INTERRELATIONS: THE BIOLOGICAL AND PHYSICAL SCIENCES

Robert T. Blackburn
SHIMER COLLEGE

W99

Scott, Foresman and Company

CHICAGO   ATLANTA   DALLAS   PALO ALTO   FAIR LAWN, N.J.

Library of Congress Catalog Card No. 66–14839
Copyright © 1966 by Scott, Foresman and Company
All Rights Reserved
Printed in the United States of America

To
M. J. B.

Preface

The conception of a course built around the interrelations of the biological and physical sciences, a course for which the readings in this book have become the core, dates back to about 1950. The course was conceived in The College at The University of Chicago as the culmination of a required three-year sequence of work in the natural sciences, and it continues to serve this purpose at Shimer College.

Among my University of Chicago colleagues at that time were Harold Gall, Benson Ginsberg, Aaron Sayvetz, Joseph Schwab, Howard Stein, and David Weiser. My thanks go to each of these gentlemen and to the others who were centrally involved in the formulation and crystallization of the course. I am doubly indebted to Dave Weiser, my continuing colleague at Shimer College, for his critical reading of the Note on Physics and for the ideas we have shared over the years.

Every book, even one whose essence is a collection of readings, must have a procreator. Marvin Bram is that person, and the idea of the Guide to Inquiry is his also.

Finally, the richness of the papers, the insights and increased understandings I have of them, obtain from the students who have engaged with me in their study. The book is indebted to those students; it exists for them and for their successors in pursuits of truths.

Robert T. Blackburn
Shimer College
Mt. Carroll, Illinois

Contents

Introduction

The bulk of this book, and its *raison d'être*, is a collection of fifteen readings. Although they have been gathered from a variety of sources and although their authors represent a variety of affiliations and special interests, one theme runs through each work: There has been in the past, is today, and will always be a certain definable relationship between the biological and physical sciences. Consideration of this relationship has been, is, and will continue to be important for students who would have a deep understanding of the natural sciences.

Since the last remarks might be considered as no more than the truisms they are, let me point out that the common element in each reading is a question: What is the *nature* of the relationship between the biological and physical sciences, past, present, and future? The authors of the papers in this collection, each a distinguished scientist, did not, of course, write specifically in answer to the question; in almost every case, the papers were prepared for particular audiences on particular occasions. Hence, for me to say that each contributes significantly to the question—which I believe each does—must be understood as a personal value-judgment. That this is an open question is proven by the fact that the papers of these scientists present diametrically opposed views—and biologists and physicists disagree among themselves as well as with members of the other discipline.

Even if the question of the nature of the relationship is ultimately unanswerable, a belief in a particular view of it is not without value and consequence. Like a good theory—namely, one with "explicative" and "explanative" virtues—a soundly reasoned view of a relationship suggests new research and new modes of attack, sets previous research on the shelf as outmoded or unfruitful, places problems in one perspective and out of another, and so on. Moreover, a "pure" science, with its succinct syntax and abstract symbolism, is barren and sterile and requires interpretation, even within its own domain. It is no surprise that scientists cannot resist the temptation to enrich the meaning of their efforts; their work begs for speculation as to its larger significance.

The central problem of scientific interrelations, then, has intellectual significance for the scientific specialist, for the student of the humanities, and for the so-called educated layman because it is intrinsically interesting and challenging. There is reason to believe that the solution to the problem lies outside the realm of the "purely scientific"—which not only does not detract from its importance but enhances its intellectual richness.

I have not grouped the readings in this book under the usual taxonomic headings (vitalism vs. mechanism, teleology vs. causality, reductionism vs. holism, etc.), nor have I interjected editorial comments and interpretations in an attempt to clarify key terms, identify obscure phenomena, or criticize or defend particular statements. Were I to do so, I should defeat one of the main purposes of the book, which is to sharpen the reader's ability to analyze scientific arguments. This ability must be developed by practice, with guidance but without overly specific instruction. Certain terms recur throughout the selections, and the careful reader will soon discover that they have different meanings for different authors and that they are emotionally loaded and frequently employed rhetorically. As the reader learns to distinguish among their varying applications and inferences, he will acquire alternative definitions and sets of meaningful terms with which to classify the positions taken.

Inasmuch as the question that runs through the readings is of topical concern, recent papers dominate the collection. Cross references among them are frequent and invite comparison. For example, Schrödinger utilizes Delbrück's model (but Delbrück reaches a different conclusion) and credits Heitler's contribution (but Heitler argues for quite a different relationship), Oparin criticizes Schrödinger, Novikoff attacks Haldane, Mayr cites Simpson, Delbrück credits Bohr, and so on.

The first reading, though not addressed to the specific fundamental problem of interrelations, sets a stage. An excerpt from a panel discussion at the Darwin Centennial, held at The University of Chicago in 1959, it serves partly as an introduction to the questions raised in later selections, partly as a witness to the sincere diversity existing among contemporary scientists, and partly as pure entertainment.

The Müller and Bernard papers were chosen as representative classics of the nineteenth century and in one way represent the opposite poles ("pure vitalism" and "pure mechanism") to which the remaining papers frequently refer. Therefore, in addition to their inherent worth, they are important background materials for study of the twentieth-century scientists, who confronted the subject of interrelations with an immensely increased knowledge of biology and physics and who worked from the vantage of changed theoretical constructs.

The dozen works that complete the collection, dating from the 1930's to the 1960's, may rightfully be called contemporary. They are not chronologically arranged, however; to the extent that there is an organizing principle for the presentation of the papers, it is juxtaposition of diverse positions.

The papers were chosen as well-written and representative expressions of different views of the interrelations among the sciences—different in the particular relationships argued (most often explicitly but on occasion implicitly), in the kinds of evidence cited, in the kinds of argument adduced, or in the interpretation of the past and present relationships and the extrapolation to the future. The reader should bear in mind that the readings constitute but a small portion of the material written on this subject. The intent of the book is not to exhaust the literature or even to provide a bibliography (bibliographies included in the readings, of course, permit the reader to continue his exploration) but only to offer a sample. Primarily because of the limitations of space, no works by "professional" philosophers are included; but these works are a rich source, readily accessible, and well worth considered attention.

An apology is due those authors whose articles or books have been excerpted; although a sincere effort was made to present each point of view in full, with supporting evidence and arguments, the deletion of any part of a book or an article is a pernicious act because it destroys the integrity of a whole and implies that some of the author's words are not important. This is certainly not true. I urge the reader to consult the original sources in their entirety.

This book presupposes a general background in the fundamental principles of biology, chemistry, and physics. Naturally, the broader and firmer one's knowledge, the more he can profit from the readings. Fortunately, however, the appeal to data made by most of the authors is not at a highly specialized level. To the extent that one need be acquainted with specific aspects of these disciplines, an understanding of genetics, cellular chemistry, and conceptual physics (i.e., the notions of quantum theory) would be most helpful. The Note on Physics (in the Appendix) is a synoptic description of several concepts central to contemporary physics. Unless the reader is reasonably knowledgeable about current work in this science, he should probably refer to the Note before undertaking his study of the more recent papers.

While I believe that any interested reader will profit from the readings, this volume was conceived primarily as the object of a discussion class. Each reading stands by itself, but the real richness and subtlety of the selections and their diverse approaches to the nature of scientific interrelations emerge most effectively under the dialectic of comparison and discussion. I have attempted to suggest the essentials of this dialectical process in the Guide to Inquiry (also in the Appendix), which contains at least one question on every reading (the panel discussion excepted) and sometimes refers to two or more readings in comparative questions. Using the Guide on his own, a reader should be able to question the readings, singly and in combination; still, my experience with these materials in the classroom indicates that sharing insight through active discussion is the most rewarding use to which they can be put.

The questions and discussions constituting the Guide necessarily reveal my own interpretations of the readings. My views may or may not merit consideration; their primary function, through the questions as paradigms, is to suggest fruitful lines of inquiry—that is, the kinds of questions which provide meaningful insights into reports of scientific investigation and reflection. The Guide is by no means exhaustive, and the reader is expected to ask each type of question about each reading. For example: What are the author's key terms? What does he believe to be the fundamental nature of each science? What evidence does he present? What potentially relevant evidence does he omit? What is the form of his argument? Is it valid? How and why does one author's argument differ from that of another? What does the author believe the future holds for the sciences? Why?

An instructor who finds the collection as a whole beyond the reasonable scope of assignments for his course can make almost any selection that suits his fancy or serves his immediate purposes. Choosing on the basis of any one of several principles, he can still provide for his students' attainment of basic knowledge and analytical ability.

The papers in this collection form the heart of the fourth and final required course in the general program in the natural sciences at Shimer College. This course is an integrative one for us, and our experience with it over the years has been rewarding. The pedagogical value of most of the readings has been proved through use; they are rich in the dialogue that results when subtly argued papers are compared with one another. The collection might also be profitably used toward the conclusion of a rigorous biology course or in a philosophy of science course.

Finally, I cannot resist a word of warning based upon my classroom experience with these readings. As stated at the outset of this Introduction and as supported by the papers in the collection, the nature of the relationship between the biological and physical sciences is an open question. But the reader is very likely to approach the question with an answer already formulated in his mind. He thus tends to be agile in finding flaws in the positions taken by those whose beliefs are different from his but negligent in his critical analysis of the author who argues in favor of his preconception. The danger is not unique to this subject, and my remarks will not eliminate it. They might, however, raise the appropriate flag and remind the reader that the analytical task before him is not an easy one. It is exciting and enriching, but not easy.

THE ORIGIN OF LIFE

CHAIRMEN

Harlow Shapley and Hans Gaffron

PANELISTS

Sir Charles Darwin; Theodosius Dobzhansky;
Earl A. Evans, Jr.; G. F. Gause; Ralph W. Gerard;
Hermann J. Muller; C. Ladd Prosser

MULLER: I think that, in the course of discussing the origin of life, we shall necessarily come closer to a definition of what life is, so that it is not necessary to define it now. I think the most fundamental property distinguishing a living thing—and that can therefore be used to define life—is its ability to form copies of itself. We call this "reproduction"; but such copies must also include innovations—mutations—that distinguish a given living thing from its parents. It is this property of not merely reproducing itself but also reproducing its mutant types that inevitably led the first multiplying objects through the three-, four-, or five-billion-year course of evolution by which all present-day living things, including ourselves, have gradually taken shape under the directing influence of natural selection. Natural selection could not go on without the necessary basis of an ability or faculty of the material to copy not merely itself but its variations. That, I think, is the heart of life, and such material, when it arose, is rightly called "living."

GERARD: I should want a little more said before I am quite willing to call matter "living." Perhaps this is a good opportunity to make the point that, while one has to think and use words in terms of fairly sharp categories, in reality there are always transitions and continua. It may be a little unwise to think of life and not-life as if these suddenly were or suddenly were not—aside from all the vast changes that have occurred in living things since the appearance of anything that we

From "The Origin of Life," in Sol Tax and Charles Callender, eds., *Issues in Evolution*, Vol. III in *Evolution After Darwin* (Chicago: The University of Chicago Press, 1960), pp. 69, 71–73, 92–93. Reprinted by permission of The University of Chicago Press. Copyright 1960 by The University of Chicago Press.

should agree was living. Not as a geneticist or a microbiologist but as one dealing primarily with more complex organisms, I am certainly aware of some other properties, even of simple organisms, which I should like to see included in any definition of life.

You have certainly put your hand on the essence of life in this ability to reproduce—and reproduce not only substance but pattern. But I should also like to think of life as something that is going on: there must be some kind of dynamic equilibrium, a flow of matter and energy through the system. Moreover, a living system maintains its integrity. It has an equilibrium state and either maintains that state or attempts to return to it when displaced by the impact of environmental stimuli. So I should include dynamic equilibrium and the ability to use its own energy to restore disturbances—which is called "adaptive amplification"—as well as specific synthesis. Then I should like to add still another quality. I think there must be a certain level of architectural complexity—levels upon levels upon levels. One has subnucleons in a nucleus, and these in an atom, and atoms in a molecule, and molecules in certain patterned groups, and these in still larger patterned groups; and only when a system has gone quite a long way in that direction of onion skin around onion skin do I think you could reasonably call it living.

SHAPLEY: You make life sound difficult.

GERARD: It is.

GAFFRON: Matter can practically always be defined in terms of physics, chemistry, and biochemistry. This certainly is not enough to define life. We might ask: If we ingest food, at what moment does the food become living? Of course it never does. One could follow a particle of assimilated food, no matter how complex, and wherever one finds it in the living organism, it is dead. It is the process in which it takes part that defines life, and not the matter of which it is composed. One may freeze a cell at such low temperature that every reaction ceases. No one could distinguish this cell from a dead one. To see whether it is alive or has the capacity of being alive, one would have to bring the cell back to normal temperature and see whether it still does what it is expected to do: to grow and, particularly, to multiply. So the essence of life is found in the process of living and not in any constituents of living cells.

GERARD: Your frozen cell, which is sufficiently frozen so that nothing is happening in it, when warmed up, will presumably (if it is still alive) show certain processes that a dead cell under the same conditions will not show. Now, what is the difference between the dormant and the dead cell?

GAFFRON: When defrosted, the dead cell will disintegrate, and the dormant cell will multiply.

GERARD: This is good operationalism.

MULLER: I wish to register my disagreement with nearly everything Gerard said. In my opinion all the properties he mentioned are results of the evolution of living matter by the mechanism that Darwin called "natural selection." We do not have an original adaptiveness on the part of life, but adaptation comes as a result of evolution.

PROSSER: My definition of life tends to be a little closer to Gerard's than to Muller's, because I think integration is the term that best covers our ignorance of life. Perhaps it would be useful here to refer to the concept of emergent properties. With each level of increasing complexity of organization, properties emerge that certainly could not have been predicted from the properties of the subunits. Molecules have different properties from atoms, macromolecules add new complexities, subcellular particles are organized chemical systems, and intact cells are much more than the sum of their parts.

GERARD: I think that this discussion brings out the point that the definition of life is a problem of where along a continuum you wish to draw a line. This, of course, is a matter of definition and therefore an individual option. This question of a sharp break or a transition or, as Prosser put it, the emergence of something new is going to appear in almost every panel. It is a choice between demanding the full thing and taking a preliminary stage. Here, one could speak of "proto-life." If you wish to define proto-life as having just the limited properties you specify, then I am happy. If you don't wish to include the other properties as minimal, that is your privilege. I think it should be made clear that these are successive demands we are making when we wish to call a thing "living."

MULLER: I should draw the line where the Darwinian process of natural selection begins to come in, and that is at the appearance of replication of the self-copying kind — that is, the replication of mutations.

. . . .

SHAPLEY: . . . I have been asked to poll the panel for opinions about Gaffron's estimate that life can be created in test tubes in a thousand years.

GAFFRON: That statement probably comes from one of those news releases, in which an article of fifty pages is condensed into fifty sentences and certain things simply get lost. On the same page of my paper where I said it might be possible to solve our problem within the next thousand years, I also said, "provided that one of these famous improbable events is not involved." With one of those interposed, we shall never create life.

SHAPLEY: It seems to me you evaded that rather well.

DARWIN: Do you mean that there will have to be a gestation of the brains of the human race for a thousand years before we see how it can be done, or do you mean that the development itself would take the thousand years? These are two quite different matters.

GAFFRON: If we have to deal with an improbable event, which happened in the course of evolution, we have to wait a little too long for it to happen also in the test tube.

SHAPLEY: Do we believe that before a thousand years life can be created in a test tube? Without any definition of what I mean by "life," do you wish to say "yes" or "no"?

DARWIN: I don't ask for a definition of life because I am afraid you can't define it. But, as I understand it, you think that the researchers will not understand what life means so as to produce it until they have worked for a thousand years.

DOBZHANSKY: I am optimistic enough to believe that in a thousand years we shall know a great deal that we do not know now. I see no reason why the problem of the origin of life should take even that long to be solved. This may be overoptimistic, but I think it is not unjustified.

EVANS: If you are talking in terms of a replicating and mutating macromolecule, then I would say that it is quite possible within a thousand years.

GAUSE: I think it is better to be optimistic.

SHAPLEY: Isn't a thousand years rather long to wait for this to happen?

GAUSE: If we believe we can do it in a thousand years, perhaps we shall make it in five hundred.

GAFFRON: You auction it off.

SHAPLEY: What will you give, Gerard?

GERARD: I think I am really the optimist. When you remember that practically all we now know has been learned in 250 years of science and most of this in one-quarter of that time; when you find out—as Panel Four will show later in the week—that the growth of human mental capacity is perhaps very great; then Heaven knows what can be done in a good deal less than one thousand years. I am willing to repeat a prediction I made once about understanding one of the important mental diseases: I said that I was quite confident that it would be solved during my lifetime. I am safe on that.

MULLER: I think I am going to shock Gerard, if he thinks he is optimistic. My answer is that those who define life as I do will admit that the most primitive forms of things that deserve to be called living have already been made in the test tube by A. Kornberg.

SHAPLEY: Muller's estimate is minus some years.

PROSSER: I would certainly say that molecules of the DNA type will soon be made to replicate even in the absence of appropriate protein catalysts. Even if you add to this other criteria, such as those Gerard stipulated earlier—most of which I will support—I think one thousand years is pessimistic rather than optimistic. However, it must be recognized that Miller has not found purine-pyrimidine bases, much less nucleotides, in his "primitive" system.

SHAPLEY: I have written down: "It will be accomplished before the end of this century."

ELEMENTS OF PHYSIOLOGY

J. Müller

Prolegomena on general physiology

Physiology is the science which treats of the properties of organic bodies, animal and vegetable, of the phenomena they present, and of the laws which govern their actions. Inorganic substances are the objects of other sciences, — physics and chemistry.

In entering upon the study of physiology, the first point to be ascertained regards the distinctions between these two great classes of bodies — the organic and the inorganic, — and the following questions suggest themselves for discussion: — Do organic and inorganic substances differ in their material composition? and since the phenomena presented by them are obviously so different, are the forces or principles on which these phenomena depend, also different; or are the forces which give rise to the phenomena of the organic kingdom merely modifications of those which produce physical and chemical actions?

. . . .

Of organism and life

Organised beings are composed of a number of essential and mutually dependent dissimilar parts. — The manner in which their elements are combined, is not the only difference between organic and inorganic

---

From *Elements of Physiology*, tr. William Baly, 2nd ed. (London: Taylor & Walton, 1839), pp. 1, 19–29, 40–41, 682–685, 689.

bodies; there is in living organic matter a principle constantly in action, the operations of which are in accordance with a rational plan, so that the individual parts which it creates in the body, are adapted to the design of the whole; and this it is which distinguishes organism. Kant says, "The cause of the particular mode of existence of each part of a living body resides in the whole, while in dead masses each part contains this cause within itself." This explains why a mere part separated from an organized whole generally does not continue to live; why, in fact, an organized body appears to be one and indivisible. And since the different parts of an organized body are heterogeneous members of one whole, and essential to its perfect state, the trunk cannot live after the loss of one of these parts.

It is only in very simple animals or plants which possess a certain number of similar parts, or where the dissimilar parts are repeated in each successive segment of the individual, that the body can be divided, and the two portions, each still possessing all the essential parts of the whole, though in smaller number, continue to live. Branches of plants separated from the trunk, being planted, form new individuals. The different parts of plants are so similar, that they are convertible one into another, branches into roots, and stamens into petals.[1] This is the case also with some simple polypes. The experiments of Trembley, Roesel, and others, prove that portions of a divided polype will continue to grow until each half becomes a perfect animal. In the same way some worms, as the Naïdes, in which each segment contains nearly the same essential parts,—the intestine, nerves, and blood-vessels,—have been observed to propagate by spontaneous division. Bonnet states, that he has seen this new growth and reproduction in the portions of a divided earthworm: but this animal, when thus divided, could not continue to live; for neither portion would contain all the parts essential to the whole.

In the higher animals, and in man, there are certain organs,—that is, parts differing in their properties and functions,—which cannot be removed without destruction of life, and of our idea of the whole; and such organs also only occur singly, as brain, spinal marrow, lungs, heart, and intestinal canal. Other parts, on the contrary, which are not members essentially necessary to our idea of the whole being, or which are several in number, may be removed with impunity: no part, however, of one of the higher animals can continue to live when separated from the body, for no one part contains all the organs essential to the whole. The ovum, the germ itself, alone possesses this power; for, at the time of its separation from the parent animal, the vital force has not formed in it the essential parts of the whole; and yet it becomes developed into a new integral being. There is, then, a unity in the organism, to which its composition of dissimilar parts is subordinate. From the facts above stated, however, it appears that organized bodies are not absolutely indivisible; they may, indeed, always be divided, and still retain their properties, if each portion contains the essential heterogeneous mem-

---

1.   Goethe, Metamorphose der Pflanzen.

bers of the whole, and in the generation even of the highest animals and plants a division takes place.

Inorganic bodies are divisible in a much more extended sense, without the parts losing the chemical properties of the whole; they may be divided (to use the common expression) *ad infinitum*,—that is, according to the atomic theory, into the ultimate atoms which, on account of their minuteness, elude the senses; and in chemical compounds, into molecules which are formed of the different component atoms, and which are likewise not recognisable by the senses. To this charcter of inorganic bodies, however, crystals form an exception, since they cannot be reduced by division to their ultimate particles without losing some of their properties. These bodies can be divided with facility only in certain directions, and the portions thus obtained are often different in form from the whole; for which reason some persons regard crystals also as "individuals," which exist from the continuance of the force which formed them, and cease to exist when external influences, chemical (atmospheric) or mechanical, overcome their force of crystallisation or hardness.[2] But even if crystals are regarded as individuals in this sense, there is still this great distinction between them and organized bodies,—that the molecules of crystals are homogeneous thoughout, and that crystals are divisible, at least, into homogeneous aggregates of molecules; while organized bodies are composed of parts perfectly dissimilar from each other, such as tissues endowed with peculiar properties. Organic combinations, moreover, never occur in a state of crystallisation in organised bodies during life. Again, in an inorganic body which is composed of heterogeneous substances aggregated together, these parts have no reference to the design and existence of the whole.

Adaptation displayed in organised bodies.—Organised bodies being composed of a certain number of dissimilar essential parts all adapted to the plan of the whole individual, it necessarily follows that their external and internal conformation are such as to distinguish them entirely from inorganic bodies. That which we admire in the whole animal, is not merely the manifestation of the ruling forces, as crystallisation is the consequence and manifestation of a certain force in a binary compound; but the form of the animals and of their organs evidences also an arrangement rationally adapted to the exercise of the forces, a pre-ordained harmony of the organisation with the faculties intended to be exercised. Crystals, on the contrary, present no adaptation of form to an intended action of the whole; because the whole crystal is not a body composed of a number of dissimilar mutually adapted tissues, but is produced merely by the aggregation of similar elements or formative particles, all subject to the same laws of crystalline attraction. Crystals, therefore, increase by the aggregation of new particles on the external surface of the parts already formed; while in the organised body, the formation of the parts situated side by side,

---

2. See Mohs, Grundriss der Mineralogie, i. Vorrede, p. 6.

each having a different organisation, is for the most part contemporane-
ous; so that the growth of organised bodies takes place in all particles of
their substance at the same time, while the increase of the mass in
inorganic bodies is produced by external apposition.[3]

This law of organic conformation,—adaptation to an end,—regulates
the form, not only of entire organs, but also of the simplest elementary
tissues. Thus it will in a future page be shown, that the manifold forms
of secreting glandular structures depend simply on the various modes
in which a large secreting surface can be realised in a small space. The
fibrous structure of muscles is necessary to enable these organs to
shorten themselves in a determined direction by the zigzag flexure of
the fibres. So, also in treating of the Physiology of the Nerves it will be
shown, that unless the nerves had been divided into a certain number
of primitive fibres, which do not communicate one with another, their
local action,— local circumscribed sensation,— would be impossible.
The same adaptation is seen to be equally necessary in the organisation
of plants. The organs of plants are less heterogeneous; and, in place of
being so much enclosed in the interior, are expanded on the
surface,— the reciprocal actions with the external world being effected
by the whole surface rather than by particular points. Hence the general character of the conformation of plants is that extension of surface
which is effected by means of the various forms of leaves, in ways more
manifold than the most lively fancy could have imagined; so that a
great part of botanical terminology is only an attempt to form, logically
and conformably to nature, a scheme of the possible varieties in the
increase of surface produced by variations of the leaves, and of their
relations to pedicle, twig, branch, and stem.

. . . .

The organic force is creative.—Hitherto I have examined merely that
peculiarity of organised bodies which consists in their being systems of
dissimilar organs, the existence of each of which has its source, not in
itself, but in the entire system, as Kant expressed it. *The organic force*,
which resides in the whole, and on which the existence of each part
depends, has however also the property of generating from organic
matter the individual organs necessary to the whole. Some have believed that life,— the active phenomena of organised bodies,— is only
the result of the harmony of the different parts— of the mutual action, as
it were, of the wheels of the machine,— and that death is the consequence of a disturbance of this harmony. This reciprocal action of parts
on each other evidently exists; for respiration in the lungs is the cause
of the activity of the heart, and the motion of the heart at every moment sends blood, prepared by respiration, to the brain, which thus
acquires the power of animating all other organs, and again gives
occasion to the respiratory movements. The external impulse to the
whole machinery is the atmospheric air in respiration. Any injury to
one of the principal moving powers in the mechanism, any considera-

---

3.   Professor E. H. Weber has made some other very interesting comparisons between
organisation and crystallisation in his General Anatomy. Hildebrandt's Anat. 1[ster] Band.

ble lesion of the lungs, heart, or brain, may be the cause of death; hence these organs have been named the *atria mortis*. But the harmonious action of the essential parts of the individual subsists only by the influence of a force, the operation of which is extended to all parts of the body, which does not depend on any single organs, and which exists before the harmonising parts, these being, in fact, formed by it during the developement of the embryo. A complicated piece of machinery, constructed in adaption to an end,—for example, a watch,—may present an action resulting from the co-operation of individual parts, and originating in one cause: but organic beings do not subsist merely by virtue of an accidental combination of elements; but, on the contrary, by the vital force inherent in them they generate from organic matter their essential constituent organs. This rational creative force is exerted in every animal strictly in accordance with what the nature of each requires; it exists already in the germ, and creates in it the essential parts of the future animal. The germ is "potentially" the whole animal; during the developement of the germ, the essential parts which constitute the "actual" whole are produced. The developement of the separate parts out of the simple mass is observable in the incubated egg. All the parts of the egg, except the germinal membrane or blastoderma, are destined for the nutrition of the germ; the entire vital principle of the egg resides in the germinal disk alone; and since the external influences which act on the germs of the most different organic beings are the same, we must regard the simple germinal disk, consisting of granular amorphous matter, as the "potential" whole of the future animal, endowed with the essential and specific force or principle of the future being, and capable of increasing the very small amount of this specific force and matter which it already possesses, by the assimilation of new matter. The germ expands to form the germinal membrane, which grows so as to surround the yolk; and by transformation of this germ the organs of the future animal are produced, the elements merely of the nervous and vascular systems, and of the intestinal canal, being first formed, and from these elements the details of the organisation afterwards more fully developed; so that the first trace of the central parts of the nervous system must be regarded neither as brain nor as spinal marrow, but as the "potential" whole of the nervous centres. In the same manner the different parts of the heart are seen to be developed from a uniform tube; and the first trace of the intestinal tube when there are no salivary glands and liver, is more than the mere intestinal tube; it is the "potential" whole,—the representative of the entire digestive apparatus; for, as Baer first discovered, liver, salivary glands, and pancreas are in the further progress of the vegetative process really developed from that which appears to be merely the rudiment of the intestinal canal. It can, indeed, no longer be doubted that the germ is not the miniature of the future being with all its organs, as Bonnet and Haller believed, but is merely "*potentially*" this being, with the specific vital force of which it is endued, and which it becomes "*actually*" by developement, and by the production of the organs essential to the active state of the "*actual*" being. For the germ itself is formed merely of amorphous matter, and a high magnifying power is not necessary to distinguish the earliest rudiments of the separate organs; on the contrary, these are from their first appearance distinct and pretty large, but simple; so that the later-complicated state of a particular organ can be seen to arise by transformation from its simple rudiment. These remarks are now no longer mere opinions, but facts; and nothing is more distinct than the developement of glands from the intestinal tube, and of the intestinal tube itself from a portion of the germinal membrane.

The creative organic force is not identical with the mind. — If Ernst Stahl had been acquainted with the above facts, he would have been still more confirmed in his famous theory, that the *rational soul* itself is the "primum movens" of organisation; that it is the ultimate and sole cause of organic activity; that the soul constructs and maintains the organisation of its body in adaptation to the laws of its intended actions; and that by its organic operations the cure of diseases is effected. Stahl's contemporaries and followers have partly misunderstood this great man, in believing that, according to his view, the soul, which forms mental conceptions, also conducts with consciousness, and designedly, the organisation of the body. The *soul* (anima) spoken of by Stahl is the organising power or principle which manifests itself in conformity with a rational law. But Stahl has gone too far in placing the manifestations of soul, combined with consciousness, on a level with the organising principle; the operations of which, though in accordance with design, obey a blind necessity. The organising principle, which according to an eternal law creates the different essential organs of the body, and animates them, is not itself seated in one particular organ; it continues in operation up to the time of birth in anencephalous monsters; it modifies the already existing nervous system, as well as all the other organs in the larvae of insects, during their transformation, causing the disappearance of several of the ganglia of the nervous cord, and the coalescence of others; by its operation during the transformation of the tadpole to the frog, the spinal marrow is shortened in proportion as the tail becomes atrophied, and the nerves of the extremities are formed. This principle, thus acting conformably to design, but without consciousness, is also manifested in the phenomena of instinct. There is great beauty and truth in the saying of Cuvier, that animals acting from instinct are, as it were, possessed by an innate idea, by a dream. But that which excites this dream can be nothing else than the organising principle, the "ultimate cause" of the being.

The existence of the organic principle in the germ, and its apparent independence of any special organ in the adult, as well as the fact that it is manifested in plants, in which both nervous system and consciousness are wanting, prove that this principle cannot be compared with mental consciousness, which is an after product of developement, and has its seat in one particular organ. Mind can generate no organic products, it can merely form conceptions; our ideas of the organised being are mere conscious conceptions of the mind. The formative or organising principle, on the contrary, is a creative power modifying matter, blindly and unconsciously, according to the laws of adaptation.

Origin of genera and species. — Organism, or the organised state, is the result of the union of the organic creative power and organic matter. Whether the two have ever been separate, whether the creative archetypes, the *eternal ideas* of Plato, as he taught in his "Timaeus," have at some former period been infused into matter, and from that time forward perpetuated in each animal and plant, is not an object of science, but of the fables and traditions which cannot be proved, and which distinctly indicate to us the limits of our mere consciousness. All that we know is, that each form of animal or plant is continued unchanged in its products, and that, in a roughly calculated number of many thousand species of animals and plants, there are no true transitions of one species to another, or of one genus to another; each family of plants and animals, each genus, and each species, is connected with certain physical conditions of its existence, with a certain temperature, and with determinate physico-geographical relations, for which it is, as it were, created. In this endless variety of creatures, in this regularity of the natural classes, families, genera, and species, is manifested one common creative principle, on which life generally throughout the world depends. But all these varieties of organism, all these animals, which may be regarded as so many modes in which the surrounding world may be enjoyed by means of sensation and reaction, are, from the moment of their creation, independent. The species perishes when the productive individuals are all destroyed; the genus is no longer capable of generating the species, nor the family of restoring the genus. In the course of the earth's history, species of animals have perished by the revolutions of its surface, and have been buried in the ruins; these belong partly to extinct genera, partly to genera still existing.

The study of the successive strata of the earth, in which the remains of organic beings occur, seems to prove that the beings, which have thus left their remains on the earth, have not all existed at the same time, that the simplest creatures have first inhabited the earth; while the remains of the higher animals, and particularly those of man, are not met with except in the most superficial of the deposits which contain organic remains. But no fact justifies us in speculations concerning the primitive, or subsequent origin of living beings; no fact indicates the possibility of explaining all these varieties by transformation, for all creatures maintain unchanged the forms which they originally received.

Nature of the organic force. — The unity resulting from the combination of the organising force with organic matter could be better conceived, if it were possible to prove that the organising force and the phenomena of life are the result, manifestation, or property of a certain combination of elements. The difference of animate and inanimate organic matter would then consist, in that state of combination of the elements, which is necessary to life, having in the latter undergone some change. Reil has stated this bold theory in his famous treatise on the "vital energy,"[4] which some physiologists, — Rudolphi, for example, — regard

---

4.   Reil, Archiv. für Physiologie, Bd. i.

as a masterpiece, on which the principles of physiology must be founded.

Reil refers the organic phenomena to original difference in the composition and form of the organic bodies. Differences in composition and form are, according to his theory, the cause of all the variety in organised bodies, and in their endowments. But if these two principles be admitted, still the problem remains unsolved; it may still be asked, how the elementary combination acquired its form, and how the form acquired its elementary combination. That the form of the organic matter does not determine originally the mode of its action, is proved indisputably by the fact, that the matter from which all animal forms are produced is at first almost without form. The germ in all Vertebrata, and probably also in the Invertebrata, from what is known of a few species, and from what I have observed in the Planaria, is a round disk of simple matter; here is no difference of form corresponding to the difference of the animals. On the other hand, the form of inorganic bodies is always determined by their elements, or by the combination of their elements. And this Reil himself admits; for he says, "Form of matter is itself a phenomenon, which depends on another phenomenon, namely, the elective affinity of the elements and their products." Hence it would follow, that if the elementary composition were alone the cause of the organic forces, it would be at the same time the formative principle itself. Now, since in organised bodies immediately after death the elementary composition of the organic matter does not appear to be different from that of bodies still living, Reil must admit the existence of other more subtile elements not recognisable by chemical analysis, which are present in the living body, but are wanting after death. Into the composition of the organic matter of the living body there must enter an unknown (according to Reil's theory, subtile material) principle, or the organic matter must maintain its properties by the operation of some unknown forces. Whether this principle is to be regarded as an imponderable matter, or as a force or energy, is just as uncertain as the same question is in reference to several important phenomena in physics; physiology in this case is not behind the other natural sciences, for the properties of this principle as displayed in the functions of the nerves are nearly as well known as those of light, caloric, and electricity, in physics.

At all events, the mobility of the organic principle is certain: its motion is evident in innumerable vital phenomena. Parts frozen, stiff, and deprived of sensation and motion, are observed gradually to recover animation, which extends into them from the borders of the living parts. This passage of the vital principle from one part to another, is still more manifest on the removal of pressure from a nerve, after that state has been produced in which the limb is said to be "asleep." The fibrin effused in inflammation on the surface of an organ, is observed to become endowed with life and organisation. This same organic principle exerts its influence even beyond the surface of an organ, as is shown by the changes produced in the animal matter contained in the vessels, for instance, in the lymph and chyle, which latter fluid during its progress through the lacteals acquires new properties:

from the coats of the blood-vessels, again, the organic principle exerts an influence on the blood, maintaining its fluidity; for out of the vessels the blood coagulates under almost all circumstances, unless it has undergone some chemical change. Lastly, I may with Autenrieth adduce that property of animal tissues, by virtue of which vital energy is at one time withdrawn from them, and then again imparted to them, and is often quickly accumulated in one organ. I do not think with Hunter that it is the influence of the vital energy which in an unincubated egg preserves the yolk and white from putrefaction; but it is certain that an extravasated, enclosed, or morbidly collected fluid, even morbid animal matter, as pus, is preserved from putrefaction longer in the living body than out of it; which does not arise merely from the exclusion of air, since, when the vital powers are low, blood and pus rapidly undergo decomposition even in the body.[5] From all these facts the existence of a force which is often rapid in its action, and is capable of extending from one part to another, or of an imponderable matter, is evident; nevertheless we are by no means justified in regarding it as identical with the known imponderable matters, or general physical forces, — caloric, light, and electricity, a comparison which is refuted by any close examination. The researches on the so-called animal magnetism at first promised to throw some light on this enigmatical principle, or imponderable matter. It was thought that, by one person laying his hand upon, or passing it along the surface of another, and by other procedures, remarkable effects were produced, arising from the overflow of the animal magnetic fluid; some indeed have imagined that by certain operations they could produce accumulation of this hypothetic fluid. These tales, however, are a lamentable tissue of falsehood, deception, and credulity; and from them we have only learned how incapable most medical men are of instituting an experimental investigation, how little idea they have of a logical criticism, which in other natural sciences has become a universal method. There is no single fact relating to this doctrine which is free from doubt, except the certainty of endless deceptions; and in the practice of medicine there is also no fact which can be connected with these wonders, except the often repeated, but still unconfirmed accounts of the cure of paralysis by investing the limbs with the bodies of animals just killed, and the willingly credited fables of the restoration of youth to the old and diseased by their being in the proximity and exposed to the exhalation of healthy children, and vice versâ.

We have thus seen that organic bodies consist of matters which present a peculiar combination of their component elements — a combination of three, four, or more to form one compound, which is observed only in organic bodies, and in them only during life. Organised bodies moreover are constituted of organs, — that is, of essential members of one whole, — each member having a separate function, and each deriving its existence from the whole; and they not merely consist of these organs, but by virtue of an innate power they form them within themselves. Life, therefore, is not simply the result of the

---

5.   Autenrieth, Physiologie, i.

harmony and reciprocal action of these parts; but is first manifested in a principle or imponderable matter which is in action in the substance of the germ, enters into the composition of the matter of this germ, and imparts to organic combinations properties which cease at death.

. . . .

Sources of new organised matter and vital force. — The nutriment of animals consists of organic matters, animal and vegetable; the nutriment of plants consists partly of vegetable and animal matters not wholly decomposed, and partly of binary compounds, namely, carbonic acid and water. It has been imagined that plants can nourish themselves from carbonic acid and water alone; the experiments of Hassenfratz, M. de Saussure, Giobert, and Link, have proved however that plants under these circumstances, if they grow at all, do so very imperfectly, and seldom flower and bear fruit.[6] It appears, therefore, that it is only when they are at the same time nourished by organic compounds in solution, which have not wholly undergone decomposition, that plants generate organic matter from binary compounds.

The power of generating organic from mineral compounds cannot, however, be entirely denied to plants; for, were it not for this power, the vegetable and animal kingdoms would soon perish. The unceasing destruction of organic bodies presupposes the formation by plants of new organic matter from binary compounds and elementary substances.

Now, by the growth and propagation of organized bodies, the organic force seems to be multiplied; for from one being many others are produced, and from these in their turn many more; while, on the other hand, with the death of organised bodies the organic force also seems to perish. But the organic force is not merely transmitted from one individual to another, — on the contrary, a plant, after producing yearly the germs of very many productive individuals, may still remain capable of the same production. Hence the source of the increase of the organic or vital force likewise would seem to lie in the organisation of new matter; and, if this be admitted, we must suppose that plants, while they form new organic matter from inorganic substances under the influence of light and caloric, are also endowed with the power of increasing the organic force from unknown external sources, and that animals also in their turn generate the organic force from their nutriment under the influence of the vital stimuli, and distribute it to the germs during propagation. Whether during life the organic force, as well as the organic matter, is constantly suffering destruction, is quite unknown. This much however seems certain, that, at the death of organic bodies, the vital force is resolved into its general natural causes, from which it appears to be generated anew by plants. If this increase of the vital principle in existing organised bodies from unknown sources in the external world be rejected, the apparently endless multiplication of the vital force in the process of growth and in propagation, must be regarded as a mere evolution of germs encased

---

6. Tiedemann, Physiolog. i. 218. Translation, p. 83.

one within another, or it must be admitted that the division of the organic force which takes place in propagation does not weaken its intensity; a supposition which appears absurd. But the fact would still remain, that, by the death of organised bodies, organic force is constantly becoming inert, or resolved into its general physical causes.

· ·

Of the active principle of the nerves

The older physiologists had no determinate ideas regarding either the nature of the nervous principle or the laws governing its action. They supposed that what they denominated "nervous spirits" were transmitted from the brain through the nerves and their ramifications to the different organs. And when the actions of common electricity, and the modes in which it is conducted, became more fully known, physiologists imagined that the action of the nerves was rendered more intelligible by comparing them with electric apparatus. But it was not until the discovery of galvanism that the grounds of this and similar hypotheses were submitted to an exact inquiry.

Many observers, as Aldini, Galvani, Von Humboldt, Fowler, and others, were inclined to attribute the galvanic phenomena to an animal principle or force hitherto unknown; while Pfaff, Volta, and Monro, on the other hand, ascribed them to an electric agency developed by the action of metals and moisture on each other, quite independently of the animal organs. Volta demonstrated the electric nature of this agency, and his view was in fine confirmed and placed beyond a doubt by the discovery that galvanic phenomena can be excited in other bodies without the aid or presence of animal substances. Monro likewise was at an early period of the inquiry led by his experiments to the correct conclusion that the galvanic fluid, which thus excites that action of the nerves, is electric in its nature, and altogether different from the nervous principle, acting merely as a stimulus of the nervous force, which then causes the muscles to contract.[7] Humboldt inferred, from several experiments which he performed, that the nerves are surrounded with a sensible atmosphere; his reason for that opinion was, that the galvanic influence transmitted through a divided nerve will pass from one portion to the other, even though the ends are not in contact. But we know now, that in such a case the interspace between the ends of the nerve is occupied by watery vapour, and that the circumstance adduced as a proof of the existence of a sensible atmosphere can be regarded only as an instance of the capability of gaseous exhalations to conduct the electric fluid. And here we perceive a marked distinction between electricity and the nervous principle: the action of the latter is interrupted by the ligature or division of a nerve; while, if

---

7.   Monro's and Fowler's Abhandlungen über thierische Electricität. Leipzig, 1796. Fowler's experiments and observations relative to the influence called Animal Electricity. London, 1793.

the poles of a galvanic apparatus be applied to a divided nerve, or to a nerve tied with a ligature, one pole above the point of division or seat of the ligature, the other below it, the electric fluid is transmitted as readily as before.

Although it is now certain that the phenomena produced in animals by galvanism are not due to an animal electricity, still many physiologists and men of science have not ceased to regard electricity and nervous power as principles in a certain degree similar. A closer inquiry, however, shows that they are totally different. The experiments of Dr. Ure, and those of Dr. Wilson Philip, have among others given rise to misconceptions. In Dr. Ure's experiments, one of the wires connected with a galvanic battery of two hundred and seventy pairs of plates was applied to the spinal cord laid bare in the body of a criminal who had died, by hanging, an hour previously, while the other wire was applied to the ischiadic nerve. At the moment that the circle was closed, the muscles of the trunk were thrown into contraction as in a violent shudder. The motions of a laboured respiration, with the alternate rising and falling of the abdomen, were imitated by including between the wires the phrenic nerve and diaphragm, and alternately opening and closing the circle. In the same way horrid grimaces of the features were produced. But in all this there was nothing more extraordinary than in the most common galvanic experiment, except that the human body was the subject of it. The experiments of Dr. Wilson Philip, in like manner, by no means justify the conclusions drawn from them. Even if it were a fact that a galvanic current, passed through the divided vagus nerve to the stomach, can cause digestion to be performed in the same way as is effected by the influence of the nerve itself in the sound state, this would not prove the identity of the nervous principle and electricity; for the portion of a divided nerve, which is separated from the brain, retains for a certain time the power of exercising its ordinary functions when stimulated. Further, the repetition of Dr. Philip's experiments by Dr. Dieckhof and myself has not been attended with exactly the same results.

The neurilema and the surrounding parts being moist, electricity would not remain insulated in the nerves, were it in action in them. It has, indeed, been imagined that the nerves have an insulating property. Fechner compares the nervous fibres to conducting wires covered with silk. But the neurilema itself is an excellent conductor of the galvanic fluid, and the nerves, as we shall show, have not a greater conducting power than other moist animal textures; for the galvanic current does not necessarily follow the ramifications of the nerves; it is only the nervous principle which takes that course. The galvanic current is conducted off from the nerves by the neighbouring tissues as readily as it is conducted by the nerves themselves, if a more direct course to the pole is thus afforded. Again, the passage of the nervous principle is interrupted by a ligature, while this has no effect on the transmission of the galvanic fluid.

Electricity is known by the bodies which insulate it, and which are conductors of it; these are its sole and certain tests, and in respect of them the nervous principle differs from it, and consequently cannot be identical with it. Other proofs however, derived from properties of the nervous principle already alluded to, may be adduced: —

1. When both poles of a galvanic battery are applied to a nerve, so that a galvanic current is transmitted transversely through it, the muscle to which it is distributed contracts, not because the galvanism reaches the muscle, but because the galvanic current passed through the nerve affects it in the same way as mechanical violence, or the application of heat or caustic potash would do; that is to say, it stimulates its motor power, the action of which is propagated only in the peripheral direction.

2. But if one pole is applied to the nerve, the other to the muscle, the galvanism does not fly transversely through the nerve, but from one pole to the other in a line from the nerve to the muscle; and the effect is the same as if both poles had been connected with the muscle. Here the excitability of the nerve is acted on in its whole course to the muscle.

3. If the nerve is bruised, or tied with a ligature, between the point where both the wires are applied and the muscle, no contractions of the latter are excited. The galvanic fluid passes transversely through the nerve, as in the first case; but the action of the nervous principle is interrupted by the mechanical injury or ligature.

4. If, on the contrary, the poles are applied one above and the other below the injured spot or ligature, the galvanic fluid is conducted through it with perfect facility, and, stimulating the lower part of the nerve, gives rise to muscular contractions.

5. Nerves, even when perfectly dead, are, like all moist animal textures, still capable of conducting the galvanic fluid, though they have lost the power of exciting contractions in muscles.

6. Lastly, the experiments of myself and Dr. Sticker have shown that, when the vital influence of the nerves on the muscles has been interrupted for any considerable period, the stimulus of a simple galvanic circle is incapable of exciting their contraction. We found this to be the case in Mammalia, in which we had several months previously divided the nerves in such a manner as to prevent their perfect reunion.

. . . .

The conclusions which must be drawn from the preceding considerations are: — 1. That the vital actions of the nerves are not attended with the developement of any galvanic currents which our instruments can detect.   2. That the laws of action of the nervous principle are totally different from those of electricity.   3. To speak, therefore, of an electric current in the nerves, is to use quite as symbolical an expression as if we compared the action of the nervous principle with light or magnetism. Of the nature of the nervous principle we are as ignorant as of the nature of light and electricity; while with its properties we are nearly as well acquainted as with those of light and other imponderable agents. However much these various principles differ from each other, the same question applies to all; namely, are their effects produced by currents of an imponderable matter travelling through space, or by the undulations of a fluid? The decision as to which theory is correct in the case of the nervous principle, is at present a matter not affecting the study of the laws of its action; just as the laws of optics must remain the same, whichever theory of the nature of light be adopted.

EXPERIMENTAL MEDICINE

Claude Bernard

Part One, Chapter I
OBSERVATION AND EXPERIMENT

Only within very narrow boundaries can man observe the phenomena which surround him; most of them naturally escape his senses, and mere observation is not enough. To extend his knowledge, he has had to increase the power of his organs by means of special appliances; at the same time he has equipped himself with various instruments enabling him to penetrate inside of bodies, to dissociate them and to study their hidden parts. A necessary order may thus be established among the different processes of investigation or research, whether simple or complex: the first apply to those objects easiest to examine, for which our senses suffice; the second bring within our observation, by various means, objects and phenomena which would otherwise remain unknown to us forever, because in their natural state they are beyond our range. Investigation, now simple, again equipped and perfected, is therefore destined to make us discover and note the more or less hidden phenomena which surround us.

But man does not limit himself to seeing; he thinks and insists on learning the meaning of the phenomena whose existence has been revealed to him by observation. So he reasons, compares facts, puts questions to them, and by the answers which he extracts, tests one by another. This sort of control, by means of reasoning and facts, is what constitutes experiment, properly speaking; and it is the only process

From *An Introduction to the Study of Experimental Medicine* (New York: Dover Publications, Inc., 1957), pp. 5, 31–32, 57–99, 183–184.

that we have for teaching ourselves about the nature of things outside us.

. . . .

Part One, Chapter II
THE A PRIORI IDEA AND DOUBT IN EXPERIMENTAL REASONING

I. *Experimental truths are objective or external*

. . . .

An experimenter facing natural phenomena is like a spectator watching a dumb show. He is in some sort the examining magistrate for nature; only instead of grappling with men who seek to deceive him by lying confessions or false witness, he is dealing with natural phenomena which for him are persons whose language and customs he does not know, persons living in the midst of circumstances unknown to him, yet persons whose designs he wishes to learn. For this purpose he uses all the means within his power. He observes their actions, their gait, their behavior, and he seeks to disengage their cause by means of various attempts, called experiments. He uses every imaginable artifice, and, as the popular expression goes, he often makes a false plea in order to learn the truth. In all this, the experimenter reasons necessarily according to his own character and lends to nature his own ideas. He makes suppositions about the cause of actions taking place before his eyes; and to learn whether the hypothesis which serves as groundwork for his interpretation is correct, he takes measures to make facts appear which in the realm of logic may be either the confirmation or the negation of the idea which he has conceived. Now, I repeat, only this logical verification can teach him and give him *experience*. The naturalist observing animals whose behavior and habits he wishes to know, the physiologist and the physician wishing to study the hidden functions of living bodies, the physicist and the chemist defining the phenomena of inert matter,—they are all in the same situation; they have manifestations before them which they can interpret only with the help of the experimental criterion, the only one which we need to consider here.

. . . .

VIII. *Proof and counterproof*

. . . .

Experimental reasoning, whose different terms we have examined in the preceding section, sets itself the same goal in all the sciences. Experimenters try to reach determinism; with the help of reasoning and of experiment they try to connect natural phenomena with their necessary conditions or, in other words, with their immediate causes. By this means, they reach the law which enables them to master phenomena. All natural philosophy is summarized in *knowing the law of phenomena*. The whole experimental problem may be reduced to foreseeing and directing phenomena. But this double goal can be attained, in living bodies, only by certain special principles of experimentation which we must point out in the following chapters.

Part Two, Chapter I
EXPERIMENTAL CONSIDERATIONS COMMON TO
LIVING THINGS AND INORGANIC BODIES

I. *The spontaneity of living beings is no obstacle to the use of experimentation*

The spontaneity enjoyed by beings endowed with life has been one of the principal objections urged against the use of experimentation in biological studies. Every living being indeed appears to us provided with a kind of inner force, which presides over manifestations of life more and more independent of general cosmic influence in proportion as the being rises higher in the scale of organization. In the higher animals and in man, for instance, this vital force seems to result in withdrawing the living being from general physico-chemical influences and thus making the experimental approach very difficult.

Inorganic bodies offer no parallel; whatever their nature, they are all devoid of spontaneity. As the manifestation of their properties is therefore absolutely bound up in the physico-chemical conditions surrounding them and forming their environment, it follows that the experimenter can reach them and alter them at will.

On the other hand, all the phenomena of a living body are in such reciprocal harmony one with another that it seems impossible to separate any part without at once disturbing the whole organism. Especially in higher animals, their more acute sensitiveness brings with it still more notable reactions and disturbances.

Many physicians and speculative physiologists, with certain anatomists and naturalists, employ these various arguments to attack experimentation on living beings. They assume a vital force in opposition to physico-chemical forces, dominating all the phenomena of life, subjecting them to entirely separate laws, and making the organism an organized whole which the experimenter may not touch without destroying the quality of life itself. They even go so far as to say that inorganic bodies and living bodies differ radically from this point of view, so that experimentation is applicable to the former and not to the latter. Cuvier, who shares this opinion and thinks that physiology should be a science of observation and of deductive anatomy, expresses himself thus: "All parts of a living body are interrelated; they can act only in so far as they act all together; trying to separate one from the whole means transferring it to the realm of dead substances; it means entirely changing its essence."

If the above objections were well founded, we should either have to recognize that determinism is impossible in the phenomena of life, and this would be simply denying biological science; or else we should have to acknowledge that vital force must be studied by special methods, and that the science of life must rest on different principles from the science of inorganic bodies. These ideas, which were current in other times, are now gradually disappearing; but it is essential to extirpate their very last spawn, because the so-called vitalistic ideas still remaining in certain minds are really an obstacle to the progress of experimental science.

I propose, therefore, to prove that the science of vital phenomena must have the same foundations as the science of the phenomena of inorganic bodies, and that there is no difference in this respect between the principles of biological science and those of physico-chemical science. Indeed, as we have already said, the goal which the experimental method sets itself is everywhere the same; it consists in connecting natural phenomena with their necessary conditions or with their immediate causes. In biology, since these conditions are known, physiologists can guide the manifestation of vital phenomena as physicists guide the natural phenomena, the laws of which they have discovered; but in doing so, experimenters do not act on life.

Yet there is absolute determinism in all the sciences, because every phenomenon being necessarily linked with physico-chemical conditions, men of science can alter them to master the phenomenon, i.e., to prevent or to promote its appearing. As to this, there is absolutely no question in the case of inorganic bodies. I mean to prove that it is the same with living bodies, and that for them also determinism exists.

II. *Manifestation of properties of living bodies is
connected with the existence of certain
physico-chemical phenomena which regulate their appearance*

The manifestation of properties of inorganic bodies is connected with surrounding conditions of temperature and moisture by means of which the experimenter can directly govern mineral phenomena. Living bodies at first sight do not seem capable of being thus influenced by neighboring physico-chemical conditions; but that is merely a delusion depending on the animal having and maintaining within himself the conditions of warmth and moisture necessary to the appearance of vital phenomena. The result is that an inert body, obedient to cosmic conditions, is linked with all their variations, while a living body on the contrary remains independent and free in its manifestations; it seems animated by an inner force that rules all its acts and liberates it from the influence of surrounding physico-chemical variations and disturbances. This quite different aspect of the manifestations of living bodies as compared with the behavior of inorganic bodies has led the physiologists, called vitalists, to attribute to the former a vital force ceaselessly at war with physico-chemical forces and neutralizing their destructive action on the living organism. According to this view, the manifestations of life are determined by spontaneous action of this special vital force, instead of being, like the manifestations of inorganic bodies, the necessary results of conditions or of the physico-chemical influences of a surrounding environment. But if we consider it, we shall soon see that the spontaneity of living bodies is simply an appearance and the result of a certain mechanism in completely determined environments; so that it will be easy, after all, to prove that the behavior of living bodies, as well as the behavior of inorganic bodies, is dominated by a necessary determinism linking them with conditions of a purely physico-chemical order.

Let us note, first of all, that this kind of independence of living beings in the cosmic environment appears only in complex higher animals. Inferior beings, such as the infusoria, reduced to an elementary organism, have no real independence. These creatures exhibit the vital properties with which they are endowed, only under the influence of external moisture, light or warmth, and as soon as one or more of these conditions happens to fail, the vital manifestation ceases, because the parallel physico-chemical phenomenon has stopped. In vegetables the manifestation of vital phenomena is linked in the same way with conditions of warmth, moisture and light in the surrounding environment. It is the same again with cold-blooded animals; the phenomena of life are benumbed or stimulated according to the same conditions. Now the influences producing or retarding vital manifestations in living beings are exactly the same as those which produce, accelerate or retard manifestations of physico-chemical phenomena in inorganic bodies, so that instead of following the example of the vitalists in seeing a kind of opposition or incompatibility between the conditions of vital manifestations and the conditions of physico-chemical manifestations, we must note, on the contrary, in these two orders of phenomena a complete parallelism and a direct and necessary relation. Only in warm-blooded animals do the conditions of the organism and those of the surrounding environment seem to be independent; in these animals indeed the manifestation of vital phenomena no longer suffers the alternations and variations that the cosmic conditions display; and an inner force seems to join combat with these influences and in spite of them to maintain the vital forces in equilibrium. But fundamentally it is nothing of the sort; and the semblance depends simply on the fact that, by the more complete protective mechanism which we shall have occasion to study, the warm-blooded animal's internal environment comes less easily into equilibrium with the external cosmic environment. External influences, therefore, bring about changes and disturbances in the intensity of organic functions only in so far as the protective system of the organism's internal environment becomes insufficient in given conditions.

III. *Physiological phenomena in the higher animals
take place in perfected internal organic environments
endowed with constant physico-chemical properties*

. . . .

Physicists and chemists experimenting on inert bodies need consider only the external environment; by means of the thermometer, barometer and other instruments used in recording and measuring the properties of the external environment, they can always set themselves in equivalent conditions. For physiologists these instruments no longer suffice; and yet the internal environment is just the place where they should use them. Indeed, the internal environment of living beings is always in direct relation with the normal or pathological vital manifestations of organic units. In proportion as we ascend the scale of living beings, the organism grows more complex, the organic units become more delicate and require a more perfected internal environment. The circulating liquids, the blood serum and the intra-organic fluids all constitute the internal environment.

In living beings the internal environment, which is a true product of the organism, preserves the necessary relations of exchange and equilibrium with the external cosmic environment; but in proportion as the organism grows more perfect, the organic environment becomes specialized and more and more isolated, as it were, from the surrounding environment. In vegetables and in cold-blooded animals, as we have said, this isolation is less complete than in warm-blooded animals; in the latter the blood serum maintains an almost fixed and constant temperature and composition. But these differing conditions do not constitute differences of nature in different living beings; they are merely improvements in the isolating and protecting mechanisms of their environment. Vital manifestations in animals vary only because the physico-chemical conditions of their internal environments vary; thus a mammal, whose blood has been chilled either by natural hibernation or by certain lesions of the nervous system, closely resembles a really cold-blooded animal in the properties of its tissues.

To sum up, from what has been said we can gain an idea of the enormous complexity of vital phenomena and of the almost insuperable difficulties which their accurate determination opposes to physiologists forced to carry on experimentation in the internal or organic environments. These obstacles, however, cannot terrify us if we are thoroughly convinced that we are on the right road. Absolute determinism exists indeed in every vital phenomenon; hence biological science exists also; and consequently the studies to which we are devoting ourselves will not all be useless. General physiology is the basic biological science toward which all others converge. Its problem is to determine the elementary condition of vital phenomena. Pathology and therapeutics also rest on this common foundation. By normal activity of its organic units, life exhibits a state of health; by abnormal manifestation of the same units, diseases are characterized;

and finally through the organic environment modified by means of certain toxic or medicinal substances, therapeutics enables us to act on the organic units. To succeed in solving these various problems, we must, as it were, analyze the organism, as we take apart a machine to review and study all its works; that is to say, before succeeding in experimenting on smaller units we must first experiment on the machinery and on the organs. We must, therefore, have recourse to analytic study of the successive phenomena of life, and must make use of the same experimental method which physicists and chemists employ in analyzing the phenomena of inorganic bodies. The difficulties which result from the complexity of the phenomena of living bodies arise solely in applying experimentation; for fundamentally the object and principles of the method are always exactly the same.

. . . .

V. *The necessary conditions of natural phenomena are absolutely determined in living bodies as well as in inorganic bodies*

We must acknowledge as an experimental axiom that in living beings as well as in inorganic bodies the necessary conditions of every phenomenon are absolutely determined. That is to say, in other terms, that when once the conditions of a phenomenon are known and fulfilled, the phenomenon must always and necessarily be reproduced at the will of the experimenter. Negation of this proposition would be nothing less than negation of science itself. Indeed, as science is simply the determinate and the determinable, we must perforce accept as an axiom that, in identical conditions, all phenomena are identical and that, as soon as conditions are no longer the same, the phenomena cease to be identical. This principle is absolute in the phenomena of inorganic bodies as well as in those of living beings, and the influence of life, whatever view of it we take, can nowise alter it. As we have said, what we call vital force is a first cause analogous to all other first causes, in this sense, that it is utterly unknown. It matters little whether or not we admit that this force differs essentially from the forces presiding over manifestations of the phenomena of inorganic bodies, the vital phenomena which it governs must still be determinable; for the force would otherwise be blind and lawless, and that is impossible. The conclusion is that the phenomena of life have their special law because there is rigorous determinism in the various circumstances constituting conditions necessary to their existence or to their manifestations; and that is the same thing. Now in the phenomena of living bodies as in those of inorganic bodies, it is only through experimentation, as I have already often repeated, that we can attain knowledge of the conditions which govern these phenomena and so enable us to master them.

Everything so far said may seem elementary to men cultivating the physico-chemical sciences. But among naturalists and especially among physicians, we find men who, in the name of what they call vitalism, express most erroneous ideas on the subject which concerns us. They believe that study of the phenomena of living matter can have no relation to study of the phenomena of inorganic matter. They look on life as a mysterious supernatural influence which acts arbitrarily by freeing itself wholly from determinism, and they brand as materialists all who attempt to reconcile vital phenomena with definite organic and physico-chemical conditions. These false ideas are not easy to uproot when once established in the mind; only the progress of science can dispel them. But vitalistic ideas, taken in the sense which we have just indicated, are just a kind of medical superstition,—a belief in the supernatural. Now, in medicine, belief in occult causes, whether it is called vitalism or is otherwise named, encourages ignorance and gives birth to a sort of unintentional quackery; that is to say, the belief in an inborn, indefinable science. Confidence in absolute determinism in the phenomena of life leads, on the contrary, to real science, and gives the modesty which comes from the consciousness of our little learning and the difficulty of science. This feeling incites us, in turn, to work toward knowledge; and to this feeling alone, science in the end owes all its progress.

I should agree with the vitalists if they would simply recognize that living beings exhibit phenomena peculiar to themselves and unknown in inorganic nature. I admit, indeed, that manifestations of life cannot be wholly elucidated by the physico-chemical phenomena known in inorganic nature. I shall later explain my view of the part played in biology by physico-chemical sciences; I will here simply say that if vital phenomena differ from those of inorganic bodies in complexity and appearance, this difference obtains only by virtue of determined or determinable conditions proper to themselves. So if the sciences of life must differ from all others in explanation and in special laws, they are not set apart by scientific method. Biology must borrow the experimental method of physico-chemical sciences, but keep its special phenomena and its own laws.

In living bodies, as in inorganic bodies, laws are immutable, and the phenomena governed by these laws are bound to the conditions on which they exist, by a necessary and absolute determinism. I use the word determinism here as more appropriate than the word fatalism, which sometimes serves to express the same idea. Determinism in the conditions of vital phenomena should be one of the axioms of experimenting physicians. If they are thoroughly imbued with the truth of this principle, they will exclude all supernatural intervention from their explanations; they will have unshaken faith in the idea that fixed laws govern biological science; and at the same time they will have a reliable criterion for judging the often variable and contradictory appearance of vital phenomena. Indeed, starting with the principle that immutable laws exist, experimenters will be convinced that phenomena can never be mutually contradictory, if they are observed in the same conditions; and if they show variations, they will know that this is necessarily so because of the intervention or interference of other conditions which alter or mask phenomena. There will be occasion thenceforth to try to learn the conditions of these variations, for there can be no effect without a cause. Determinism thus becomes the foundation of all scientific progress and criticism. If we find disconcerting or even contradictory results in performing an experiment, we must never acknowledge exceptions or contradictions as real. That would be unscientific. We must simply and necessarily decide that conditions in the phenomena are different, whether or not we can explain them at the time.

I assert that the word exception is unscientific; and as soon as laws are known, no exception indeed can exist, and this expression, like so many others, merely enables us to speak of things whose causation we do not know. Every day we hear physicians use the words: ordinarily, more often, generally, or else express themselves numerically by saying, for instance: nine times out of ten, things happen in this way. I have heard old practitioners say that the words "always" and "never" should be crossed out of medicine. I condemn neither these restrictions nor the use of these locutions if they are used as empirical approximations about the appearances of phenomena when we are still more or less ignorant of the exact conditions in which they exist. But certain physicians seem to reason as if exceptions were necessary; they seem to believe that a vital force exists which can arbitrarily prevent things from always happening alike; so that exceptions would result directly from the action of mysterious vital force. Now this cannot be the case; what we now call an exception is a phenomenon, one or more of whose conditions are unknown; if the conditions of the phenomena of which we speak were known and determined, there would be no further exceptions, medicine would be as free from them as is any other science. For instance, we might formerly say that sometimes the itch was cured and sometimes not; but now that we attack the cause of this disease, we cure it always. Formerly it might be said that a lesion of the nerves brought on paralysis, now of feeling, and again of motion; but now we know that cutting the anterior spinal nerve paralyzes motion only. Motor paralysis occurs consistently and always, because its condition has been accurately determined by experimenters.

The certainty with which phenomena are determined should also be, as we have said, the foundation of experimental criticism, whether applied to one's self or to others. A phenomenon, indeed, always appears in the same way if conditions are similar; the phenomenon never fails if the conditions are present, just as it does fail to appear if the conditions are absent. Thus an experimenter who has made an experiment, in conditions which he believes were determined, may happen not to get the same results in a new series of investigations as in his first observation; in repeating the experiment, with fresh precautions, it may happen again that, instead of his first result, he may encounter a wholly different one. In such a situation, what is to be done? Should we acknowledge that the facts are indeterminable? Certainly not, since that cannot be. We must simply acknowledge that experimental conditions, which we believed to be known, are not known. We must more closely study, search out and define the experimental conditions, for the facts cannot be contradictory one to another; they can only be indeterminate. Facts never exclude one another, they are simply explained by differences in the conditions in which they are born. So an experimenter can never deny a fact that he has seen and observed, merely because he cannot rediscover it. In the third part of this introduction, we shall cite instances in which the principles of experimental criticism which we have just suggested, are put in practice.

VI. *To have determinism for phenomena, in biological as in physico-chemical sciences, we must reduce the phenomena to experimental conditions as definite and simple as possible*

As a natural phenomenon is only the expression of ratios and relations and connections, at least two bodies are necessary to its appearance. So we must always consider, first, a body which reacts or which manifests the phenomenon; second, another body which acts and plays the part of environment in relation to the first. It is impossible to imagine a body wholly isolated in nature; it would no longer be real, because there would be no relation to manifest its existence.

In phenomenal relations, as nature presents them to us, more or less complexity always prevails. In this respect mineral phenomena are much less complex than vital phenomena; this is why the sciences dealing with inorganic bodies have succeeded in establishing themselves more quickly. In living bodies, the complexity of phenomena is immense, and what is more, the mobility accompanying vital characteristics makes them much harder to grasp and to define.

The properties of living matter can be learned only through their relation to the properties of inorganic matter; it follows that the biological sciences must have as their necessary foundation the physico-chemical sciences from which they borrow their means of analysis and their methods of investigation. Such are the necessary reasons for the secondary and backward evolution of the sciences concerned with the phenomena of life. But though the complexity of vital phenomena creates great obstacles, we must not be appalled, for, as we have already said, unless we deny the possibility of biological science, the principles of science are everywhere the same. So we may be sure that we are on the right road and that in time we shall reach the scientific result that we are seeking, that is to say, determinism in the phenomena of living beings.

We can reach knowledge of definite elementary conditions of phenomena only by one road, viz., by experimental analysis. Analysis dissociates all the complex phenomena successively into more and more simple phenomena, until they are reduced, if possible, to just two elementary conditions. Experimental science, in fact, considers in a phenomenon only the definite conditions necessary to produce it. Physicists try to picture these conditions to themselves, more or less ideally in mechanics or mathematical physics. Chemists successively analyze complex matters; and in thus reaching either elements or definite substances (individual compounds or chemical species), they attain the elementary or irreducible conditions of phenomena. In the same way, biologists should analyze complex organisms and reduce the phenomena of life to conditions that cannot be analyzed in the present state of science.

Experimental physiology and medicine have no other goal. When faced by complex questions, physiologists and physicians, as well as physicists and chemists, should divide the total problem into simpler and simpler and more and more clearly defined partial problems. They will thus reduce phenomena to their simplest possible material conditions and make application of the experimental method easier and more certain. All the analytic sciences divide problems, in order to experiment better. By following this path, physicists and chemists have succeeded in reducing what seemed the most complex phenomena to simple properties connected with well-defined mineral species. By following the same analytic path, physiologists should succeed in reducing all the vital manifestations of a complex organism to the play of certain organs, and the action of these organs to the properties of well-defined tissues or organic units. Anatomico-physiological experimental analysis, which dates from Galen, has just this meaning, and histology, in pursuing the same problem to-day, is naturally coming closer and closer to the goal.

Though we can succeed in separating living tissues into chemical elements or bodies, still these elementary chemical bodies are not elements for physiologists. In this respect biologists are more like physicists than chemists, for they seek to determine the properties of bodies and are much less preoccupied with their elementary composition. In the present state of the science, it would be impossible to establish any relation between the vital properties of bodies and their chemical composition; because tissues and organs endowed with the most diverse properties are at times indistinguishable from the point of view of their elementary chemical composition. Chemistry is most useful to physiologists in giving them means of separating and studying individual compounds, true organic products which play important parts in the phenomena of life.

Organic individual compounds, though well defined in their properties, are still not active elements in physiological phenomena; like mineral matter, they are, as it were, only passive elements in the organism. For physiologists, the truly active elements are what we call anatomical or histological units. Like the organic individual compounds, these are not chemically simple; but physiologically considered, they are as simplified as possible in that their vital properties are the simplest that we know,—vital properties which vanish when we happen to destroy this elementary organized part. However, all ideas of ours about these elements are limited by the present state of our knowledge; for there can be no question that these histological units, in the condition of cells and fibres, are still complex. That is why certain naturalists refuse to give them the names of elements and propose to call them elementary organisms. This appellation is in fact more appropriate; we can perfectly well picture to ourselves a complex organism made up of a quantity of distinct elementary organisms, uniting, joining and grouping together in various ways, to give birth first to the different tissues of the body, then to its various organs; anatomical mechanisms are themselves only assemblages of organs which present endlessly varied combinations in living beings. When we come to analyze the complex manifestations of any organism, we should therefore separate the complex phenomena and reduce them to a certain number of simple properties belonging to elementary organisms; then synthetically reconstruct the total organism in thought, by reuniting and ordering the elementary organisms, considered at first separately, then in their reciprocal relations.

When physicians, chemists or physiologists, by successive experimental analyses, succeed in determining the irreducible element of a phenomenon in the present state of their science, the scientific problem is simplified, but its nature is not changed thereby; and men of science are no nearer to absolute knowledge of the essence of things. Nevertheless, they have gained what it is truly important to obtain, to wit, knowledge of the necessary conditions of the phenomenon and determination of the definite relation existing between a body manifesting its properties and the immediate cause of this manifestation. The object of analysis, in biological as in physico-chemical science, is, after all, to determine and, as far as possible, to isolate the conditions governing the occurrence of each phenomenon. We can act on the phenomena of nature only by reproducing the natural conditions in which they exist; and we act the more easily on these conditions in proportion as they have first been better analyzed and reduced to a greater state of simplicity. Real science exists, then, only from the moment when a phenomenon is accurately defined as to its nature and rigorously determined in relation to its material conditions, that is, when its law is known. Before that, we have only groping and empiricism.

. . . .

VIII. *In biological as in physico-chemical science,*
determinism is possible, because matter in living as in inorganic bodies
can possess no spontaneity

To sum up, the study of life includes two things: (1) Study of the properties of organized units; (2) study of the organic environment, i.e., study of the conditions which this environment must fulfill to permit the appearance of vital activities. Physiology, pathology and therapeutics rest on this double knowledge; apart from this, neither medical science nor any truly scientific or effectual therapeutics exists.

In living organisms it is convenient to distinguish between three kinds of definite bodies: first, chemical elements; second, organic and inorganic individual compounds; third, organized anatomical units. Of about 70 elements known to chemistry to-day, only 16 are found in that most complex of organisms, the organism of man. But these 16 elements combine with one another to form the various liquid, solid and gaseous substances of the organism. Oxygen and nitrogen, howev.er, are merely dissolved in the organic fluids; and in living beings, seem to act as elements. The inorganic individual compounds (earthy salts, phosphates, chlorides, sulphates, etc.) are essential constituents in the composition of living bodies, but are taken ready-made directly from the outer world. Organic individual compounds are also constituents of living bodies, but by no means borrowed from the outer world; they are made by the vegetable or animal organism; among such substances are starch, sugar, fat, albumen, etc., etc. When extracted from the body, they preserve their properties because they are not alive; they are organic products, but not organized. Anatomical units stand alone as organized living parts. These parts are irritable and, under the influence of various stimulants, exhibit properties exclusively characteristic of living beings. They live and nourish themselves, and their nourishment creates and preserves their properties, which means that they cannot be cut off from the organism without more or less rapidly losing their vitality.

Though very different from one another in respect to their functions in the organism, these three classes of bodies all show physico-chemical reactions under the influence of the outer stimuli,—warmth, light, electricity; but living parts also have the power of being irritable, i.e., reacting under the influence of certain stimuli in a way specially characteristic of living tissues, such as muscular contraction, nervous transmission, glandular secretion, etc. But whatever the variety presented by the three classes of phenomena, whether the reaction be physico-chemical or vital, it is never in any way spontaneous. The phenomenon always results from the influence exerted on the reacting body by a physico-chemical stimulant outside itself.

Every definite substance, whether inorganic, organic or organized, is autonomous; that is to say, it has characteristic properties and exhibits independent action. Nevertheless, each one of these bodies is inert, that is, it is incapable of putting itself into action; to do this, it must always enter into relation with another body, from which it receives a stimulus. Thus every mineral body in the cosmic environment is stable; it changes its state only when the circumstances in which it is placed are rather seriously changed, either naturally or through experimental interference. In any organic environment, the substances created by animals and vegetables are much more changeable and less stable, but still they are inert and exhibit their properties only as they are influenced by agents outside themselves. Finally, anatomical units themselves, which are the most changeable and unstable of substances, are still inert, that is, they never break into vital activity unless some foreign influence invites them. A muscle-fibre, for instance, has the vital property peculiar to itself of contracting, but this living fibre is inert in the sense that if nothing changes in its environmental or its inner conditions, it cannot bring its functions into play, and it will not contract. For the muscular fibre to contract, a change must necessarily be produced in it, by its coming into relation with a stimulation from without, which may come either from the blood or from a nerve. We may say as much of all the histological units, nerve units, blood units, etc. Different living units thus play the part of stimuli, one in relation to another; and the functional manifestations of an organism are merely the expression of their harmonious reciprocal relations. The histological units react either separately or one against another by means of vital properties which are themselves in necessary connection with surrounding physico-chemical conditions; and this relation is so intimate that we may say the intensity of physico-chemical phenomena taking place in an organism may be used to measure the intensity of its vital phenomena. Therefore, as has already been said, we must not set up an antagonism between vital phenomena and physico-chemical phenomena, but, on the contrary, we must note the complete and necessary parallelism between the two classes of phenomena. To sum up, living matter is no more able than inorganic matter to get into activity or movement by itself. Every change in matter implies intervention of a new relation, i.e., an outside condition or influence. The rôle of men of science is to try to define and determine the material conditions producing the appearance of each phenomenon. These conditions once known, experimenters master the phenomenon in this sense, that they can give movement to matter, or take it away, at pleasure.

What we have just said is equally true for the phenomena of living bodies and the phenomena of inorganic bodies. Only in the case of the complex higher organisms, physiologists and physicians must study the stimuli of vital phenomena, not in the relations of the whole organism with the general cosmic environment, but rather in the organic conditions of the inner environment. Considered in the general cosmic environment, the functions of man and of the higher animals seem to us, indeed, free and independent of the physico-chemical conditions of the environment, because its actual stimuli are found in an inner, organic, liquid environment. What we see from the outside is merely the result of physico-chemical stimuli from the inner environment; that is where physiologists must build up the real determinism of vital functions.

Living machines are therefore created and constructed in such a way that, in perfecting themselves, they become freer and freer in the general cosmic environment. But the most absolute determinism still obtains, none the less, in the inner environment which is separated more and more from the outer cosmic environment, by reason of the same organic development. A living machine keeps up its movement because the inner mechanism of the organism, by acts and forces ceaselessly renewed, repairs the losses involved in the exercise of its functions. Machines created by the intelligence of man, though infinitely coarser, are built in just this fashion. A steam engine's activity is independent of outer physico-chemical conditions, since the machine goes on working through cold, heat, dryness and moisture. But physicists going down into the inner environment of the machine, find that this independence is only apparent, and that the movement of its every inner gear is determined by physical conditions whose law they know. As for physiologists, if they can go down into the inner environment of a living machine, they find likewise absolute determinism that must become the real foundation of the science of living bodies.

IX. *The limits of our knowledge are the same in the phenomena of living bodies and in the phenomena of inorganic bodies*

. . . .

In the knowledge that we acquire, we should distinguish between two sets of notions: the first corresponds to the *cause* of phenomena, the second to the *means* of producing them. By the cause of a phenomenon we mean the constant and definite condition necessary to existence; we call this the relative determinism or the *how* of things, i.e., the immediate or determining cause. The means of obtaining phenomena are the varied processes by whose aid we may succeed in putting in action the single determining cause which produces the phenomenon. The necessary cause in the formation of water is the combination of two volumes of hydrogen with one of oxygen; this is the single cause which always determines the phenomenon. We cannot conceive of water apart from this essential condition. Subordinate conditions or processes in the formation of water may be extremely varied; only all these processes reach the same result, viz., combination of oxygen and hydrogen in invariable proportions. Let us take another example. I assume that we wish to transform starch into glucose; we have any number of means or processes for doing this, but fundamentally there will always be the identical cause, and a single determinism will beget the phenomenon. This cause is fixation of one more unit of water in the substance, to bring about its transformation. Only we may produce this hydration in any number of conditions and by any number of methods: by means of acidulated water, of heat, of animal or vegetable enzymes; but all these processes finally come to a single condition, hydrolysis of the starch. The determinism, i.e., the cause of the phenomenon, is therefore single, though the means for making it appear may be multiple and apparently very various. It is most important to establish this distinction especially in medicine, where the greatest confusion reigns, precisely because physicians recognize a multitude of causes for the same disease. To convince ourselves of what I am urging we have only to open a treatise on pathology. By no means all the circumstances enumerated are causes; at most they are means or processes by which a disease can be produced. But the real and effective cause of a disease must be *constant* and *determined*, that is unique; anything else would be a denial of science in medicine. It is true that determining causes are much harder to recognize and define in the phenomena of living beings; but they exist nevertheless, in spite of the seeming diversity of means employed. Thus in certain toxic phenomena we see different poisons lead to one cause and to a single determinism for the death of histological units, for example, the coagulation of muscular substance. In the same way, varied circumstances producing the same disease must all correspond to a single and determined pathogenic action. In a word, determinism which insists on identity of effect bound up with identity of cause is an axiom of science which can no more be transgressed in the sciences of life than in the sciences of inorganic matter.

. . . .

Part Two, Chapter II
EXPERIMENTAL CONSIDERATIONS PECULIAR TO
LIVING BEINGS

I. *The phenomena of living beings must be considered as*
a harmonious whole

So far we have been explaining experimental considerations applicable to both living and inorganic bodies; for living bodies the
difference consists merely in the greater complexity of phenomena,
making experimental analysis and determination of the conditions
incomparably harder. But in the behavior of living bodies we must call
the reader's attention to their very special interdependence; in the
study of vital functions, if we neglected the physiological point of
view, even if we experimented skilfully, we should be led to the most
false ideas and the most erroneous deductions.

We saw in the last chapter that the object of the experimental
method is to reach the determinism of phenomena, no matter of what
nature, whether vital or mineral. We know, moreover, that what we call
determinism of a phenomenon means nothing else than the determining cause or immediate cause determining the appearance of
phenomena. Thus we necessarily obtain the conditions in which the
phenomena exist, and on which the experimenter must act to make the
phenomena vary. We therefore consider the various expressions above
as equivalents; and the word determinism sums them all up.

It is indeed true, as we have said, that life brings absolutely no
difference into the scientific experimental method which must be
applied to the study of physiological phenomena, and that in this
respect physiological science and physico-chemical science rest on
exactly the same principles of investigation. But still we must recognize that determinism in the phenomena of life is not only very complex, but that it is at the same time harmoniously graded. Thus complex physiological phenomena are made up of a series of simpler
phenomena each determining the other by associating together or
combining for a common final object. Now the physiologist's prime
object is to determine the elementary conditions of physiological
phenomena and to grasp their natural subordination, so as to understand and then to follow the different combinations in the varied
mechanism of animal organisms. The ancient emblem representing life
as a closed circle, formed by a serpent biting its own tail, gives a fairly
accurate picture of things. In complex organisms the organism of life
actually forms a closed circle, but a circle which has a head and a tail in
this sense, that vital phenomena are not all of equal importance,
though each in succession completes the vital circle. Thus the muscular
and nervous organs sustain the activity of the organs preparing the
blood; but the blood in its turn nourishes the organs which produce it.
Here is an organic or social interdependence which sustains a sort of
perpetual motion, until some disorder or stoppage of a necessary vital
unit upsets the equilibrium, or leads to disturbance or stoppage in the
play of the animal machine. The problem for experimenting physicians

consists, therefore, in finding the simple determinism of an organic disorder, that is to say, in grasping the initial phenomenon which brings all the others in its train through a complex determinism as necessary in character as the initial determinism. This initial determinism is like Ariadne's thread guiding the experimenter in the dark labyrinth of physiological and pathological phenomena, and enabling him to understand how their varied mechanisms are still bound together by absolute determinisms. By examples cited further on, we shall see how a dislocation of the organism or an apparently highly complex disorder may be traced back to an initial simple determinism which later produces more complex determinisms. A case in point is poisoning by carbon monoxide. I am devoting my whole course at the Collège de France this year to the study of *curare*, not for the sake of the substance itself, but because this study shows us how the simplest single determinism, such as the lesion of a terminal motor nerve, re-echoing successively from all the other vital units, leads to secondary determinisms which grow more and more complicated till death ensues. I wish thus to establish experimentally the existence of intraorganic determinisms to which I shall later return, because I consider study of them the true basis of pathology and of scientific therapeutics.

Physiologists and physicians must never forget that a living being is an organism with its own individuality. Since physicists and chemists cannot take their stand outside the universe, they study bodies and phenomena in themselves and separately without necessarily having to connect them with nature as a whole. But physiologists, finding themselves, on the contrary, outside the animal organism which they see as a whole, must take account of the harmony of this whole, even while trying to get inside, so as to understand the mechanism of its every part. The result is that physicists and chemists can reject all idea of final causes for the facts that they observe; while physiologists are inclined to acknowledge an harmonious and pre-established unity in an organized body, all of whose partial actions are interdependent and mutually generative. We really must learn, then, that if we break up a living organism by isolating its different parts, it is only for the sake of ease in experimental analysis, and by no means in order to conceive them separately. Indeed when we wish to ascribe to a physiological quality its value and true significance, we must always refer it to this whole, and draw our final conclusion only in relation to its effects in the whole. It is doubtless because he felt this necessary interdependence among all parts of an organism, that Cuvier said that experimentation was not applicable to living beings, since it separated organized parts which should remain united. For the same reason, other physiologists or physicians, called vitalists, have proscribed and still proscribe experimentation in medicine. These views, which have their correct side, are nevertheless false in their general outcome and have greatly hampered the progress of science. It is doubtless correct to say that the constituent parts of an organism are physiologically inseparable one from another, and that they all contribute to a common vital result; but we may not conclude from this that the living machine must not be analyzed as we analyze a crude machine whose parts also have their rôle to play in a whole. With the help of experimental analysis we must transfer physiological functions as much as possible outside the organism; segregation allows us to see and to grasp hidden conditions of the phenomena, so as to follow them later inside the organism and to interpret their vital rôle. Thus we establish artificial digestion and fecundation, so as to know natural digestion and fecundation better. Thanks to their organic self-regulation, we can also detach living tissues, and by means of artificial circulation or otherwise, we can place them in conditions where we can better study their characteristics. We occasionally isolate an organ by using anesthetics to destroy the reactions of its general group; we reach the same result by cutting the nerves leading to a part, but preserving the blood vessels. By means of experimental analysis, I have even transformed warm-blooded animals, as it were, into cold-blooded animals, so as to study better the characteristics of their histological units; I have succeeded in poisoning glands separately and in making them work, by means of dissected nerves, quite apart from the organism. In this last case we can have a gland, at will, in a state, first, of absolute rest, then, of exaggerated action; when both extremes of the phenomenon are known we can later easily grasp all the intervening stages, and we then understand how a completely chemical function can be regulated by a nervous system, so as to supply organic fluids in conditions that are always the same. We will not further amplify these suggestions about experimental analysis; we sum up by saying that proscribing experimental analysis of organs means arresting science and denying the experimental method; but, on the other hand, that practising physiological analysis, while losing sight of the harmonious unity of an organism, means misunderstanding the science of life and individuality, and leaving it characterless.

After carrying out an analysis of phenomena, we must therefore always reconstruct our physiological synthesis, so as to see the joint action of all the parts we have isolated. *À propos* of the phrase physiological synthesis, we must further explain our thought. It is generally agreed that synthesis reunites what analysis has divided, and that synthesis therefore verifies analysis, of which it is merely the counterproof or necessary complement. This definition is entirely true for analysis and synthesis of matter. In chemistry, synthesis produces, weight for weight, the same body made up of identical elements combined in the same proportions; but in the case of analyzing and synthesizing the properties of bodies, i.e., synthesizing phenomena, it is much harder. Indeed, the properties of bodies result not merely from the nature and proportions of matter, but also from the arrangement of matter. Moreover, as we know, it happens that properties, which appear and disappear in synthesis and analysis, cannot be considered as simple addition or pure subtraction of properties of the constituent bodies. Thus, for example, the properties of oxygen and hydrogen do not account for the properties of water, which result nevertheless from combining them.

I do not intend to go into these difficult yet fundamental problems about the relative properties of combined or combining bodies; they will find their proper place elsewhere. I shall here only repeat that phenomena merely express the relations of bodies, whence it follows that, by dissociating the parts of a whole, we must make phenomena cease if only because we destroy the relations. It follows also, in physiology, that analysis, which teaches us the properties of isolated elementary parts, can never give us more than a most incomplete ideal synthesis; just as knowing a solitary man would not bring us knowledge of all the institutions which result from man's association, and which can reveal themselves only through social life. In a word, when we unite physiological elements, properties appear which were imperceptible in the separate elements. We must therefore always proceed experimentally in vital synthesis, because quite characteristic phenomena may result from more and more complex union or association of organized elements. All this proves that these elements, though distinct and self-dependent, do not therefore play the part of simple associates; their union expresses more than addition of their separate properties. I am persuaded that the obstacles surrounding the experimental study of psychological phenomena are largely due to difficulties of this kind; for despite their marvellous character and the delicacy of their manifestations, I find it impossible not to include cerebral phenomena, like all other phenomena of living bodies, in the laws of scientific determinism.

. . . .

The primary essence of life is a developing organic force, the force which constituted the mediating nature of Hippocrates and the *archeus faber* of Van Helmont. But whatever our idea of the nature of this force, it is always exhibited concurrently and parallel with the physico-chemical conditions proper to vital phenomena. Through study, then, of physico-chemical details, physicians will learn to understand individualities as special cases included in a general law, and will discover there, as everywhere, an harmonious generalization of variety in unity. But since physicians deal with variety, they must always seek to define it jn their studies and to comprehend it in their generalizations.

If I had to define life in a single phrase, I should clearly express my thought by throwing into relief the one characteristic which, in my opinion, sharply differentiates biological science. I should say: life is creation. In fact, a created organism is a machine which necessarily works by virtue of the physico-chemical properties of its constituent elements. To-day we differentiate three kinds of properties exhibited in the phenomena of living beings: physical properties, chemical properties and vital properties. But the term "vital properties" is itself only provisional; because we call properties vital which we have not yet been able to reduce to physico-chemical terms; but in that we shall doubtless succeed some day. So that what distinguishes a living machine is not the nature of its physico-chemical properties, complex as they may be, but rather the creation of the machine which develops under our eyes in conditions proper to itself and according to a definite idea which expresses the living being's nature and the very essence of life.

When a chicken develops in an egg, the formation of the animal body as a grouping of chemical elements is not what essentially distinguishes the vital force. This grouping takes place only according to laws which govern the chemico-physical properties of matter; but the guiding idea of the vital evolution is essentially of the domain of life and belongs neither to chemistry nor to physics nor to anything else. In every living germ is a creative idea which develops and exhibits itself through organization. As long as a living being persists, it remains under the influence of this same creative vital force, and death comes when it can no longer express itself; here as everywhere, everything is derived from the idea which alone creates and guides; physico-chemical means of expression are common to all natural phenomena and remain mingled, pell-mell, like the letters of the alphabet in a box, till a force goes to fetch them, to express the most varied thoughts and mechanisms. This same vital idea preserves beings, by reconstructing the living parts disorganized by exercise or destroyed by accidents or diseases. To the physico-chemical conditions of this primal development, then, we must always refer our explanation of life, whether in the normal or the pathological state. We shall see, indeed, that physiologists and physicians can really act only indirectly through animal physico-chemistry, that is to say, through physics and chemistry worked out in the special field of life, where the necessary conditions of all phenomena of living organisms develop, create and support each other according to a definite idea and obedient to rigorous determinisms.

II. *Experimental practice with living beings*

As we have said, the experimental method and the principles of experimentation are identical for the phenomena of inorganic bodies and the phenomena of living bodies. But it cannot be the same with experimental practice, and it is easy to conceive that the peculiar organization of living bodies requires special processes for its analysis and must offer difficulties *sui generis*. However, the considerations and special precepts, which we shall present to physiologists, to forearm them against sources of error in experimental practice, have to do only with the delicacy, mobility and fugitiveness of vital qualities and the complexity of the phenomena of life. Physiologists, indeed, have only to take apart the living machine, and with the help of tools and processes borrowed from physics and chemistry, to study and measure the various vital phenomena whose law they seek to discover.

Each of the sciences possesses, if not an individual method, at least particular processes; and the sciences, moreover, serve as instruments one for another. Mathematics serves as an instrument for physics, chemistry and biology in different degrees; physics and chemistry serve as powerful instruments for physiology and medicine. In the mutual service which sciences render one another, we must of course distinguish between the men of science, who use, and those who carry forward each science. Physicists and chemists are not mathematicians because they make calculations; physiologists are not chemists or physicists because they make use of chemical reagents or physical instruments, any more than chemists and physicists are physiologists because they study the composition or properties of certain animal or vegetable fluids or tissues. Each science has its problem and its point of view which we may not confuse without risk of leading scientific investigation astray. Yet this confusion has often occurred in biological science which, because of its complexity, needs the help of all the other sciences. We have seen, and we still often see chemists and physicists who, instead of confining themselves to the demand that living bodies furnish them suitable means and arguments to establish certain principles of their own sciences, try to absorb physiology and reduce it to simple physico-chemical phenomena. They offer explanations or systems of life which tempt us at times by their false simplicity, but which harm biological science in every case, by bringing in false guidance and inaccuracy which it then takes long to dispel. In a word, biology has its own problem and its definite point of view; it borrows from other sciences only their help and their methods, not their theories. This help from other sciences is so powerful that, without it, the development of the science of vital phenomena would be impossible. Previous knowledge of the physico-chemical sciences is therefore decidedly not, as is often said, an accessory to biology, but, on the contrary, is essential to it and fundamental. That is why I think it proper to call the physico-chemical sciences allied sciences, and not sciences accessory to physiology. We shall see that anatomy is also a science allied to physiology, just as physiology itself, which requires the help of anatomy and of all the physico-chemical sciences, is the science most closely allied to medicine and forms its true scientific foundation.

The application of physico-chemical sciences to physiology and the use of their processes as instruments, suited to the analysis of the phenomena of life, present a great many difficulties inherent, as we have said, in the mobility and fugitiveness of vital phenomena. The spontaneity and mobility enjoyed by living beings make the properties of organized bodies very hard to fix and to study. . . .

. . . .

To sum up, if we wish to find the exact conditions of vital manifestations in man and the higher animals, we must really look, not at the outer cosmic environment, but rather at the inner organic environment. Indeed, as we have often said, it is in the study of these inner organic conditions that direct and true explanations are to be found for the phenomena of the life, health, sickness and death of the organism. From the outside, we see only the resultant of all the inner activities of the body, which therefore seem like the result of a distinct vital force in only the most distant relations with the physico-chemical conditions of the outer environment, and manifesting itself always as a sort of organic personality endowed with specific tendencies. We have elsewhere said that ancient medicine considered the influence of the cosmic environment, of water, air and locality; we may indeed find useful suggestions here as to hygienic and as to morbid changes. But modern experimental medicine will be distinguished for being espe-

cially founded on knowledge of the inner environment where normal
and morbid as well as medicinal influences take action. But how are we
to know this inner environment of the organism, so complex in man and
in the higher animals, unless we go down and, as it were, penetrate into
it, by means of experimentation applied to living bodies? That is to
say, to analyze the phenomena of life, we must necessarily penetrate
into living organisms with the help of the methods of vivisection.

To sum up, only in the physico-chemical conditions of the inner
environment can we find the causation of the external phenomena of
life. The life of an organism is simply the resultant of all its inmost
workings; it may appear more or less lively, or more or less enfeebled
and languishing, without possible explanation by anything in the outer
environment, because it is governed by the conditions of the inner
environment. We must therefore seek the true foundation of animal
physics and chemistry in the physico-chemical properties of the inner
environment. However, as we shall see further on, it is necessary to
consider not only the physico-chemical conditions indispensable to
life, but also the peculiar, evolutionary, physiological conditions which
are the *quid proprium* of biological science. I have always greatly emphasized this distinction because I believe that it is basic, and that
physiological considerations must predominate in a treatise on experimentation applied to medicine. Here indeed we shall find the differences due to influences of age, sex, species, race, or to state of fasting or
digestion, etc. That will lead us to consider, in the organism, reciprocal
and simultaneous reactions of the inner environment on the organs,
and of the organs on the inner environment.

. . . .

Part Three, Chapter II
EXAMPLES OF
EXPERIMENTAL PHYSIOLOGICAL CRITICISM

. . . .

IV. *Experimental criticism should bear on*
facts alone and never on words

At the beginning of this chapter, I said that we are often deceived by
false values ascribed to words. I wish to explain my idea by examples.

First example. — In 1859 I made a report to the Philomathic Society,
in which I discussed Brodie's and Magendie's experiments on ligature
of the bile duct, and I showed that the divergent results which the two
experimenters reached, depended on the fact that one operated on dogs
and tied only the bile duct, while the other operated on cats and, without suspecting it, included in his ligature, both the bile duct and a
pancreatic duct. Thus I showed the reason for the difference in the
results they reached, and I concluded that, in physiology as everywhere

else, experiments are rigorous and give identical results whenever we operate in exactly similar conditions.

À *propos* of this, a member of the society took the floor to attack my conclusions; it was Gerdy, surgeon at the Charité, professor in the faculty of medicine, and known through various works on surgery and physiology. "Your anatomical explanation of Brodie's and Magendie's experiments," said he, "is correct, but I cannot accept your general conclusion. You say, in fact, that the results of experiments in physiology are identical; I deny it. Your conclusion would be correct for inert nature, but it cannot be true for living nature. Whenever life enters into phenomena," he went on, "conditions may be as similar as we please; the results may still be different." To support his opinion, Gerdy cited cases of individuals with the same disease, to whom he had given the same drugs, with different results. He also recalled cases of like operations for the same disease, but followed by cure in one case and death in another. These differences, according to him, all depended on life itself altering the results, though the experimental conditions were the same; but this could not happen, he thought, in phenomena of inert bodies, into which life does not enter. Opposition to these ideas was prompt and general in the Philomathic Society. Everyone pointed out to Gerdy that his opinions were nothing less than a denial of biological science; and that, in the cases of which he spoke, he completely deceived himself as to the identity of conditions, in this sense, that the diseases which he regarded as similar or identical were not in the least alike, and that he attributed to the influence of life what should be accounted for by our ignorance about phenomena as complex as those of pathology. Gerdy continued to maintain that life had the effect of altering phenomena so as to make them differ in different individuals, even when the conditions in which they took place were identical. . . .

THE UNIVERSE
IN ITS BIOLOGICAL ASPECT

J. S. Haldane

Different aspects of the universe of our experience have given rise to different branches of science or knowledge. The temporal and spatial aspects have, for instance, given rise to the mathematical sciences, the physical aspects to the physical sciences, and the psychological aspects to the "humanistic" sciences which deal with conscious behaviour.

For ordinary scientific purposes we can separate these aspects, though we can also readily see that they cannot ultimately be separated. What I wish to discuss is the biological aspect, with its corresponding branches of biological science.

Although biology is among the oldest branches of knowledge, and biological ideas played a large part in Greek culture, as represented for instance by Aristotle, yet in modern times biology as a really distinct branch of science has to fight for its acknowledgment. My lecture must therefore perforce be a fighting lecture. If it were true that life can be regarded as no more than a complex physical and chemical process, apart from the mysterious fact of consciousness which may accompany it, then biology would be no more than a branch of the physical sciences. I shall try to show you that this is not so, and that biology can rightly claim to be an independent science, representing its own aspect of experience. In making this claim I must at the same time protest against the assumption made by many writers that the "science" of nature means simply mathematical physics. In the clear and fascinating

---

"The Universe in Its Biological Aspect," an address to the British Institute of Philosophical Studies, January 12, 1932. Reprinted from *Materialism* by J. S. Haldane (London: Hodder and Stoughton, Limited, 1932), pp. 47–86.

writings of Sir Arthur Eddington and Sir James Jeans, for instance, this assumption seems to be constantly made; and biology is treated as if it were, or at least might be, only a complicated, and therefore backward, branch of mathematical physics.[1] To be more specific, living organisation is treated as if it were only machinery, to the working of which the second law of thermodynamics can be applied legitimately. A complete *petitio principii* is involved in the assumption that the visible and tangible world of our experience must necessarily be regarded as only a physical world.

It seems to me that in the late Renaissance time, when mathematical and physical science burst into activity with living and fruitful ideas, biology was quite unintentionally put on a wrong track. In questioning Nature by experiment and ordinary observation we need to realise what questions can be answered, and what cannot be, because they are meaningless. The success of physicists and chemists with their own questions led biologists to put similar questions in connection with the phenomena of life, and to assume that they are capable of being answered. The result has been, as it seems to me, that though biology has made very striking progress in modern times, it has also suffered from much confusion; and as one result biologists scarcely know where they are as regards the question whether biology is in reality any more than a branch of the physical sciences.

The characteristic feature of life is that living organisms present a highly specific structure and set of activities, reproduced indefinitely often. In the light of detailed investigation it is evident that all the phenomena in a living organism are dependent on its environment. But it is equally evident that the manner of this dependence is, in its turn, dependent on the organism itself, and is, or tends to be, of such a nature that the specific structure and activities of the organism are developed, maintained for a certain time, and sooner or later reproduced from part of its living body. When we examine any part of this living body we find that it is the seat of constant activity of such a nature that from a physical standpoint both its substance and its energy are constantly being lost, but are at the same time constantly being replaced. Thus both the structure and the activities tend to be maintained in the characteristic manner, in spite of the losses.

Not only the general conception which we frame of life, but also the detailed study based on this conception, must correspond with our experience of life. In ordinary physical and chemical study we analyse our experience into that of separable events or processes occurring in separable material units; and it may at first sight seem that we must be able to do the same with the phenomena of life. Indeed, it is at present usually taken as self-evident that we can do so, and that the phenomena of life can therefore be included as part of a universe which can be so analysed, whether or not a mechanical analysis is possible. In actual

---

1. I may perhaps point out that if we accept Planck's contention (*Nature*, April 18, 1931) that "the conception of wholeness must . . . be introduced into physics, as in biology, to make the orderliness of Nature intelligible and capable of formulation," mathematical physics can be regarded as a backward branch of biology.

fact, however, we can only do so if at the same time we can account in some way for the characteristic features with which biology deals.

If we persist in the attempt to analyse the phenomena into separable events or processes, we are either driven into the vitalistic assumption that a special influence, which has been called the vital principle, or by various other names, is determining the phenomena within an organism in such a manner as to give them their specific character, or else into the mechanistic conception that the specific character is an appearance dependent on extremely definite and complex physico-chemical structure in living organisms. Both of these hypotheses are represented in the forms which biological theory has taken since the time of Galileo, but it seems to me that to both of them there are insuperable objections, which I shall now state.

The vitalistic hypothesis, which may be discussed first, seemed to make it possible to retain the physical interpretation of the visible universe, with the one provision that what occurs, or part of what occurs, in living organisms is determined in a special and characteristic manner. As a matter of fact, physicists and chemists were usually inclined to accept vitalism, since they very readily recognised the peculiarities of life, and vitalism seemed to leave them quite unencumbered in what they regarded as their own domain. It was also the prevailing belief among biologists from the seventeenth to the middle of the nineteenth century, and still survives among them to some extent, though often in a disguised form. At the present time the difficulty in framing any mechanistic conception of what are known as quantum phenomena is driving physicists towards a conception very similar to that of vitalism extended to phenomena existing throughout what we at present call the inorganic world.

The vital principle was conceived as something which grows and multiplies within living organisms with their growth and multiplication, death being its disappearance. Its influence was manifested in the otherwise unexplained fact that the characteristic co-ordinated details of living structure and living activities are developed and maintained. It was conceived as an influence constantly guiding the otherwise unco-ordinated or chaotic reactions between the substances present in the body, and between these substances and those present in the environment. The characteristic features of life were therefore due to its influence, and the manner of this influence was specific in each species of organism.

The fatal difficulty associated with vitalism is that observation and experiment have shown with ever-increasing clearness that the supposed influence of the vital principle is dependent on what were admitted by the vitalists to be ordinary physical and chemical conditions in the environment. A lack or excess of something (for instance, oxygen or carbon dioxide) in these conditions, or some abnormality in them, is sufficient, not merely to hinder life for the time, but to pervert or entirely destroy it. This is shown by the discovery and study of all kinds of diseases or abnormalities due to deficiencies or excesses in the environment, of the action of poisons, and of various other facts demonstrating how completely all the influences in living organisms are ultimately dependent on conditions in the environment. In multicellular organisms, moreover, the specific behaviour of each living cell is clearly dependent on the specific character of the environment produced for it by the other cells. With the absence of these environmental conditions the specific behaviour disappears.

In view of all this, biologists have almost unanimously abandoned vitalism as an acknowledged belief, and I do not think that they are ever in the least likely to return to it. But the abandonment of vitalism during the latter half of last century led them, since they still held firmly to the Renaissance ideas as to visible reality, to assume that a physico-chemical or mechanistic interpretation of life must be an ultimate possibility, in which case biology must be regarded as a branch of the physical sciences. Let us now examine this conception. We can do so quite generally, without going much into detail.

The general difficulty which at once confronts the mechanistic conception of life is that of giving any account of the maintained co-ordination which is characteristic of life. The phenomena in a living organism are of such a nature that they are not only co-ordinated in a highly specific manner, but are maintained and reproduced from generation to generation. On the mechanistic interpretation these peculiar characters must be due to great complications of structure within what is called "living matter." In other words, a living organism must be conceived as an elaborately arranged physico-chemical automaton. Descartes, whom Huxley and other representatives of the physico-chemical theory of life acknowledged as their historical leader, stated this general hypothesis very clearly in his short physiological books *De Homine* and *De Formatione Fœtus*. We can further extend this hypothesis by supposing that the elaboration is the result of natural selection, acting over millions of years, and not, as various mechanistic theologians and others inferred, of an act of creation by a God possessing superhuman skill and knowledge of physics and chemistry.

But whether in its purely scientific, or in its theological, form, the mechanistic conception does not cover the facts. What is interpreted on the mechanistic conception as the physico-chemical structure of a living organism is constantly passing away and being renewed. In reproduction of a whole organism this process occurs in a gross manner, so that only a very minute portion of the parent organism may pass into the offspring; and this may be repeated indefinitely often. The theory of natural selection is, moreover, of no help in a mechanistic theory of heredity, since the fact of heredity, including hereditary transmission of variations, is taken for granted in the theory, and so cannot be accounted for by it. It is mere confusion of thought to suppose that the fact of natural selection contributes to a mechanistic theory of life.

Before detailed study of the metabolism associated with life, attempts at a mechanistic theory of heredity were mainly confined to the reproduction of characteristic form. The type of such attempts was the so-called "box within box" theory, according to which the germ contains a small image of the adult organism. Development was supposed to consist in a mere expansion of this small image to the adult size. All the required physico-chemical complication was thus supposed to be present in the small image, and further far smaller ones within it, to provide for future generations.

When no trace of any such images could be found in the earliest stages of developing organisms, mechanistic theories of development took the form of assuming that in these stages there is present a molecular arrangement or system of the definiteness and complication needed to bring it about that, in response to the nutritional and other stimuli of the environment, the adult organism is developed. This is the form which the mechanistic theory takes at present. I need not enter into the elaborations required in order to bring it into harmony with the mass of microscopical and other observation which has meanwhile accumulated with regard to cells, nuclei, chromosomes and their elements, and sexual union. It is evident that, among all these details, important as they are, we are apt to lose sight of the main thread of argument in the mechanistic theory. That argument is that the germ of an organism must contain a physico-chemical system of such extraordinary complication and definiteness that, in response to the action of its structureless physico-chemical environment, an adult organism is formed with its endless features of minute resemblance to both the form and the metabolic activities of the parent organism or organisms. This structure or system must also be capable of reproduction indefinitely often.

Now when we examine this conception we can very soon see that it contains all the essential defects of the "box within box" conception, as well as greater defects resulting from our far greater knowledge of how characteristic not only the form, but also the activities, of any organism are. Let us suppose that there is such a structure or system within a germ. In sexual reproduction it must in the first place have been produced by some sort of fusion of a male and a female structure. We may picture to ourselves this process as one in which definite portions of a male have been exchanged for corresponding portions of a female structure. A very intelligent ultra-microscopic mechanician might effect this selective exchange, but we can form no conception of how it could be effected by any physico-chemical process. Apart from this preliminary question there is the further and more fundamental question as to how the male or female structure could originate. Many biologists, following the lead of Weismann, have been content to say that the offspring is like the parent because the substance from which the offspring develops is the same in character as that from which the parent has developed, since both originate from the same stock of growing living matter or germ-plasm. But from the mechanistic standpoint this is a mere putting of empty words in place of explanation. By a plasma is ordinarily meant a solution of very large molecules and molecular aggregates, that is to say, a colloidal solution; and a solution has no definite structure, since its molecules or parts move about freely. A germ on the mechanistic theory must have a quite definite and enormously complex physico-chemical structure, and the structure of the germ of the offspring must have been formed by physico-chemical means in a perfectly definite manner from the parent organism, the germ of the parent organism having within it, in its turn, the molecular machinery for the formation of not only its own adult form, but that of all its direct offspring, including the millions which never develop; and so on *ad infinitum.* From this we can see that the mechanistic theory of reproduction lands us in absurdities. The attempts to render intelligible in a mechanistic sense how it is that living organisms reproduce what is normal to them seem to me almost childish in their futility. From the mechanistic standpoint reproduction is a miracle; but such an admission would be a negation of science. The attempt at mechanistic explanation tends to drive us back towards vitalism, with the vital principle as a dumping-place for what seems miraculous.

What we can perhaps realise most clearly in the case of reproduction of a whole organism is, however, no isolated fact in biology; for reproduction is taking place in all living activity. We can everywhere observe the breaking-down processes, with formation of various end-products, in the ever-present metabolism of living tissues; but along with these go characteristic processes of reproduction. What is reproduced is living structure and activity with all their delicacy of detail. We can form no coherent mechanistic conception of how it is that the intensely labile structure tends to return always to normality, or, to put the matter differently, how the breaking-down process is so co-ordinated that the building-up process accompanies it. The failure of the mechanistic theory extends over the whole field of the phenomena of life. We can only adhere to this theory if we obstinately close our eyes to facts. The orthodox credulity with which so many writers continue to refer to the "mechanisms" of various living activities is to my mind pathetic in its blind clinging to what has come to be regarded as sacred scientific authority.

Up to a certain point biologists can work on quite comfortably with either mechanistic or vitalistic principles. The mechanists can accept as simply given in experience all of what seem to them the individual physical and chemical facts which the study of life presents; and they can at the same time accept the characteristic peculiarities of life and account in their minds for them by assuming that further similar study, to which there are no limits whatsoever, will gradually reveal physical and chemical interpretations of them. They can also point to the great apparent progress which has been made in physico-chemical analysis of phenomena on the fringes of life. This progress seems evident so long, but only so long, as no attention is paid to the element of co-ordinated maintenance which enters into all these phenomena. When they look only on this partial picture of life they feel satisfied with mechanistic interpretation. The trouble is, however, that, as has already been pointed out, mechanistic interpretation is quite useless in the interpretation of what is characteristic, namely, the co-ordinated maintenance and reproduction involved in all the apparent physico-chemical phenomena which have been discovered. The more there are of the latter the more hopeless does the problem of accounting physically for the co-ordinated maintenance and reproduction become. Moreover, the farther the attempt at physico-chemical analysis is pushed onward towards intimate phenomena within living structure the more hazy do the results become. Thus the substances which have been produced by or separated from living or dead structures are definite enough in the chemical sense, but within living substance their nature and properties seem undefinable. The "protoplasm," for instance, which Huxley imagined to be a physically and chemically definable substance is, from the physical and chemical standpoints, now only an indefinite name.

The vitalists, on the other hand, are as ready as the mechanists to apply physico-chemical interpretation in the case of everything to which it apparently can be, or has been, applied successfully. They lay stress, however, on the aspects of living activity, where physico-chemical analysis is not only an actual present failure, but shows not the slightest sign of becoming anything else than a failure. These they account for by attributing them to the influence of the "vital principle," which thus becomes a waste-heap for all that cannot be interpreted on mechanistic principles. The trouble of the vitalists is, however, just as serious as that of the mechanists. Whatever influence is attributed to the vital principle can be shown by experiment to depend on the influence of environment, and therefore on what the vitalists have themselves admitted to be physico-chemical in nature. It is only in so far as the vitalists shut their eyes to this fact that vitalism seems at all satisfying; and the fact is now too evident, particularly to physiologists, to allow overt vitalism to survive.

Since we cannot form a coherent vitalistic or mechanistic conception of life, we must find a different theoretical basis for biology, and we can only find it by looking more closely at the observed facts of life. In life we find that all the phenomena concerned — structure, activity, and active relations with environment — are, or tend towards being, so co-ordinated that they express what is normal for an adult organism. This is the fundamental feature of what we observe. If we attempt to analyse life into various separable events or processes, whether physico-chemical events alone, or such events plus others due to the interfering influence of a "vital principle," we are, as has already been pointed out, confronted by the impossibility of doing so. The analysis can never be carried out, since its nature prevents it from expressing the co-ordination which is everywhere present; and the failure is specially evident when we consider the phenomena of reproduction. The more closely we consider the phenomena of life, the more clear does it become that we can only describe them in terms of the conception that what we call the life of an organism is something regarded as objective in our experience, and manifests itself in the co-ordinated development and maintenance of normal structure, normal activity, and normal relationship with environment outside what we regard as the living body.

This is no new conception: we find it substantially expressed in Greek thought of over two thousand years ago, and it is always present in our minds, even though since the Renaissance it has hardly been acknowledged scientifically. It has, in fact, just as good a claim to be a "common-sense" conception as has the physical conception of what we perceive. When we say that anything is alive what we mean is that it shows in its structure, activity, and relations with environment a tendency towards development and maintenance of the specific form of unity which a particular form of life implies. A living germ is the incomplete manifestation of such unity—incomplete through its separation from the parent life; and it therefore develops naturally to the more complete manifestation in the adult form. There is no other kind of explanation of individual development. It is thus vain to look for the explanation of the development of a germ or the maintenance of life at a number of separable points within the body or environment. Life as simply life is the reality which must be assumed in biological interpretation; and the word "life" is indispensable for denoting what we find. The reality of life implies that spatial arrangement does not mean the separate existences of elements thus arranged.

What, then, is biological explanation, as compared with physical or chemical explanation? Biological explanation is certainly not physico-chemical analysis, since from the nature of the facts such analysis is impossible. In other words, it is not causal explanation. Its real nature is just the demonstration by observation and experiment that an observed phenomenon comes under the general conception of the life of an organism, since it is something which tends to be maintained in definite relation to the other phenomena of its life—in other words, that the phenomenon is a normal expression of life. We observe innumerable facts with regard to living animals—for instance, the fact that they take up oxygen. When we also find that restriction of oxygen-intake is resisted in various ways, and that if it nevertheless occurs every activity in the body is deranged and minute structure seriously affected, we have definitely shown that what we might simply call a certain transfer of oxygen is an act of physiological respiration, and, as such, an active and normal manifestation of the organism's life. The presence of oxygen in the air breathed and in the blood, the structure of the lungs, the circulation of the blood, and the presence in it of hæmoglobin and other substances, are similar manifestations. These phenomena, to which very many others have been added, and are being added by further investigation, are seen to be connected as the maintenance of a life. The demonstration of this connection constitutes biological explanation of them, and this kind of explanation is what, in actual fact, biological investigation is always aiming at the extension of. Through the advancing demonstration we gain enormously in power of prediction and practical control, wherever we are in presence of biological phenomena.

This is true even if we are only using purely anatomical methods of investigation; for we are seeking for and finding maintained co-ordinated relationship in structure; and the discovery of this gives us the great powers of prediction which a scientific anatomist possesses. But in seeking out these relationships, anatomists have also always in mind to a greater or less extent the relationship of structures to their activities and to the nature of environment, in accordance with the conception that life is a whole which realises itself, not only in structural arrangement, but also in activity, including the relations between organism and environment. Mere anatomical methods do not, however, suffice for more than a partial realisation of this conception. Physiological methods must be added.

It is useless to regard anatomy as dealing simply with structure, and physiology with its activities; for the structure with which anatomy actually deals is living and therefore active structure, while change in structure itself is involved in all the activity with which physiology deals. A widespread idea exists that physiology deals with nothing but physical and chemical facts relating to life, and may thus be properly called biophysics and biochemistry. The reasons which make this identification impossible have already been given, but the point involved is one which, with our upbringing in the scientific conceptions which have come down to us from Renaissance times, it is at first hard to grasp. The matter and energy which physical and chemical science present have come to be regarded by us as unquestionable realities apart from our own interpretation of them. It therefore seems natural to us to ask, for instance, what happens to molecules as they enter living substance, or what the immediate source is of the energy which leaves it. Such partial answers as we can get to these questions throw no light on the co-ordinated maintenance observed in what we are endeavouring to describe. The questions we are putting are not capable of being answered, because they involve a presupposition which is inconsistent with our experience of life. This presupposition is that we can analyse the phenomena of life into separable events and processes.

The life of an organism embodies a conception which embraces inseparably the details which it covers, so that when we pass from the physically interpreted to the biologically interpreted world, our standpoint becomes radically different. It is this difference in standpoint which I wish to emphasise in this lecture. In the universe of our experience we find, and I think we shall always find, both kinds of interpretation present. We must realise this fact, and not attempt to gloss it over by vain attempts at compromise, or imaginary deductions of the one method of interpretation from the other.

Though it is true that physico-chemical interpretation of life is impossible, this mere negative fact does not give us biological interpretation. The latter mode of interpretation is already present in our experience, and we have only, by further investigation, to extend its application. In so doing we find that it fits the observations with which biology deals, and gives to biologists an extremely fruitful working conception. With this conception they can work profitably, in place of having to struggle with problems that are insoluble because they involve assumptions which are inconsistent with experience of life.

Let me illustrate this by physiological examples. I shall first take the physiology of renal secretion. If we assume that this must be a process which is ultimately physical, we naturally ask by what mechanism the urine, with its various constituents, is separated from the blood. The mechanism which has always suggested itself is that the kidneys act as some kind of filter. But this theory, in whatever way modified, has been found to be quite unsatisfactory, and we can say the same about all further attempts at mechanistic explanation. The more complex, moreover, such attempts become, the more urgent becomes the further question as to how the mechanism is produced and maintained. Continuation of these attempts is by no means an inspiring ideal, and in any case it now seems evident that any mechanistic conception of how urine is secreted would directly involve a mechanistic explanation of how the structure of the kidneys is developed and maintained. We can, however, put aside as meaningless the search for a mechanistic explanation, and proceed to investigate the manner in which renal secretion expresses the life of the organism. Not only the fact of renal excretion, but the variations in the amount and composition of the urine, then begin to become intelligible physiologically. We find more and more clearly by experiment that in various ways the activity of the kidneys is keeping normal the composition of the blood, intercellular, and intracellular fluids, and so contributing to the normality of other bodily structures and activities; and we can proceed to investigate from this standpoint the activities of the kidneys and the associated activities of the circulation and of other organs. We are thus furnished with a working theory which inspires experimental investigation in all directions, and is extremely fruitful and important practically, in contrast to the fruitlessness of endeavouring to discover a mechanism of secretion.

As a second example I may take the physiology of blood-circulation. The fact that blood circulates through all parts of the body is physiologically intelligible, because by this means the composition of the blood and other interstitial liquids, and the body-temperature, can be kept normal. The conception of this normality gives a working hypothesis for investigation as to how the circulation is co-ordinated or regulated. Physiologists have proceeded to investigate the manner in which the circulation through various parts of the body maintains conditions of normality, and therefore varies with varying requirements for its maintenance. We can see at once that circulation is only intelligible in relation to knowledge of varying bodily activities, such as breathing, muscular and nervous activity, and activity of various glands. The intelligibility is, however, biological and not physical. If we seek for a physico-chemical explanation of why the heart contracts rhythmically in a certain manner, why the blood-vessels respond as they do to certain stimuli, or why the whole circulatory system develops and maintains itself as it does, we can obtain no definite answer. What we can investigate and progressively understand is the manner in which the circulation fulfils its functions in maintaining what is normal within the body; and maintenance of normality is just maintenance of a life. In this investigation, just as in the investigation of renal secretion, we require the most exact physical and chemical methods. But what we are always dealing with are not the mere individual results given by these methods, but the maintained relations of these results to other results.

Maintenance of normality is a fact present in all physiological activity, and cannot be analysed into separable physico-chemical processes. This maintenance enters into every observation of life; and the more we discover as to any part of physiology, the more clearly does the fact appear. This is so in the case of even what may at first sight appear to be grossly mechanical activities, such as the contraction of a muscle or the passage of a nerve-impulse. During a muscular contraction the contracting elements are performing innumerable metabolic cycles, in each of which there is a return to the normal; and we can say the same of the passage of a nerve-impulse. The living structures as a whole express also the tendency towards development and maintenance of what is normal; and the uses to which muscles and nerves are put in the living body express the tendency towards maintenance of either a biological normal or the wider "interest" of personality.

The same considerations apply, of course, to sensory phenomena, reflexes, tropisms, etc. It is only by confusion of thought that so many persons imagine that preliminary physical and chemical interpretations of these phenomena can stand when the light of physiological investigation is turned on them. The comparison of reflex physiological action to reflection of light is, for instance, a useful preliminary simile, but soon ceases to be useful to a physiologist, since the co-ordinated metabolism which is characteristic of life is found to enter into all reflex action. While it may be true that since the Renaissance physiologists have set before themselves an ideal of either mechanistic or vitalistic interpretation, it seems to me that the actual progress of physiology has been steadily in the direction of extending the application of the conception of life as always a maintained whole embracing relation to environment.

When we regard the life of an organism as a real objective unity which shows itself in the phenomena of life, we can, by progressive observation and experiment, bring these phenomena into more and more clear scientific order. Organic structure is then no longer an arrangement of self-existent material parts in an environment of similar character, but, along with its environment, the active expression of life; and organic activity is no longer the passage of self-existent energy from part to part, and between organism and environment, but simply another aspect of the expression of a life. We thus do not artificially separate in theory the structure from the activity, and we recognise the artificiality of separating them. The biological facts which have been discovered fit the conception of life, thus making knowledge of life progressively more extensive. We are also furnished with a conception which stimulates further research, just as fundamental physical conceptions stimulate further research when life is not taken into account.

Since we cannot in theory separate organism from environment, it is evident that biological interpretation is without spatial limitation. It therefore represents a definite interpretation of our whole experience, not a conception which is only applicable to the bodies of living organisms. Hence biology is in the truest sense an independent science, co-equal with mathematical or physical science. Since, however, it covers phenomena which from their very nature can only be interpreted imperfectly by means of physical conceptions, it stands on a higher theoretical level than physical science. In other words, its interpretations take us nearer to reality. For biology the universe is a universe of lives, and not of separable events and processes. Saturated as we still are with Galilean ideas, we commonly regard life as something which is intruded into a surrounding physically interpretable universe, and death of an individual as a cessation of this intrusion. But for biology there is no such intrusion, and death of an individual is only a phenomenon through which development of further life is facilitated. Life represents a deeper interpretation of what is interpreted physically, and the physical world is not something outside life. The facts which physical and chemical investigation reveal in connection with life are interpreted more adequately in biology.

In the extension of biological interpretation we use as raw material experiences or observations which we have at first interpreted physically or chemically. For instance, we observe details which appear at first as if they could be interpreted as mere details of physical structure or physical action; and similarly for what appear as details of chemical composition and reaction. When, however, further investigation shows us that these details are determined, in their relations to one another, with reference to a life, or as an expression of what is normal in the life of an organism, we realise that they cannot actually be interpreted physically or chemically. Nevertheless, it is as apparent physical and chemical phenomena that what we are led, when we put them together, to interpret as phenomena of life appear to us first. In this sense biology is based on physics and chemistry; and unless the provisional physical and chemical observation is sufficient, the biological interpretation will not be accurate. In physiological and morphological work we may require the most delicate of physical and chemical methods. If they do not already exist we have to devise them with the greatest care. Much of my own time and that of other physiologists has been devoted to devising such methods.

The fact that crude data of biology appear as physical and chemical data has led to the widespread misunderstanding that biology can be nothing more than physical and chemical science, and to the still more widespread misunderstanding that, however mysterious a phenomenon of life may be, the only profitable way of investigating it is by assuming provisionally that it can be interpreted physically and chemically. This way, however, leads to no intelligible results, as we have already seen; and mechanistic physiology is not only extraordinarily barren, but fails completely as a practical working creed, if we regard it as physiology, and not as mere bio-physics or bio-chemistry. It is only through specifically biological interpretation that biology can make progress as a science. The progress of abstract bio-physics or bio-chemistry does not represent that of biology.

Biological interpretation is essentially concerned with function. The whole life of an organism is expressed in the function of any particular part or activity, and just in proportion as we understand the whole life do we understand the function of any particular part or activity. The idea that each part of the body has only one limited function is derived from the conception of the body as a machine. The conception of a whole which is not merely the sum of its parts or activities, but in which their own nature is expressed, became in Renaissance times something foreign to the spirit of natural science, so that it was only in an unacknowledged form that the conception persisted among biologists. The acknowledged form of biological theory was either vitalistic or mechanistic; and in either of these forms the Aristotelian or Hippocratic conception of a life as a whole, of which it is the nature to express itself in each of its details, was lost. For the Hippocratic tradition and for Aristotle it was just Nature that manifests itself in the phenomena of life.

Though unity is expressed in the phenomena of a life, it is evident that the unity is very imperfect. All sorts of accompanying phenomena seem irrelevant to life, or at least cannot at present be related to it. Because of the imperfection in biological interpretation biology leaves endless scope for physical interpretation, and never tends to abolish it except in so far as it re-interprets phenomena which are found to be related to life. For biological interpretation the life of one organism overlaps that of others, though the association of different lives may express a wider biological unity, as in the association of the lives of different cells in the bodies of higher organisms, or the association of plant life with bacterial and animal forms of life.

We can carry biological interpretation backwards in time to earlier forms of life, and we can extend it to very simple existing forms of life. So-called micro-organisms appear to represent a simpler form of life than do cells; and it would seem that a cell must be regarded as a colony of simple units of life. The facts which Mendel first discovered in relation to heredity accord well with this conception. An ultra-microscopic virus seems to represent a form of organism which may perhaps be of not more than molecular size. The study of so minute an organism may possibly furnish a link in the extension of biological interpretation into what we at present regard as the inorganic world of molecules and atoms. The discovery of quantum phenomena strongly suggests the possibility of such an extension, which must be regarded as one of the scientific aims of biology. This is a very different aim from the essentially meaningless one of tracing life backwards to conditions which can be interpreted in terms of traditional physical and chemical conceptions. The fact that biology has not yet definitely extended itself into the details of what we at present call the inorganic world, is no argument for the impossibility of this extension. Meanwhile, however, we must never forget that biological interpretation extends over the whole field of our experience, however imperfectly in detail.

The lives of all higher animals are associated with what we recognise as conscious behaviour. In our own bodies we readily distinguish between the structures and activities of which we are aware as under direct conscious control, and mere organic activities and structures such as circulation, digestion, or nervous reflexes, with the corresponding structures. Moreover, such phenomena as hunger, thirst, brightness, colour, sound, odours, tactile sensations, sense of effort, pain, and various emotions are experienced by us whether we will or not. Although we are conscious of them their actual occurrences are not directly under voluntary control. Although, to take another instance, breathing is largely under voluntary control, yet physiological investigation shows that in the long run it is regulated involuntarily in a very exact manner, and without the slightest knowledge on our part of what is effected in breathing.

The unconscious or involuntary features in all these phenomena enter clearly into biology. Even though we are conscious of such phenomena as brightness, they can still be treated from a purely physiological standpoint in so far as we do not take into consideration the fact of their appearing to us as constitutive of perceived objects. We are apt to imagine that such things as brightness or colour can be regarded as running parallel to physically interpreted phenomena. It requires very little investigation to show that this is not the case; but I have not time to discuss here how, as it seems to me, sensory phenomena necessitate distinctively physiological interpretation.[2]

In conscious behaviour, including both perception and voluntary action, we are in presence of what we quite naturally distinguish from mere life. As already pointed out, we regard any phenomenon of life as expressing in itself the unity of a whole life. But in the case of mere life this unity is only regarded as extending over spatially related phenomena. In the case of conscious behaviour, we are dealing with unity extending not only over spatial, but also over temporal, relations. In perceptions or voluntary actions the past and future, unified by the interest which extends over them, are no less expressed directly than the immediate present. The test which we apply when we wish to discover whether an organism is conscious consists in ascertaining whether it learns from each experience, so that past experience is directly represented in present and future behaviour. When unity extends as interest over the past and future, as well as the spatially arranged present, we call the unity personality, in contrast to the blind immediacy of the unity we call life; while what we distinguish as tending to be maintained in the unity of personality is interpreted as of value.

Biology does not deal with personality, nor with values. The science which deals with them is psychology; and we cause confusion if we fail to distinguish biology from psychology, just as we cause confusion by failing to distinguish biology from physical science.

In conclusion let me endeavour to state shortly the main point which I have placed before you. It is that in biological science we are, whether we are clearly aware of it or not, regarding the world of our experience from a standpoint which is peculiar to biology and different from that of other sciences, particularly the physical sciences and psychology. It is no mere matter of arbitrary choice that we do so, but because it is the least we can do in the direction of interpreting our experience of life. Biological conceptions are more penetrating than those of the physical sciences. In other words, they take us nearer to reality. We might, by applying psychological conceptions to the phenomena of life, endeavour to penetrate still more deeply towards reality. But in the details with which biology deals there is nothing to necessitate the use of psychological conceptions, except in so far as we

---

2. A short discussion of this point will be found in my book, *The Philosophical Basis of Biology*, p. 87.

actually infer from their behaviour that living organisms are behaving consciously.

Biology is thus an independent science, using its own method of interpreting the world of our experience, and its own method of explanation and prediction, which is not causal. To regard natural science as simply physical science seems to me only a sign of failure to realise an essential aspect of the facts of visible and tangible experience. The universe for biology is a universe of lives, no one of which excludes others spatially, since spatial exclusion is nonexistent for life. Biology represents, not a philosophy, but a point of view from which we can profitably regard our universe, just as we do in mathematics or physics. I have tried to indicate the biological point of view, and how, in general, it is actually employed in scientific investigation.

THE LIMITATIONS OF ANALYSIS IN BIOLOGY

E. S. Russell

I had originally intended to discuss the analogy which exists between the organismal conception of the living thing and Gestalt theory, but it seemed to me on reflection that this analogy is too obvious to require any elaborate treatment. The word organismal was introduced by the American zoologist Ritter[1] to characterize the view that the living thing is essentially an organized whole and not a mere summation of parts. Precisely the same view is taken of the perceptual field by the upholders of the Gestalt theory.

I have thought it preferable, therefore, to discuss a problem which is common to both these views and is of considerable importance both theoretically and practically. It is this: if we agree that neither the organism nor the perceptual field is a mere summation of parts, can we properly apply the method of analysis at all, and, if so, within what limits?

The more skilful opponents of the organismal view, like Dr. Joseph Needham, raise this very point. We agree, they say, that the organism is not strictly comparable with a machine, which is constructed by fitting together or assembling, in a particular order, parts which are originally independent and do not change when they take their place as constituents of the machine. In the living organism, it is agreed, the parts are not strictly independent, but are determined to some extent by their relations to one another and to the whole organism. The living thing is

---

"The Limitations of Analysis in Biology," *Proceedings of the Aristotelian Society*, New Series, XXXIII (1933), 147–158. Reprinted by courtesy of the Editor of The Aristotelian Society.
    1. *The Unity of the Organism*, Boston, 1919.

therefore an individual whole, and not a pure summation of parts. But, they say, while this view may be philosophically sound, it is of no use for the practical purposes of research. Defined in this way, "an organism is something which the scientific method cannot deal with; it is a hard, round, smooth nut, which experimental analysis can neither crack nor lever open at any point. As soon as a hole is made in it, it explodes like a Prince Rupert drop and vanishes away."[2] While then the biologist may agree that the living thing is an organism, he cannot do anything with it unless he forgets that it is in the strict sense of the word an organism, unless he treats it as if it were a machine, that is, an assemblage of parts, and therefore susceptible of analysis to an indefinite degree.

This is an interesting view, and one for which there is a great deal to be said. The brilliant results achieved in the fields of physiology and biochemistry prove conclusively the practical value of this causal-analytic method of attack on biological problems. To apply the method it is necessary to make abstraction of certain features of the living organism, those that differentiate it from a mechanism, but it is of the essence of science that it abstracts from perceptual reality and deals only with simplified measurable aspects of it. Hence the physiologist may be entirely justified in ignoring those aspects of the living organism which do not fit into the abstract but useful mechanistic schema. The physiologist, perhaps, but not, I think, the biologist. This abstract method may be adequate for the special purposes of the physiologist and the biochemist, who deal by preference with isolated parts or isolated processes of the organism, but it seems to me to be gravely defective as a general method for biology.

In the first place, biology can, and does, deal with the activities of the whole intact animal. The old natural history, which superior persons are apt to dismiss as unscientific, but which nevertheless is, as W. M. Wheeler says, "the perennial rootstock or stolon of biological science," was concerned with the habits of animals as naively observed, and with their adaptation to environmental conditions. We should do well to remember that both the main theories of organic evolution, Lamarckism and Darwinism, developed out of this despised natural history study of living and intact animals. Of recent years, two young and vigorous branches of biology have differentiated out of this original matrix of natural history — the study of behaviour, and the study of animal ecology.

My second objection to the limitations imposed by the mechanistic method in biology is this: if the mechanistic scheme is acknowledged to be over abstract by its more enlightened adherents, why should we be content with this Ignorabimus, merely for the sake of piling up an endless amount of exact and numerical research results? If our aim is to understand living things better, why accept with unnatural piety a method which we know for certain will never give us full satisfaction?

It is indubitable that the organism is an integrated unity, in which the parts are characterized and determined in large measure by their

---

2. Joseph Needham, *The Sceptical Biologist*, London, 1929, p. 82.

relations to the whole. This unity is there at the beginning of development and persists throughout its course. The organism is a unity in time; its activities are essentially transitive; they prepare for the future. Take the process of individual development—there is a definite course, trajectory or cycle, through which it passes; it has a beginning, a middle and an end, and much of the detail of development is comprehensible only with reference to the stage and the end. Take any example of conative behavior—there is here the same continuity and directedness of effort; here also we must interpret the parts of the action in their relation to the end pursued. The relations of the parts to the whole are, therefore, not merely static or spatial, but spatio-temporal relations to the continuing activities of the organism. These whole-activities may be maintenance, or reproduction, or development, and the partial processes can be understood only if their relations to these master-activities are laid clear.

If this general statement be true, it is clearly impossible to compress the characteristic activities of life within the bounds of mechanism. If we insist on fitting life to the Procrustean bed of mechanism, we must perforce lop off its head and its feet, and content ourselves with studying the truncated corpse.

Can we not do better than this? Let us try. Obviously we must start with the most highly integrated activity of the animal, namely its behaviour. Now it is perfectly possible, as the work of the last few years has shown, to study animal behaviour in a scientific and objective way, without accepting the absurd restrictions of the rigid behaviourist. I need only refer to the work of Köhler, of Bierens de Haan, of Adams, of McDougall, to prove this point. In such work the animal is accepted as a living whole, showing certain characteristic activities, which can be accurately observed and recorded, which can be modified experimentally, submitted to scientific study. It is true that the point of view adopted is quite different from that of the physical investigator; the fact that the animal is an active and striving agent is taken at its face value, and the psychologist is not afraid to assume that the animal has its own perceptual world, the existence of which can be deduced from its behaviour. His conception of organism is much richer, less abstract, than that formed by the mechanist.

The practicability of a science of animal behaviour may be taken as proved. It is clear also that the *rôle* of analysis in this psychological study of behaviour is a very limited one. The psychologist must take behaviour as he finds it, as a series of unitary and continuous actions; he finds also in many cases, in accordance with Gestalt theory, that the perceptual world of the animal is an organized whole, in which separate parts or elements cannot properly be distinguished. The animal in many instances reacts, not to isolated elements in the perceptual field, but to relations or patterns within it.

But the study of behaviour is only a small part of biology, and the question arises, how we can connect up this study of relatively un-analysed whole-activities with the study of the physiological processes which underly and condition them. Probably the best line of approach to this difficult and crucial question is to consider in some detail a typical case of animal behaviour. Let us take for this purpose a bird building its nest.

We have first of all to put this activity in its proper setting. It is a part or link in a long chain of actions whose aim is reproduction. Behaviour preparatory to this end begins long before the actual building of the nest. In many birds there is a long migration in the spring from their wintering areas in the south to their breeding ground in the north. Often the male arrives first, and marks out for himself, his prospective mate and offspring, a definite breeding territory, sufficient in extent to supply the necessary food in a month or two's time for his growing young. By song he attracts to himself a mate, and warns intruders off; if his territory is invaded by a rival he drives him off with vigour. Later on, as the year advances, the pair undertake the construction of the nest. The pattern of this is fixed and specific, and the general location of it is also predetermined; much variation, however, occurs in detail. The birds seek far and wide for suitable and specific material for the nest, but unusual materials may also be employed. The nest is built of a size big enough to accommodate the normal number of young. In it the eggs are laid and brooded, and when they are hatched the laborious task of feeding the hungry young begins. After one brood has been reared, the whole business of nest building, laying and hatching may be gone through again.

That is a cursory sketch of the overt behaviour shown during the breeding cycle. There goes on at the same time a definite physiological cycle in the reproductive organs, which is closely correlated with the behaviour cycle. It would be more accurate perhaps to say that there is one reproductive cycle which manifests itself, on the one hand, in physiological changes, and on the other in overt behaviour. This cycle is a unitary and continuous process, moving through a definite trajectory to a definite end; all the activities of the organism, behavioural and physiological alike, are integrated in one movement towards the goal of the reproduction of the species.

We can, of course, analyse the process; we can take little bits of it and study them separately; we can interfere with the physiological processes experimentally and find out the effect upon behaviour; we can study the effect of external conditions, such as light, upon the different stages of the process. The organismalist has never denied the possibility of applying analytical methods to the study of living things, nor does he deny the value of such methods. It is one thing, however, to analyse organic events, with due regard to the necessary limitations of analysis, and quite another to assume, as do the mechanists, that these events can be completely built up or synthesized from the parts or elements distinguished by analysis. It is this assumption that the organismalist rejects. He rejects it because he sees that to study a part or part-process by itself is to consider it apart from its relations to the whole, and it is precisely these relations that are important. If it is convenient or useful to study parts or processes in isolation — which no one denies — there should follow upon this procedure, not a resynthesis or fitting together of abstract elements, but a reintegration of the parts in the whole, by the restoration of those relations to the whole of which abstraction has been made in the process of analysis. The action of a bird in building its nest is, as we have seen, but a part or link in the general reproductive cycle of activities, and it cannot be fully understood except in relation to that cycle. We can for convenience consider it separately, in abstraction from what goes before and what follows after, and we can also analyse the very complex neuro-muscular organization which underlies it.

Clearly the nest-building activity is dependent upon, and conditioned by, the existence of an elaborate and specific organization of sense-organs, central nervous system, and executive organs. We can profitably study the mode of action of this system and of the parts of it. Thus we could study the physiology of vision, of flying or running, the mechanism by which the beak works in picking up nest-material, and so on—all parts of the nest-building activity. We could study more general aspects of the mechanism—the nature of muscular contraction, considered as a physico-chemical event, the nature of the nervous impulse. But these studies of isolated elements of the main activity, though they undoubtedly add to our knowledge and understanding, would not by themselves suffice to give us complete comprehension of the nest-building activity. And they would help towards understanding only if they were seen in their proper relations to the whole activity, only if they were reintegrated in that activity.

This brings us to the important question of the hierarchy of activities, and the relation between the different levels of function. In the case we have been considering the action of nest-building is the integration of a great number of partial functions; it is the main or comprehensive activity, to which all the others are subordinated. The physiological activities of running, flying, picking up nest-material, and so on, are all subordinate parts of the main action. Underlying these are certain structural and physiological relations, and certain properties of nervous and muscular tissue. These may all be regarded as *conditions* of the whole-action, and in general we may say that there are levels of functional activity, physico-chemical, physiological, behavioural, of which the highest is conditioned but not completely determined by the lower levels. It follows that the highest, most integrated, activity is not fully explicable or interpretable in terms of the lower levels.

Let us turn now to another characteristic of living things which throws further light upon this fundamental problem of the relation of the parts to the whole. It is characteristic of living things, and of no other objects, that they undergo a process of development which is essentially differentiation. By differentiation I mean the gradual appearance of an organized complexity from simpler beginnings. This differentiation does not take place by addition or assemblage of parts. Thus the unicellular egg does not become multicellular by the addition of other cells, but by doubling and redoubling. Furthermore, the egg-cell is demonstrably a unitary organism from its first formation; it is already the (undifferentiated) organism which by growth and differentiation becomes the adult and fully-formed organism. Certain environmental conditions, certain supplies of energy, are necessary for development, but the process is not essentially determined by environment; organization goes on from within. Many theories of development have assumed that there is present at the beginning an inner and invisible complexity, comparable to that of the adult organism, and that this original complexity is merely made manifest as visible differentiation proceeds. But such theories are only scientific fantasies invented to get round the difficulty of conceiving how the simple can become the complex.

The development of a living thing is then essentially a process whereby a simple but unitary organism becomes differentiated into a more complex, and generally larger, but still unitary organism — differentiation takes place within a whole.

As Bergson pointed out long ago, this process is not obviously explicable in terms either of mechanism or of machine-teleology. If we desire to make a complex thing we do so by adding one part to another, proceeding according to a previously thought-out plan. But, as Bergson says, the merest glance at the development of an embryo shows that life proceeds in quite a different way — not by association and addition of elements, but by dissociation and doubling.[3]

If we reject, as I think we must, any vitalistic interpretation in terms of an entelechy or other organizing agent, we have no alternative but to accept the observed facts of development and make the best of them. It follows that the unity of the organism, which is there at the beginning, must be accepted as fundamental; unity or integration is not a problem for biology, but an axiom, a master-fact to which we must relate all other facts about the organism. If we analyse organic activities, we must correct this procedure by relating the parts back to the whole, by reintegrating them in the whole.

Let me illustrate this fundamental point that development is a differentiation of parts within a whole by referring briefly to some recent work on the development of behaviour.

A very careful study was made by Coghill of the development of the nervous system in *Amblystoma* (the axolotl) in relation to the development of its behaviour. Naturally he found the two closely correlated. The really interesting thing that emerged was the demonstration that behaviour is from the beginning a whole or integrated activity. It begins by mass movements of the body as a whole, including the curling up of the tail. This movement soon develops into the activity of swimming, which at this tadpole-like stage consists in wagging the tail from side to side. A little later the movements of the limbs take shape; at first they are dominated by the movements of the trunk, but gradually become more independent; they still, however, form part of the general pattern of movements. Coghill summarises the process as follows: "Behaviour develops from the beginning through the progressive expansion of a perfectly integrated total pattern and the individuation within it of partial patterns which acquire various degrees of discreteness."[4]

Wholeness is there from the beginning; the special movements develop by differentiation within the total pattern. Only at a relatively

---

3. H. Bergson, *L'Evolution créatrice*, 5th ed., p. 97.
4. G. E. Coghill, *Anatomy and the Problem of Behaviour*, Cambridge, 1929, p. 38.

late stage do apparently discrete and separate reflexes appear. To quote
Coghill again: "In *Amblystoma* the total pattern first extends through
the trunk and the tail. As this pattern enlarges, the parts involved are
always perfectly integrated. This totally integrated pattern then extends
into the gills, next into the fore limbs, and finally into the hind limbs.
But as the totally integrated pattern expands through the organism, its
parts, one after the other, in the same order as they were invaded by
the total pattern, begin to acquire a measure of individuality of their
own: first the gills, then the fore limbs, and finally the hind limbs. This
means that local reflexes emerge as, in the language of 'Gestalt,' a
'quality upon a ground'; that is to say, they emerge as a special feature
within a more diffuse but dominant mechanism of integration of the
whole organism. They cannot be regarded as simply the action of a
chain of neurones, excepting as every link of the chain is conceived to
be welded into the organism as a whole."[5]

The theory that the reflex arc is the basal unit of behaviour, and that
all behaviour can be satisfactorily accounted for as a concatenation of
reflexes, conditioned or unconditioned, has been a favourite assumption of the physiologist. It is a theory which does considerable violence to the observable facts of behaviour, but it is of theoretical
interest as an attempt to build up or synthesize behaviour by the addition or summation of supposedly separate units. Actually the attempt
must fail because the units are abstractions—parts artificially isolated
and considered without reference to their relations to the whole. It is
not possible to reconstitute an organic unity by addition of abstract
parts. And exact observation of the development of behaviour shows
that this unity does not come about by addition of elements; the unity
is there from the beginning and the parts appear by differentiation
within the whole.[6]

This fundamental fact, which is true not only of the development of
executive behaviour, but also of the development of the perceptual field,
indicates clearly the limitations of the method of analysis in biology.
We may quite properly analyse, but we cannot re-compose the whole
by direct summation of the parts distinguished by analysis. "Real" parts
or "differentiates"—to coin a needed word—are "parts-of-a-whole"; if
we treat them as discrete units we denature them. The antidote to
analysis is not resynthesis, in its basic meaning of putting together, but
reintegration.

If this view be true, it follows that the biologist's first task is to study
the activities of the organism as a whole. This means, in animals at
least, the study of behaviour, and, generally, of the relations of the
animal to its environment. In such studies the animal must be accepted
as an integral whole; its activities as a whole organism are "organic" or
"psycho-physical," that is to say, activities of a higher order than physiological, and irreducible to these. As soon as we, by analysis, dissolve

---

5. *Ibid.*, pp. 88–89.

6. Coghill's law of differentiation has been shown to hold good in many other
Vertebrate larvæ and embryos. See O. C. Irwin, "The Organismic Hypothesis and
Differentiation of Behaviour," *Psychological Review*, XXXIX, 1932, for a useful summary.

or *dis*-integrate this organic unity, we get parts or part-processes susceptible of physiological treatment. Such analytical or physiological study, however valuable its results may be, cannot adequately replace, or be substituted for, the study of behaviour, which retains its primary validity.

In the second place, the activities of the organism must be related to one or other of the master-functions, which are development (differentiation), maintenance and reproduction. All these are processes in time, transitive activities, and it is necessary, therefore, in studying any detail of organic activity to relate it to what has gone before and what is coming after. The need for this is very clear when we consider long trains of behaviour, such as are shown in the reproductive cycle in birds. It is a method of interpretation or understanding which is necessary also in the study of individual development.

In the third place, we must remember that unity or integration is primary in a genetic sense; it becomes fuller and richer as development proceeds, but it is there from the beginning. We cannot "explain" it scientifically, but, having accepted it, we can study the process of differentiation by considering the relations of the differentiating parts, and how they influence one another. To sum up—life appears to us only in the form of individuals or organized wholes; there is no such thing as "living matter." The proper method for the biologist is to start with the activity of the organism as a whole and work down from this to the conditions of the whole-action. Both in animals and in plants the first object of study should be the responses of the organism to its environment—behaviour-responses in animals, growth-responses in plants. The biologist may properly analyse these whole-actions with the aim of discovering the physiological processes which underly them; he may profitably study these physiological processes in isolation in order to discern the physico-chemical events of which they are made up. But he should not start with the elementary processes and attempt to build up the living reality by adding these together, for the task is an impossible one, and will sooner or later drive him into accepting some form of dualistic vitalism.

It is only by accepting the obvious fact that the living thing is an organized whole and not a mere summation of parts that the biologist can preserve the autonomy of his science and escape the Scylla of materialism on the one hand and the Charybdis of vitalism on the other.

WHAT IS LIFE?

Erwin Schrödinger

Chapter 1
THE CLASSICAL PHYSICIST'S APPROACH
TO THE SUBJECT

Cogito ergo sum.   *Descartes*

1. *The general character and the purpose of the investigation*

This little book arose from a course of public lectures, delivered by a theoretical physicist to an audience of about four hundred which did not substantially dwindle, though warned at the outset that the subject-matter was a difficult one and that the lectures could not be termed popular, even though the physicist's most dreaded weapon, mathematical deduction, would hardly be utilized. The reason for this was not that the subject was simple enough to be explained without mathematics, but rather that it was much too involved to be fully accessible to mathematics. Another feature which at least induced a semblance of popularity was the lecturer's intention to make clear the fundamental idea, which hovers between biology and physics, to both the physicist and the biologist.

For actually, in spite of the variety of topics involved, the whole enterprise is intended to convey one idea only—one small comment

From *What Is Life? The Physical Aspect of the Living Cell* (New York: Cambridge University Press, 1944), pp. 1–17, 29–34, 41–87.

on a large and important question. In order not to lose our way, it may be useful to outline the plan very briefly in advance.

The large and important and very much discussed question is:

How can the events *in space and time* which take place within the spatial boundary of a living organism be accounted for by physics and chemistry?

The preliminary answer which this little book will endeavour to expound and establish can be summarized as follows:

The obvious inability of present-day physics and chemistry to account for such events is no reason at all for doubting that they can be accounted for by those sciences.

2. *Statistical physics. The fundamental difference in structure*

That would be a very trivial remark if it were meant only to stimulate the hope of achieving in the future what has not been achieved in the past. But the meaning is very much more positive, viz. that the inability, up to the present moment, is amply accounted for.

To-day, thanks to the ingenious work of biologists, mainly of geneticists, during the last 30 or 40 years, enough is known about the actual material structure of organisms and about their functioning to state that, and to tell precisely why, present-day physics and chemistry could not possibly account for what happens in space and time within a living organism.

The arrangements of the atoms in the most vital parts of an organism and the interplay of these arrangements differ in a fundamental way from all those arrangements of atoms which physicists and chemists have hitherto made the object of their experimental and theoretical research. Yet the difference which I have just termed fundamental is of such a kind that it might easily appear slight to anyone except a physicist who is thoroughly imbued with the knowledge that the laws of physics and chemistry are statistical throughout.[1] For it is in relation to the statistical point of view that the structure of the vital parts of living organisms differs so entirely from that of any piece of matter that we physicists and chemists have ever handled physically in our laboratories or mentally at our writing desks.[2] It is well-nigh unthinkable that the laws and regularities thus discovered should happen to apply immediately to the behaviour of systems which do not exhibit the structure on which those laws and regularities are based.

The non-physicist cannot be expected even to grasp—let alone to appreciate the relevance of—the difference in 'statistical structure' stated in terms so abstract as I have just used. To give the statement life and colour, let me anticipate, what will be explained in much more detail later, namely, that the most essential part of a living cell—the

---

1. This contention may appear a little too general. The discussion must be deferred to the end of this book, §§ 67 and 68.

2. This point of view has been emphasized in two most inspiring papers by F. G. Donnan, *Scientia*, vol. 24, no. 78, p. 10, 1918 ('La science physico-chimique décrit-elle d'une façon adéquate les phénomènes biologiques?'); *Smithsonian Report* for 1929, p. 809 ('The mystery of life').

chromosome fibre—may suitably be called *an aperiodic crystal*. In physics we have dealt hitherto only with *periodic crystals*. To a humble physicist's mind, these are very interesting and complicated objects; they constitute one of the most fascinating and complex material structures by which inanimate nature puzzles his wits. Yet, compared with the aperiodic crystal, they are rather plain and dull. The difference in structure is of the same kind as that between an ordinary wallpaper in which the same pattern is repeated again and again in regular periodicity and a masterpiece of embroidery, say a Raphael tapestry, which shows no dull repetition, but an elaborate, coherent, meaningful design traced by the great master.

In calling the periodic crystal one of the most complex objects of his research, I had in mind the physicist proper. Organic chemistry, indeed, in investigating more and more complicated molecules, has come very much nearer to that 'aperiodic crystal' which, in my opinion, is the material carrier of life. And therefore it is small wonder that the organic chemist has already made large and important contributions to the problem of life, whereas the physicist has made next to none.

3. The naïve physicist's approach to the subject

After having thus indicated very briefly the general idea—or rather the ultimate scope—of our investigation, let me describe the line of attack.

I propose to develop first what you might call 'a naïve physicist's ideas about organisms', that is, the ideas which might arise in the mind of a physicist who, after having learnt his physics and, more especially, the statistical foundation of his science, begins to think about organisms and about the way they behave and function and who comes to ask himself conscientiously whether he, from what he has learnt, from the point of view of his comparatively simple and clear and humble science, can make any relevant contributions to the question.

It will turn out that he can. The next step must be to compare his theoretical anticipations with the biological facts. It will then turn out that—though on the whole his ideas seem quite sensible—they need to be appreciably amended. In this way we shall gradually approach the correct view—or, to put it more modestly, the one that I propose as the correct one.

Even if I should be right in this, I do not know whether my way of approach is really the best and simplest. But, in short, it was mine. The 'naïve physicist' was myself. And I could not find any better or clearer way towards the goal than my own crooked one.

4. Why are the atoms so small?

A good method of developing 'the naïve physicist's ideas' is to start from the odd, almost ludicrous, question: Why are atoms so small? To begin with, they are very small indeed. Every little piece of matter handled in everyday life contains an enormous number of them. Many examples have been devised to bring this fact home to an audience, none of them more impressive than the one used by Lord Kelvin: Suppose that you could mark the molecules in a glass of water; then pour the contents of the glass into the ocean and stir the latter thoroughly so as to distribute the marked molecules uniformly throughout the seven seas; if then you took a glass of water anywhere out of the ocean, you would find in it about a hundred of your marked molecules.[3]

The actual sizes of atoms[4] lie between about $\frac{1}{3000}$ and $\frac{1}{2000}$ of the wave-length of yellow light. The comparison is significant, because the wave-length roughly indicates the dimensions of the smallest grain still recognizable in the microscope. Thus it will be seen that such a grain still contains thousands of millions of atoms.

Now, why are atoms so small?

Clearly, the question is an evasion. For it is not really aimed at the size of the atoms. It is concerned with the size of organisms, more particularly with the size of our own corporeal selves. Indeed, the atom is small, when referred to our civic unit of length, say the yard or the metre. In atomic physics one is accustomed to use the so-called Ångström (abbr. Å.), which is the 10^{10}th part of a metre, or in decimal notation $0 \cdot 0000000001$ metre. Atomic diameters range between 1 and 2 Å. Now those civic units (in relation to which the atoms are so small) are closely related to the size of our bodies. There is a story tracing the yard back to the humour of an English king whom his councillors asked what unit to adopt — and he stretched out his arm sideways and said: 'Take the distance from the middle of my chest to my fingertips, that will do all right.' True or not, the story is significant for our purpose. The king would naturally indicate a length comparable with that of his own body, knowing that anything else would be very inconvenient. With all his predilection for the Ångström unit, the physicist prefers to be told that his new suit will require six and a half yards of tweed — rather than sixty-five thousand millions of Ångströms of tweed.

It thus being settled that our question really aims at the ratio of two lengths — that of our body and that of the atom — with an incontestable priority of independent existence on the side of the atom, the question truly reads: Why must our bodies be so large compared with the atom?

I can imagine that many a keen student of physics or chemistry may have deplored the fact that every one of our sense organs, forming a more or less substantial part of our body and hence (in view of the magnitude of the said ratio) being itself composed of innumerable atoms, is much too coarse to be affected by the impact of a single atom.

---

3.   You would not, of course, find exactly 100 (even if that were the exact result of the computation). You might find 88 or 95 or 107 or 112, but very improbably as few as 50 or as many as 150. A 'deviation' or 'fluctuation' is to be expected of the order of the square root of 100, i.e., 10. The statistician expresses this by stating that you would find 100 ± 10. This remark can be ignored for the moment, but will be referred to later, affording an example of the statistical $\sqrt{n}$ law.

4.   According to present-day views an atom has no sharp boundary, so that 'size' of an atom is not a very well-defined conception. But we may identify it (or, if you please, replace it) by the distance between their centres in a solid or in a liquid — not, of course, in the gaseous state, where that distance is, under normal pressure and temperature, roughly ten times as great.

We cannot see or feel or hear the single atoms. Our hypotheses with regard to them differ widely from the immediate findings of our gross sense organs and cannot be put to the test of direct inspection.

Must that be so? Is there an intrinsic reason for it? Can we trace back this state of affairs to some kind of first principle, in order to ascertain and to understand why nothing else is compatible with the very laws of Nature?

Now this, for once, is a problem which the physicist is able to clear up completely. The answer to all the queries is in the affirmative.

5. The working of an organism requires exact physical laws

If it were not so, if we were organisms so sensitive that a single atom, or even a few atoms, could make a perceptible impression on our senses — Heavens, what would life be like! To stress one point: an organism of that kind would most certainly not be capable of developing the kind of orderly thought which, after passing through a long sequence of earlier stages, ultimately results in forming, among many other ideas, the idea of an atom.

Even though we select this one point, the following considerations would essentially apply also to the functioning of organs other than the brain and the sensorial system. Nevertheless, the one and only thing of paramount interest to us in ourselves is, that we feel and think and perceive. To the physiological process which is responsible for thought and sense all the others play an auxiliary part, at least from the human point of view, if not from that of purely objective biology. Moreover, it will greatly facilitate our task to choose for investigation the process which is closely accompanied by subjective events, even though we are ignorant of the true nature of this close parallelism. Indeed, in my view, it lies outside the range of natural science and very probably of human understanding altogether.

We are thus faced with the following question: Why should an organ like our brain, with the sensorial system attached to it, of necessity consist of an enormous number of atoms, in order that its physically changing state should be in close and intimate correspondence with a highly developed thought? On what grounds is the latter task of the said organ incompatible with being, as a whole or in some of its peripheral parts which interact directly with the environment, a mechanism sufficiently refined and sensitive to respond to and register the impact of a single atom from outside?

The reason for this is, that what we call thought (1) is itself an orderly thing, and (2) can only be applied to material, i.e. to perceptions or experiences, which have a certain degree of orderliness. This has two consequences. First, a physical organization, to be in close correspondence with thought (as my brain is with my thought) must be a very well-ordered organization, and that means that the events that happen within it must obey strict physical laws, at least to a very high degree of accuracy. Secondly, the physical impressions made upon that physically well-organized system by other bodies from outside, obviously correspond to the perception and experience of the corresponding thought, forming its material, as I have called it. Therefore, the physical interactions between our system and others must, as a rule, themselves possess a certain degree of physical orderliness, that is to say, they too must obey strict physical laws to a certain degree of accuracy.

6. *Physical laws rest on atomic statistics and are therefore only approximate*

And why could all this not be fulfilled in the case of an organism composed of a moderate number of atoms only and sensitive already to the impact of one or a few atoms only?

Because we know all atoms to perform all the time a completely disorderly heat motion, which, so to speak, opposes itself to their orderly behaviour and does not allow the events that happen between a small number of atoms to enrol themselves according to any recognizable laws. Only in the co-operation of an enormously large number of atoms do statistical laws begin to operate and control the behaviour of these *assemblées* with an accuracy increasing as the number of atoms involved increases. It is in that way that the events acquire truly orderly features. All the physical and chemical laws that are known to play an important part in the life of organisms are of this statistical kind; any other kind of lawfulness and orderliness that one might think of is being perpetually disturbed and made inoperative by the unceasing heat motion of the atoms.

7. *Their precision is based on the large number of atoms intervening. First example (paramagnetism)*

Let me try to illustrate this by a few examples, picked somewhat at random out of thousands, and possibly not just the best ones to appeal to a reader who is learning for the first time about this condition of things—a condition which in modern physics and chemistry is as fundamental as, say, the fact that organisms are composed of cells is in biology, or as Newton's Law in astronomy, or even as the series of integers, 1, 2, 3, 4, 5, . . . in mathematics. An entire newcomer should not expect to obtain from the following few pages a full understanding and appreciation of the subject, which is associated with the illustrious names of Ludwig Boltzmann and Willard Gibbs and treated in textbooks under the name of 'statistical thermodynamics'.

If you fill an oblong quartz tube with oxygen gas and put it into a magnetic field, you find that the gas is magnetized.[5] The magnetization is due to the fact that the oxygen molecules are little magnets and tend to orientate themselves parallel to the field, like a compass needle. But you must not think that they actually all turn parallel. For if you double the field, you get double the magnetization in your oxygen body,

---

5.   A gas is chosen, because it is simpler than a solid or a liquid; the fact that the magnetization is in this case extremely weak, will not impair the theoretical considerations.

FIGURE 1.   Paramagnetism.

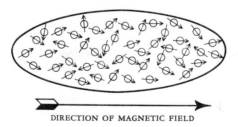

DIRECTION OF MAGNETIC FIELD

and that proportionality goes on to extremely high field strengths, the magnetization increasing at the rate of the field you apply.

This is a particularly clear example of a purely statistical law. The orientation the field tends to produce is continually counteracted by the heat motion, which works for random orientation. The effect of this striving is, actually, only a small preference for acute over obtuse angles between the dipole axes and the field. Though the single atoms change their orientation incessantly, they produce on the average (owing to their enormous number) a constant small preponderance of orientation in the direction of the field and proportional to it. This ingenious explanation is due to the French physicist P. Langevin. It can be checked in the following way. If the observed weak magnetization is really the outcome of rival tendencies, namely, the magnetic field, which aims at combing all the molecules parallel, and the heat motion, which makes for random orientation, then it ought to be possible to increase the magnetization by weakening the heat motion, that is to say, by lowering the temperature, instead of reinforcing the field. That is confirmed by experiment, which gives the magnetization inversely proportional to the absolute temperature, in quantitative agreement with theory (Curie's law). Modern equipment even enables us, by lowering the temperature, to reduce the heat motion to such insignificance that the orientating tendency of the magnetic field can assert itself, if not completely, at least sufficiently to produce a substantial fraction of 'complete magnetization'. In this case we no longer expect that double the field strength will double the magnetization, but that the latter will increase less and less with increasing field, approaching what is called 'saturation'. This expectation too is quantitatively confirmed by experiment.

Notice that this behaviour entirely depends on the large numbers of molecules which co-operate in producing the observable magnetization. Otherwise, the latter would not be constant at all, but would, by fluctuating quite irregularly from one second to the next, bear witness to the vicissitudes of the contest between heat motion and field.

8. *Second example (Brownian movement, diffusion)*

If you fill the lower part of a closed glass vessel with fog, consisting of minute droplets, you will find that the upper boundary of the fog

FIGURE 2.   Sinking fog.   FIGURE 3.   Brownian movement of a sinking droplet.

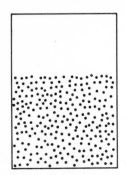

gradually sinks, with a well-defined velocity, determined by the viscosity of the air and the size and the specific gravity of the droplets. But if you look at one of the droplets under the microscope you find that it does not permanently sink with constant velocity, but performs a very irregular movement, the so-called Brownian movement, which corresponds to a regular sinking only on the average.

Now these droplets are not atoms, but they are sufficiently small and light to be not entirely insusceptible to the impact of one single molecule of those which hammer their surface in perpetual impacts. They are thus knocked about and can only on the average follow the influence of gravity.

This example shows what funny and disorderly experience we should have if our senses were susceptible to the impact of a few molecules only. There are bacteria and other organisms so small that they are strongly affected by this phenomenon. Their movements are determined by the thermic whims of the surrounding medium; they have no choice. If they had some locomotion of their own they might nevertheless succeed in getting from one place to another — but with some difficulty, since the heat motion tosses them like a small boat in a rough sea.

A phenomenon very much akin to Brownian movement is that of *diffusion*. Imagine a vessel filled with a fluid, say water, with a small amount of some coloured substance dissolved in it, say potassium permanganate, not in uniform concentration, but rather as in Fig. 4, where the dots indicate the molecules of the dissolved substance (permanganate) and the concentration diminishes from left to right. If you leave this system alone a very slow process of 'diffusion' sets in, the permanganate spreading in the direction from left to right, that is, from the places of higher concentration towards the places of lower concentration, until it is equally distributed through the water.

The remarkable thing about this rather simple and apparently not

FIGURE 4.   Diffusion from left to right in a solution of varying concentration.

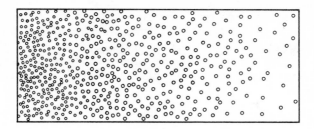

particularly interesting process is that it is in no way due, as one might think, to any tendency or force driving the permanganate molecules away from the crowded region to the less crowded one—like the population of a country spreading to those parts where there is more elbow-room. Nothing of the sort happens with our permanganate molecules. Every one of them behaves quite independently of all the others, which it very seldom meets. Every one of them, whether in a crowded region or in an empty one, suffers the same fate of being continually knocked about by the impacts of the water molecules and thereby gradually moving on in an unpredictable direction—sometimes towards the higher, sometimes towards the lower, concentrations, sometimes obliquely. The kind of motion it performs has often been compared with that of a blindfolded person on a large surface, imbued with a certain desire of 'walking', but without any preference for any particular direction, and so changing his line continuously.

That this random walk of the permanganate molecules, the same for all of them, should yet produce a regular flow towards the smaller concentration and ultimately make for uniformity of distribution, is at first sight perplexing—but only at first sight. If you contemplate in Fig. 4 thin slices of approximately constant concentration, the permanganate molecules which in a given moment are contained in a particular slice will, by their random walk, it is true, be carried with equal probability to the right or to the left. But precisely in consequence of this, a plane separating two neighbouring slices will be crossed by more molecules coming from the left than in the opposite direction, simply because to the left there are more molecules engaged in random walk than there are to the right. And as long as that is so the balance will show up as a regular flow from left to right, until a uniform distribution is reached.

When these considerations are translated into mathematical language the exact law of diffusion is reached in the form of a partial differential equation

$$\frac{\partial p}{\partial t} = D\nabla^2 p,$$

which I shall not trouble the reader by explaining, though its meaning in ordinary language is again simple enough.[6] The reason for mentioning the stern 'mathematically exact' law here, is to emphasize that its physical exactitude must nevertheless be challenged in every particular application. Being based on pure chance, its validity is only approximate. If it is, as a rule, a very good approximation, that is only due to the enormous number of molecules that co-operate in the phenomenon. The smaller their number, the larger the quite haphazard deviations we must expect—and they can be observed under favourable circumstances.

9. *Third example (limits of accuracy of measuring)*

The last example we shall give is closely akin to the second one, but has a particular interest. A light body, suspended by a long thin fibre in equilibrium orientation, is often used by physicists to measure weak forces which deflect it from that position of equilibrium, electric, magnetic or gravitational forces being applied so as to twist it around the vertical axis. (The light body must, of course, be chosen appropriately for the particular purpose.) The continued effort to improve the accuracy of this very commonly used device of a 'torsional balance', has encountered a curious limit, most interesting in itself. In choosing lighter and lighter bodies and thinner and longer fibres—to make the balance susceptible to weaker and weaker forces—the limit was reached when the suspended body became noticeably susceptible to the impacts of the heat motion of the surrounding molecules and began to perform an incessant, irregular 'dance' about its equilibrium position, much like the trembling of the droplet in the second example. Though this behaviour sets no absolute limit to the accuracy of measurements obtained with the balance, it sets a practical one. The uncontrollable effect of the heat motion competes with the effect of the force to be measured and makes the single deflection observed insignificant. You have to multiply observations, in order to eliminate the effect of the Brownian movement of your instrument. This example is, I think, particularly illuminating in our present investigation. For our organs of sense, after all, are a kind of instrument. We can see how useless they would be if they became too sensitive.

10. *The* $\sqrt{n}$ *rule*

So much for examples, for the present. I will merely add that there is not one law of physics or chemistry, of those that are relevant within an organism or in its interactions with its environment, that I might not choose as an example. The detailed explanation might be more complicated, but the salient point would always be the same and thus the description would become monotonous.

---

6. To wit: the concentration at any given point increases (or decreases) at a time rate proportional to the comparative surplus (or deficiency) of concentration in its infinitesimal environment. The law of heat conduction is, by the way, of exactly the same form, 'concentration' having to be replaced by 'temperature'.

But I should like to add one very important quantitative statement concerning the degree of inaccuracy to be expected in any physical law, the so-called $\sqrt{n}$ law. I will first illustrate it by a simple example and then generalize it.

If I tell you that a certain gas under certain conditions of pressure and temperature has a certain density, and if I expressed this by saying that within a certain volume (of a size relevant for some experiment) there are under these conditions just n molecules of the gas, then you might be sure that if you could test my statement in a particular moment of time, you would find it inaccurate, the departure being of the order of $\sqrt{n}$. Hence if the number $n=100$, you would find a departure of about 10, thus relative error$=10\%$. But if $n=1$ million, you would be likely to find a departure of about 1000, thus relative error$=\frac{1}{10}\%$. Now, roughly speaking, this statistical law is quite general. The laws of physics and physical chemistry are inaccurate within a probable relative error of the order of $1/\sqrt{n}$, where n is the number of molecules that co-operate to bring about that law—to produce its validity within such regions of space or time (or both) that matter, for some considerations or for some particular experiment.

You see from this again that an organism must have a comparatively gross structure in order to enjoy the benefit of fairly accurate laws, both for its internal life and for its interplay with the external world. For otherwise the number of co-operating particles would be too small, the 'law' too inaccurate. The particularly exigent demand is the square root. For though a million is a reasonably large number, an accuracy of just 1 in 1000 is not overwhelmingly good, if a thing claims the dignity of being a 'Law of Nature'.

Chapter II
THE HEREDITARY MECHANISM
. . . .

19. *Maximum size of a gene*

We have just introduced the term gene for the hypothetical material carrier of a definite hereditary feature. We must now stress two points which will be highly relevant to our investigation. The first is the size—or, better, the maximum size—of such a carrier; in other words, to how small a volume can we trace the location? The second point will be the permanence of a gene, to be inferred from the durability of the hereditary pattern.

As regards the size, there are two entirely independent estimates, one resting on genetic evidence (breeding experiments), the other on cytological evidence (direct microscopic inspection). The first is, in principle, simple enough. After having, in the way described above, located in the chromosome a considerable number of different (large-scale) features (say of the *Drosophila* fly) within a particular one of its chromosomes, to get the required estimate we need only divide the measured length of that chromosome by the number of features and multiply by the cross-section. For, of course, we count as different only such features as are occasionally separated by crossing-over, so that they cannot be due to the same (microscopic or molecular) structure. On the other hand, it is clear that our estimate can only give a maximum size, because the number of features isolated by genetic analysis is continually increasing as work goes on.

The other estimate, though based on microscopic inspection, is really far less direct. Certain cells of *Drosophila* (namely, those of its salivary glands) are, for some reason, enormously enlarged, and so are their chromosomes. In them you distinguish a crowded pattern of transverse dark bands across the fibre. C. D. Darlington has remarked that the number of these bands (2000 in the case he uses) is, though considerably larger, yet roughly of the same order of magnitude as the number of genes located in that chromosome by breeding experiments. He inclines to regard these bands as indicating the actual genes (or separations of genes). Dividing the length of the chromosome, measured in a normal-sized cell by their number (2000), he finds the volume of a gene equal to a cube of edge 300 Å. Considering the roughness of the estimates, we may regard this to be also the size obtained by the first method.

20. *Small numbers*

A full discussion of the bearing of statistical physics on all the facts I am recalling—or perhaps, I ought to say, of the bearing of these facts on the use of statistical physics in the living cell—will follow later. But let me draw attention at this point to the fact that 300 Å. is only about 100 or 150 atomic distances in a liquid or in a solid, so that a gene contains certainly not more than about a million or a few million atoms. That number is much too small (from the $\sqrt{n}$ point of view) to entail an orderly and lawful behaviour according to statistical physics—and that means according to physics. It is too small, even if all these atoms played the same role, as they do in a gas or in a drop of liquid. And the gene is most certainly not just a homogeneous drop of liquid. It is probably a large protein molecule, in which every atom, every radical, every heterocyclic ring plays an individual role, more or less different from that played by any of the other similar atoms, radicals, or rings. This, at any rate, is the opinion of leading geneticists such as Haldane and Darlington, and we shall soon have to refer to genetic experiments which come very near to proving it.

21. *Permanence*

Let us now turn to the second highly relevant question: What degree of permanence do we encounter in hereditary properties and what must we therefore attribute to the material structures which carry them?

The answer to this can really be given without any special investigation. The mere fact that we speak of hereditary properties indicates that we recognize the permanence to be almost absolute. For we must not forget that what is passed on by the parent to the child is not just this or that peculiarity, a hooked nose, short fingers, a tendency to rheumatism, haemophilia, dichromasy, etc. Such features we may conveniently select for studying the laws of heredity. But actually it is the whole (four-dimensional) pattern of the 'phenotype', the visible and manifest nature of the individual, which is reproduced without appreciable change for generations, permanent within centuries— though not within tens of thousands of years—and borne at each transmission by the material structure of the nuclei of the two cells which unite to form the fertilized egg cell. That is a marvel—than which only one is greater; one that, if intimately connected with it, yet lies on a different plane. I mean the fact that we, whose total being is entirely based on a marvellous interplay of this very kind, yet possess the power of acquiring considerable knowledge about it. I think it possible that this knowledge may advance to little short of a complete understanding—of the first marvel. The second may well be beyond human understanding.

Chapter III
MUTATIONS

> Und was in schwankender Erscheinung schwebt,
> Befestiget mit dauernden Gedanken.[7] *Goethe*

22. *'Jump-like' mutations—the working-ground of natural selection*

The general facts which we have just put forward in evidence of the durability claimed for the gene structure, are perhaps too familiar to us to be striking or to be regarded as convincing. Here, for once, the common saying that exceptions prove the rule is actually true. If there were no exceptions to the likeness between children and parents, we should have been deprived not only of all those beautiful experiments which have revealed to us the detailed mechanism of heredity, but also of that grand, million-fold experiment of Nature, which forges the species by natural selection and survival of the fittest.

Let me take this last important subject as the starting-point for presenting the relevant facts—again with an apology and a reminder that I am not a biologist:

We know definitely, to-day, that Darwin was mistaken in regarding the small, continuous, accidental variations, that are bound to occur even in the most homogeneous population, as the material on which natural selection works. For it has been proved that they are not inherited. The fact is important enough to be illustrated briefly. If you take a

---

7. And what in fluctuating appearance hovers,
   Ye shall fix by lasting thoughts.

FIGURE 5.   Statistics of length of awns in a pure-bred crop. The black group is to be selected for sowing. (The details are not from an actual experiment, but are just set up for illustration.)

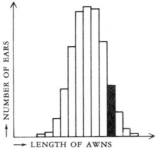

crop of pure-strain barley, and measure, ear by ear, the length of its awns and plot the result of your statistics, you will get a bell-shaped curve as shown in Fig. 5, where the number of ears with a definite length of awn is plotted against that length. In other words: a definite medium length prevails, and deviations in either direction occur with certain frequencies. Now pick out a group of ears (as indicated by blackening) with awns noticeably beyond the average, but sufficient in number to be sown in a field by themselves and give a new crop. In making the same statistics for this, Darwin would have expected to find the corresponding curve shifted to the right. In other words, he would have expected to produce by selection an increase of the average length of the awns. That is not the case, if a truly pure-bred strain of barley has been used. The new statistical curve, obtained from the selected crop, is identical with the first one, and the same would be the case if ears with particularly short awns had been selected for seed. Selection has no effect—because the small, continuous variations are not inherited. They are obviously not based on the structure of the hereditary substance, they are accidental. But about 40 years ago the Dutchman de Vries discovered that in the offspring even of thoroughly pure-bred stocks, a very small number of individuals, say two or three in tens of thousands, turn up with small but 'jump-like' changes, the expression 'jump-like' not meaning that the change is so very considerable, but that there is a discontinuity inasmuch as there are no intermediate forms between the unchanged and the few changed. De Vries called that a mutation. The significant fact is the discontinuity. It reminds a physicist of quantum theory—no intermediate energies occurring between two neighbouring energy levels. He would be inclined to call de Vries's mutation theory, figuratively, the quantum theory of biology. We shall see later that this is much more than figurative. The mutations are actually due to quantum jumps in the gene molecule. But quantum theory was but two years old when de Vries first published his discovery, in 1902. Small wonder that it took another generation to discover the intimate connection!

. . . .

28. *The necessity of mutation being a rare event*

So far we have tended to fix our attention on harmful mutations, which may be the more numerous; but it must be definitely stated that we do encounter advantageous mutations as well. If a spontaneous mutation is a small step in the development of the species, we get the impression that some change is 'tried out' in rather a haphazard fashion at the risk of its being injurious, in which case it is automatically eliminated. This brings out one very important point. In order to be suitable material for the work of natural selection, mutations must be rare events, as they actually are. If they were so frequent that there was a considerable chance of, say, a dozen of different mutations occurring in the same individual, the injurious ones would, as a rule, predominate over the advantageous ones and the species, instead of being improved by selection, would remain unimproved, or would perish. The comparative conservatism which results from the high degree of permanence of the genes is essential. An analogy might be sought in the working of a large manufacturing plant in a factory. For developing better methods, innovations, even if as yet unproved, must be tried out. But in order to ascertain whether the innovations improve or decrease the output, it is essential that they should be introduced one at a time, while all the other parts of the mechanism are kept constant.

29. *Mutations induced by X-rays*

We now have to review a most ingenious series of genetical research work, which will prove to be the most relevant feature of our analysis.

The percentage of mutations in the offspring, the so-called mutation rate, can be increased to a high multiple of the small natural mutation rate by irradiating the parents with X-rays or γ-rays. The mutations produced in this way differ in no way (except by being more numerous) from those occurring spontaneously, and one has the impression that every 'natural' mutation can also be induced by X-rays. In *Drosophila* many special mutations recur spontaneously again and again in the vast cultures; they have been located in the chromosome, and have been given special names. There have been found even what are called 'multiple alleles', that is to say, two or more different 'versions' or 'readings' — in addition to the normal, non-mutated one — of the same place in the chromosome code; that means not only two, but three or more alternatives in that particular 'locus', any two of which are to each other in the relation 'dominant-recessive' when they occur simultaneously in their corresponding loci of the two homologous chromosomes.

The experiments on X-ray-produced mutations give the impression that every particular 'transition', say from the normal individual to a particular mutant, or conversely, has its individual 'X-ray coefficient', indicating the percentage of the offspring which turns out to have mutated in that particular way, when a unit dosage of X-ray has been applied to the parents, before the offspring was engendered.

30. First law. Mutation is a single event

Furthermore, the laws governing the induced mutation rate are extremely simple and extremely illuminating. I follow here the report of N. W. Timoféëff, in *Biological Reviews,* vol. 9, 1934. To a considerable extent it refers to that author's own beautiful work. The first law is

(1) *The increase is exactly proportional to the dosage of rays, so that one can actually speak (as I did) of a coefficient of increase.*

We are so used to simple proportionality that we are liable to underrate the far-reaching consequences of this simple law. To grasp them, we may remember that the price of a commodity, for example, is not always proportional to its amount. In ordinary times a shopkeeper may be so much impressed by your having bought six oranges from him, that, on your deciding to take after all a whole dozen, he may give it to you for less than double the price of the six. In times of scarcity the opposite may happen. In the present case, we conclude that the first half-dosage of radiation, while causing, say, one out of a thousand descendants to mutate, has not influenced the rest at all, either in the way of predisposing them for, or of immunizing them against, mutation. For otherwise the second half-dosage would not cause again just one out of a thousand to mutate. Mutation is thus not an accumulated effect, brought about by consecutive small portions of radiation reinforcing each other. It must consist in some single event occurring in one chromosome during irradiation. What kind of event?

31. Second law. Localization of the event

This is answered by the second law, viz.

(2) *If you vary the quality of the rays (wave-length) within wide limits, from soft X-rays to fairly hard γ-rays, the coefficient remains constant, provided you give the same dosage in so-called r-units,* that is to say, provided you measure the dosage by the total amount of ions produced per unit volume in a suitably chosen standard substance during the time and at the place where the parents are exposed to the rays.

As standard substance one chooses air not only for convenience, but also for the reason that organic tissues are composed of elements of the same average atomic weight as air. A lower limit for the amount of ionizations or allied processes[8] (excitations) in the tissue is obtained simply by multiplying the number of ionizations in air by the ratio of the densities. It is thus fairly obvious, and is confirmed by a more critical investigation, that the single event, causing a mutation, is just an ionization (or similar process) occurring within some 'critical' volume of the germ cell. What is the size of this critical volume? It can be estimated from the observed mutation rate by a consideration of this kind: if a dosage of 50,000 ions per c.cm. produces a chance of only 1:1000 for any particular gamete (that finds itself in the irradiated district) to mutate in that particular way, we conclude that the critical

---

8.   A lower limit, because these other processes escape the ionization measurement, but may be efficient in producing mutations.

volume, the 'target' which has to be 'hit' by an ionization for that mutation to occur, is only $\frac{1}{1000}$ of $\frac{1}{50000}$ of a c.cm., that is to say, one fifty-millionth of a c.cm. The numbers are not the right ones, but are used only by way of illustration. In the actual estimate we follow M. Delbrück, in a paper by Delbrück, N. W. Timoféëff and K. G. Zimmer,[9] which will also be the principal source of the theory to be expounded in the following two chapters. He arrives there at a size of only about ten average atomic distances cubed, containing thus only about 10^3=a thousand atoms. The simplest interpretation of this result is that there is a fair chance of producing that mutation when an ionization (or excitation) occurs not more than about '10 atoms away' from some particular spot in the chromosome. We shall discuss this in more detail presently.

The Timoféëff report contains a practical hint which I cannot refrain from mentioning here, though it has, of course, no bearing on our present investigation. There are plenty of occasions in modern life when a human being has to be exposed to X-rays. The direct dangers involved, as burns, X-ray cancer, sterilization, are well known, and protection by lead screens, lead-loaded aprons, etc., is provided, especially for nurses and doctors who have to handle the rays regularly. The point is, that even when these imminent dangers to the individual are successfully warded off, there appears to be the indirect danger of small detrimental mutations being produced in the germ cells — mutations of the kind envisaged when we spoke of the unfavourable results of close-breeding. To put it drastically, though perhaps a little naïvely, the injuriousness of a marriage between first cousins might very well be increased by the fact that their grandmother had served for a long period as an X-ray nurse. It is not a point that need worry any individual personally. But any possibility of gradually infecting the human race with unwanted latent mutations ought to be a matter of concern to the community.

Chapter IV
THE QUANTUM-MECHANICAL EVIDENCE

> Und deines Geistes höchster Feuerflug
> Hat schon am Gleichnis, hat am Bild genug.[10] *Goethe*

32. *Permanence unexplainable by classical physics*

Thus, aided by the marvellously subtle instrument of X-rays (which, as the physicist remembers, revealed thirty years ago the detailed atomic lattice structures of crystals), the united efforts of biologists and physicists have of late succeeded in reducing the upper limit for the

---

9. *Nachr. a. d. Biologie d. Ges. d. Wiss. Göttingen*, vol. 1, p. 189, 1935.
10. And thy spirit's fiery flight of imagination acquiesces in an image, in a parable.

size of the microscopic structure, being responsible for a definite large-scale feature of the individual — the 'size of a gene' — and reducing it far below the estimates obtained in § 19. We are now seriously faced with the question: How can we, from the point of view of statistical physics, reconcile the facts that the gene structure seems to involve only a comparatively small number of atoms (of the order of 1000 and possibly much less), and that nevertheless it displays a most regular and lawful activity — with a durability or permanence that borders upon the miraculous?

Let me throw the truly amazing situation into relief once again. Several members of the Habsburg dynasty have a peculiar disfigurement of the lower lip ('Habsburger Lippe'). Its inheritance has been studied carefully and published, complete with historical portraits, by the Imperial Academy of Vienna, under the auspices of the family. The feature proves to be a genuinely Mendelian 'allele' to the normal form of the lip. Fixing our attention on the portraits of a member of the family in the sixteenth century and of his descendant, living in the nineteenth, we may safely assume that the material gene structure, responsible for the abnormal feature, has been carried on from generation to generation through the centuries, faithfully reproduced at every one of the not very numerous cell divisions that lie between. Moreover, the number of atoms involved in the responsible gene structure is likely to be of the same order of magnitude as in the cases tested by X-rays. The gene has been kept at a temperature around 98° F. during all that time. How are we to understand that it has remained unperturbed by the disordering tendency of the heat motion for centuries?

A physicist at the end of the last century would have been at a loss to answer this question, if he was prepared to draw only on those laws of Nature which he could explain and which he really understood. Perhaps, indeed, after a short reflection on the statistical situation he would have answered (correctly, as we shall see): These material structures can only be molecules. Of the existence, and sometimes very high stability, of these associations of atoms, chemistry had already acquired a widespread knowledge at the time. But the knowledge was purely empirical. The nature of a molecule was not understood — the strong mutual bond of the atoms which keeps a molecule in shape was a complete conundrum to everybody. Actually, the answer proves to be correct. But it is of limited value as long as the enigmatic biological stability is traced back only to an equally enigmatic chemical stability. The evidence that two features, similar in appearance, are based on the same principle, is always precarious as long as the principle itself is unknown.

33. *Explicable by quantum theory*

In this case it is supplied by quantum theory. In the light of present knowledge, the mechanism of heredity is closely related to, nay, founded on, the very basis of quantum theory. This theory was discovered by Max Planck in 1900. Modern genetics can be dated from the rediscovery of Mendel's paper by de Vries, Correns and Tschermak

(1900) and from de Vries's paper on mutations (1901–3). Thus the births of the two great theories nearly coincide, and it is small wonder that both of them had to reach a certain maturity before the connection could emerge. On the side of quantum theory it took more than a quarter of a century till in 1926–7 the quantum theory of the chemical bond was outlined in its general principles by W. Heitler and F. London. The Heitler-London theory involves the most subtle and intricate conceptions of the latest development of quantum theory (called 'quantum mechanics' or 'wave mechanics'). A presentation without the use of calculus is well-nigh impossible or would at least require another little volume like this. But fortunately, now that all work has been done and has served to clarify our thinking, it seems to be possible to point out in a more direct manner the connection between 'quantum jumps' and mutations, to pick out at the moment the most conspicuous item. That is what we attempt here.

34. *Quantum theory — discrete states — quantum jumps*

The great revelation of quantum theory was that features of discreteness were discovered in the Book of Nature, in a context in which anything other than continuity seemed to be absurd according to the views held until then.

The first case of this kind concerned energy. A body on the large scale changes its energy continuously. A pendulum, for instance, that is set swinging is gradually slowed down by the resistance of the air. Strangely enough, it proves necessary to admit that a system of the order of the atomic scale behaves differently. On grounds upon which we cannot enter here, we have to assume that a small system can by its very nature possess only certain discrete amounts of energy, called its peculiar energy levels. The transition from one state to another is a rather mysterious event, which is usually called a 'quantum jump'.

But energy is not the only characteristic of a system. Take again our pendulum, but think of one that can perform different kinds of movement, a heavy ball suspended by a string from the ceiling. It can be made to swing in a north-south or east-west or any other direction or in a circle or in an ellipse. By gently blowing the ball with a bellows, it can be made to pass continuously from one state of motion to any other.

For small-scale systems most of these or similar characteristics — we cannot enter into details — change discontinuously. They are 'quantized', just as the energy is.

The result is that a number of atomic nuclei, including their bodyguards of electrons, when they find themselves close to each other, forming 'a system', are unable by their very nature to adopt any arbitrary configuration we might think of. Their very nature leaves them only a very numerous but discrete series of 'states' to choose from.[11]

---

11. I am adopting the version which is usually given in popular treatment and which suffices for our present purpose. But I have the bad conscience of one who perpetuates a convenient error. The true story is much more complicated, inasmuch as it includes the occasional indeterminateness with regard to the state the system is in.

We usually call them levels or energy levels, because the energy is a very relevant part of the characteristic. But it must be understood that the complete description includes much more than just the energy. It is virtually correct to think of a state as meaning a definite configuration of all the corpuscles.

The transition from one of these configurations to another is a quantum jump. If the second one has the greater energy ('is a higher level'), the system must be supplied from outside with at least the difference of the two energies to make the transition possible. To a lower level it can change spontaneously, spending the surplus of energy in radiation.

35. *Molecules*

Among the discrete set of states of a given selection of atoms there need not necessarily but there may be a lowest level, implying a close approach of the nuclei to each other. Atoms in such a state form a molecule. The point to stress here is, that the molecule will of necessity have a certain stability; the configuration cannot change, unless at least the energy difference, necessary to 'lift' it to the next higher level, is supplied from outside. Hence this level difference, which is a well-defined quantity, determines quantitatively the degree of stability of the molecule. It will be observed how intimately this fact is linked with the very basis of quantum theory, viz. with the discreteness of the level scheme.

I must beg the reader to take it for granted that this order of ideas has been thoroughly checked by chemical facts; and that it has proved successful in explaining the basic fact of chemical valency and many details about the structure of molecules, their binding-energies, their stabilities at different temperatures, and so on. I am speaking of the Heitler-London theory, which, as I said, cannot be examined in detail here.

36. *Their stability dependent on temperature*

We must content ourselves with examining the point which is of paramount interest for our biological question, namely, the stability of a molecule at different temperatures. Take our system of atoms at first to be actually in its state of lowest energy. The physicist would call it a molecule at the absolute zero of temperature. To lift it to the next higher state or level a definite supply of energy is required. The simplest way of trying to supply it is to 'heat up' your molecule. You bring it into an environment of higher temperature ('heat bath'), thus allowing other systems (atoms, molecules) to impinge upon it. Considering the entire irregularity of heat motion, there is no sharp temperature limit at which the 'lift' will be brought about with certainty and immediately. Rather, at any temperature (different from absolute zero) there is a certain smaller or greater chance for the lift to occur, the chance increasing of course with the temperature of the heat bath. The best way to express this chance is to indicate the average time you will have to wait until the lift takes place, the 'time of expectation'.

From an investigation, due to M. Polanyi and E. Wigner,[12] the 'time of expectation' largely depends on the ratio of two energies, one being just the energy difference itself that is required to effect the lift (let us write W for it), the other one characterizing the intensity of the heat motion at the temperature in question (let us write T for the absolute temperature and kT for the characteristic energy).[13] It stands to reason that the chance for effecting the lift is smaller, and hence that the time of expectation is longer, the higher the lift itself compared with the average heat energy, that is to say, the greater the ratio $W{:}kT$. What is amazing is how enormously the time of expectation depends on comparatively small changes of the ratio $W{:}kT$. To give an example (following Delbrück): for W thirty times kT the time of expectation might be as short as $\frac{1}{10}$ sec., but would rise to 16 months when W is 50 times kT, and to 30,000 years when W is 60 times kT!

37. Mathematical interlude

It might be as well to point out in mathematical language — for those readers to whom it appeals — the reason for this enormous sensitivity to changes in the level step or temperature, and to add a few physical remarks of a similar kind. The reason is that the time of expectation, call it t, depends on the ratio W/kT by an exponential function, thus

$$t = \tau e^{W/kT}.$$

τ is a certain small constant of the order of 10^{-13} or 10^{-14} sec. Now, this particular exponential function is not an accidental feature. It recurs again and again in the statistical theory of heat, forming, as it were, its backbone. It is a measure of the improbability of an energy amount as large as W gathering accidentally in some particular part of the system, and it is this improbability which increases so enormously when a considerable multiple of the 'average energy' kT is required.

Actually a $W = 30kT$ (see the example quoted above) is already extremely rare. That it does not yet lead to an enormously long time of expectation (only $\frac{1}{10}$ sec. in our example) is, of course, due to the smallness of the factor τ. This factor has a physical meaning. It is of the order of the period of the vibrations which take place in the system all the time. You could, very broadly, describe this factor as meaning that the chance of accumulating the required amount W, though very small, recurs again and again 'at every vibration', that is to say, about 10^{13} or 10^{14} times during every second.

38. First amendment

In offering these considerations as a theory of the stability of the molecule it has been tacitly assumed that the quantum jump which we

---

12. *Zeitschrift für Physik*, Chemie (A), Haber-Band, p. 439, 1928.
13. k is a numerically known constant, called Boltzmann's constant. $\frac{3}{2} kT$ is the average kinetic energy of a gas atom at temperature T.

FIGURE 6.   The two isomeres of propyl-alcohol.

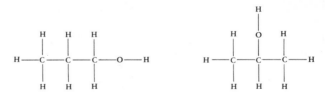

called the 'lift' leads, if not to a complete disintegration, at least to an essentially different configuration of the same atoms—an isomeric molecule, as the chemist would say, that is, a molecule composed of the same atoms in a different arrangement (in the application to biology it is going to represent a different 'allele' in the same 'locus' and the quantum jump will represent a mutation).

To allow of this interpretation two points must be amended in our story, which I purposely simplified to make it at all intelligible. From the way I told it, it might be imagined that only in its very lowest state does our group of atoms form what we call a molecule and that already the next higher state is 'something else'. That is not so. Actually the lowest level is followed by a crowded series of levels which do not involve any appreciable change in the configuration as a whole, but only correspond to those small vibrations among the atoms which we have mentioned in § 37. They, too, are 'quantized', but with comparatively small steps from one level to the next. Hence the impacts of the particles of the 'heat bath' may suffice to set them up already at fairly low temperature. If the molecule is an extended structure, you may conceive these vibrations as high-frequency sound waves, crossing the molecule without doing it any harm.

So the first amendment is not very serious: we have to disregard the 'vibrational fine-structure' of the level scheme. The term 'next higher level' has to be understood as meaning the next level that corresponds to a relevant change of configuration.

39. *Second amendment*

The second amendment is far more difficult to explain, because it is concerned with certain vital, but rather complicated, features of the scheme of relevantly different levels. The free passage between two of them may be obstructed, quite apart from the required energy supply; in fact, it may be obstructed even from the higher to the lower state.

Let us start from the empirical facts. It is known to the chemist that the same group of atoms can unite in more than one way to form a molecule. Such molecules are called isomeric ('consisting of the same parts'; ἴσος = same, μέρος = part). Isomerism is not an exception, it is the rule. The larger the molecule, the more isomeric alternatives are offered. Fig. 6 shows one of the simplest cases, the two kinds of pro-

FIGURE 7. Energy threshold (3) between the isomeric levels (1) and (2). The arrows indicate the minimum energies required for transition.

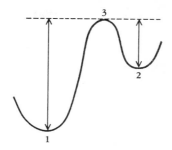

pyl-alcohol, both consisting of 3 carbons (C), 8 hydrogens (H), 1 oxygen (O).[14] The latter can be interposed between any hydrogen and its carbon, but only the two cases shown in our figure are different substances. And they really are. All their physical and chemical constants are distinctly different. Also their energies are different, they represent 'different levels'.

The remarkable fact is that both molecules are perfectly stable, both behave as though they were 'lowest states'. There are no spontaneous transitions from either state towards the other.

The reason is that the two configurations are not neighbouring configurations. The transition from one to the other can only take place over intermediate configurations which have a greater energy than either of them. To put it crudely, the oxygen has to be extracted from one position and has to be inserted into the other. There does not seem to be a way of doing that without passing through configurations of considerably higher energy. The state of affairs is sometimes figuratively pictured as in Fig. 7, in which 1 and 2 represent the two isomeres, 3 the 'threshold' between them, and the two arrows indicate the 'lifts', that is to say, the energy supplies required to produce the transition from state 1 to state 2 or from state 2 to state 1, respectively.

Now we can give our 'second amendment', which is that transitions of this 'isomeric' kind are the only ones in which we shall be interested in our biological application. It was these we had in mind when explaining 'stability' in §§ 35 – 37. The 'quantum jump' which we mean is the transition from one relatively stable molecular configuration to another. The energy supply required for the transition (the quantity denoted by W) is not the actual level difference, but the step from the initial level up to the threshold (see the arrows in Fig. 7).

Transitions with no threshold interposed between the initial and the final state are entirely uninteresting, and that not only in our biological

14.   Models, in which C, H and O were represented by black, white and red wooden balls respectively, were exhibited at the lecture. I have not reproduced them here, because their likeness to the actual molecules is not appreciably greater than that of Fig. 6.

application. They have actually nothing to contribute to the chemical stability of the molecule. Why? They have no lasting effect, they remain unnoticed. For, when they occur, they are almost immediately followed by a relapse into the initial state, since nothing prevents their return.

Chapter V
DELBRÜCK'S MODEL DISCUSSED AND TESTED

> Sane sicut lux seipsam et tenebras manifestat, sic veritas norma sui et falsi est.[15]
>
> *Spinoza,* ETHICS, P. II, Prop. 43.

40. *The general picture of the hereditary substance*

From these facts emerges a very simple answer to our question, namely: Are these structures, composed of comparatively few atoms, capable of withstanding for long periods the disturbing influence of heat motion to which the hereditary substance is continually exposed? We shall assume the structure of a gene to be that of a huge molecule, capable only of discontinuous change, which consists in a rearrangement of the atoms and leads to an isomeric[16] molecule. The rearrangement may affect only a small region of the gene, and a vast number of different rearrangements may be possible. The energy thresholds, separating the actual configuration from any possible isomeric ones, have to be high enough (compared with the average heat energy of an atom) to make the change-over a rare event. These rare events we shall identify with spontaneous mutations.

The later parts of this chapter will be devoted to putting this general picture of a gene and of mutation (due mainly to the German physicist M. Delbrück) to the test, by comparing it in detail with genetical facts. Before doing so, we may fittingly make some comment on the foundation and general nature of the theory.

41. *The uniqueness of the picture*

Was it absolutely essential for the biological question to dig up the deepest roots and found the picture on quantum mechanics? The conjecture that a gene is a molecule is to-day, I dare say, a commonplace. Few biologists, whether familiar with quantum theory or not, would disagree with it. In § 32 we ventured to put it into the mouth of a pre-quantum physicist, as the only reasonable explanation of the observed permanence. The subsequent considerations about isomerism, threshold energy, the paramount role of the ratio $W:kT$ in deter-

---

15. Truly, as light manifests itself and darkness, thus truth is the standard of itself and of error.

16. For convenience I shall continue to call it an isomeric transition, though it would be absurd to exclude the possibility of any exchange with the environment.

mining the probability of an isomeric transition — all that could very well be introduced on a purely empirical basis, at any rate without drawing explicitly on quantum theory. Why did I so strongly insist on the quantum-mechanical point of view, though I could not really make it clear in this little book and may well have bored many a reader?

Quantum mechanics is the first theoretical aspect which accounts from first principles for all kinds of aggregates of atoms actually encountered in Nature. The Heitler-London bondage is a unique, singular feature of the theory, not invented for the purpose of explaining the chemical bond. It comes in quite by itself, in a highly interesting and puzzling manner, being forced upon us by entirely different considerations. It proves to correspond exactly with the observed chemical facts, and, as I said, it is a unique feature, well enough understood to tell with reasonable certainty that 'such a thing could not happen again' in the further development of quantum theory.

Consequently, we may safely assert that there is no alternative to the molecular explanation of the hereditary substance. The physical aspect leaves no other possibility to account for its permanence. If the Delbrück picture should fail, we would have to give up further attempts. That is the first point I wish to make.

42. *Some traditional misconceptions*

But it may be asked: Are there really no other endurable structures composed of atoms except molecules? Does not a gold coin, for example, buried in a tomb for a couple of thousand years, preserve the traits of the portrait stamped on it? It is true that the coin consists of an enormous number of atoms, but surely we are in this case not inclined to attribute the mere preservation of shape to the statistics of large numbers. The same remark applies to a neatly developed batch of crystals we find embedded in a rock, where it must have been for geological periods without changing.

That leads us to the second point I want to elucidate. The cases of a molecule, a solid, a crystal are not really different. In the light of present knowledge they are virtually the same. Unfortunately, school teaching keeps up certain traditional views, which have been out of date for many years and which obscure the understanding of the actual state of affairs.

Indeed, what we have learnt at school about molecules does not give the idea that they are more closely akin to the solid state than to the liquid or gaseous state. On the contrary, we have been taught to distinguish carefully between a physical change, such as melting or evaporation in which the molecules are preserved (so that, for example, alcohol, whether solid, liquid or a gas, always consists of the same molecules, C_2H_6O), and a chemical change, as, for example, the burning of alcohol,

$$C_2H_6O + 3O_2 = 2CO_2 + 3H_2O,$$

where an alcohol molecule and three oxygen molecules undergo a rearrangement to form two molecules of carbon dioxide and three molecules of water.

About crystals, we have been taught that they form three-fold periodic lattices, in which the structure of the single molecule is sometimes recognizable, as in the case of alcohol and most organic compounds, while in other crystals, e.g. rock-salt (NaCl), NaCl molecules cannot be unequivocally delimited, because every Na atom is symmetrically surrounded by six Cl atoms, and vice versa, so that it is largely arbitrary what pairs, if any, are regarded as molecular partners.

Finally, we have been told that a solid can be crystalline or not, and in the latter case we call it amorphous.

43. *Different 'states' of matter*

Now I would not go so far as to say that all these statements and distinctions are quite wrong. For practical purposes they are sometimes useful. But in the true aspect of the structure of matter the limits must be drawn in an entirely different way. The fundamental distinction is between the two lines of the following scheme of 'equations':

$$\text{molecule} = \text{solid} = \text{crystal.}$$
$$\text{gas} \quad = \text{liquid} = \text{amorphous.}$$

We must explain these statements briefly. The so-called amorphous solids are either not really amorphous or not really solid. In 'amorphous' charcoal fibre the rudimentary structure of the graphite crystal has been disclosed by X-rays. So charcoal is a solid, but also crystalline. Where we find no crystalline structure we have to regard the thing as a liquid with very high 'viscosity' (internal friction). Such a substance discloses by the absence of a well-defined melting temperature and of a latent heat of melting that it is not a true solid. When heated it softens gradually and eventually liquefies without discontinuity. (I remember that at the end of the first Great War we were given in Vienna an asphalt-like substance as a substitute for coffee. It was so hard that one had to use a chisel or a hatchet to break the little brick into pieces, when it would show a smooth, shell-like cleavage. Yet, given time, it would behave as a liquid, closely packing the lower part of a vessel in which you were unwise enough to leave it for a couple of days.)

The continuity of the gaseous and liquid state is a well-known story. You can liquefy any gas without discontinuity by taking your way 'around' the so-called critical point. But we shall not enter on this here.

44. *The distinction that really matters*

We have thus justified everything in the above scheme, except the main point, namely, that we wish a molecule to be regarded as a solid = crystal.

The reason for this is that the atoms forming a molecule, whether there be few or many of them, are united by forces of exactly the same nature as the numerous atoms which build up a true solid, a crystal. The molecule presents the same solidity of structure as a crystal.

Remember that it is precisely this solidity on which we draw to account for the permanence of the gene!

The distinction that is really important in the structure of matter is whether atoms are bound together by those 'solidifying' Heitler-London forces or whether they are not. In a solid and in a molecule they all are. In a gas of single atoms (as e.g. mercury vapour) they are not. In a gas composed of molecules, only the atoms within every molecule are linked in this way.

45. *The aperiodic solid*

A small molecule might be called 'the germ of a solid'. Starting from such a small solid germ, there seem to be two different ways of building up larger and larger associations. One is the comparatively dull way of repeating the same structure in three directions again and again. That is the way followed in a growing crystal. Once the periodicity is established, there is no definite limit to the size of the aggregate. The other way is that of building up a more and more extended aggregate without the dull device of repetition. That is the case of the more and more complicated organic molecule in which every atom, and every group of atoms, plays an individual role, not entirely equivalent to that of many others (as is the case in a periodic structure). We might quite properly call that an aperiodic crystal or solid and express our hypothesis by saying: We believe a gene—or perhaps the whole chromosome fibre[17]—to be an aperiodic solid.

46. *The variety of contents compressed in the miniature code*

It has often been asked how this tiny speck of material, the nucleus of the fertilized egg, could contain an elaborate code-script involving all the future development of the organism? A well-ordered association of atoms, endowed with sufficient resistivity to keep its order permanently, appears to be the only conceivable material structure, that offers a variety of possible ('isomeric') arrangements, sufficiently large to embody a complicated system of 'determinations' within a small spatial boundary. Indeed, the number of atoms in such a structure need not be very large to produce an almost unlimited number of possible arrangements. For illustration, think of the Morse code. The two different signs of dot and dash in well-ordered groups of not more than four allow of thirty different specifications. Now, if you allowed yourself the use of a third sign, in addition to dot and dash, and used groups of not more than ten, you could form 88,572 different 'letters'; with five signs and groups up to 25, the number is 372,529,029,846,-191,405.

It may be objected that the simile is deficient, because our Morse signs may have different composition (e.g. $\cdot --$ and $\cdot\cdot -$) and thus they are a bad analogue for isomerism. To remedy this defect, let us pick, from the third example, only the combinations of exactly 25 symbols

---

17. That it is highly flexible is no objection; so is a thin copper wire.

and only those containing exactly 5 out of each of the supposed 5 types (5 dots, 5 dashes, etc.). A rough count gives you the number of combinations as 62,330,000,000,000, where the zeros on the right stand for figures which I have not taken the trouble to compute.

Of course, in the actual case, by no means 'every' arrangement of the group of atoms will represent a possible molecule; moreover, it is not a question of a code to be adopted arbitrarily, for the code-script must itself be the operative factor bringing about the development. But, on the other hand, the number chosen in the example (25) is still very small, and we have envisaged only the simple arrangements in one line. What we wish to illustrate is simply that with the molecular picture of the gene it is no longer inconceivable that the miniature code should precisely correspond with a highly complicated and specified plan of development and should somehow contain the means to put it into operation.

47. *Comparison with facts: degree of stability; discontinuity of mutations*

Now let us at last proceed to compare the theoretical picture with the biological facts. The first question obviously is, whether it can really account for the high degree of permanence we observe. Are threshold values of the required amount — high multiples of the average heat energy kT — reasonable, are they within the range known from ordinary chemistry? That question is trivial; it can be answered in the affirmative without inspecting tables. The molecules of any substance which the chemist is able to isolate at a given temperature must at that temperature have a lifetime of at least minutes. (That is putting it mildly; as a rule they have much more.) Thus the threshold values the chemist encounters are of necessity precisely of the order of magnitude required to account for practically any degree of permanence the biologist may encounter; for we recall from § 36 that thresholds varying within a range of about 1:2 will account for lifetimes ranging from a fraction of a second to tens of thousands of years.

But let me mention figures, for future reference. The ratios W/kT mentioned by way of example in § 36, viz.

$$\frac{W}{kT} = 30, 50, 60,$$

producing lifetimes of

$$\tfrac{1}{10} \text{ sec., } 16 \text{ months, } 30,000 \text{ years,}$$

respectively, correspond at room temperature with threshold values of

$$0 \cdot 9, 1 \cdot 5, 1 \cdot 8 \text{ electron-volts.}$$

We must explain the unit 'electron-volt', which is rather convenient for the physicist, because it can be visualized. For example, the third number $(1 \cdot 8)$ means that an electron, accelerated by a voltage of about 2 volts, would have acquired just sufficient energy to effect the transition by impact. (For comparison, the battery of an ordinary pocket flash-light has 3 volts.)

These considerations make it conceivable that an isomeric change of configuration in some part of our molecule, produced by a chance fluctuation of the vibrational energy, can actually be a sufficiently rare event to be interpreted as a spontaneous mutation. Thus we account, by the very principles of quantum mechanics, for the most amazing fact about mutations, the fact by which they first attracted de Vries's attention, namely, that they are 'jumping' variations, no intermediate forms occurring.

48. *Stability of naturally selected genes*

Having discovered the increase of the natural mutation rate by any kind of ionizing rays, one might think of attributing the natural rate to the radio-activity of the soil and air and to cosmic radiation. But a quantitative comparison with the X-ray results shows that the 'natural radiation' is much too weak and could account only for a small fraction of the natural rate.

Granted that we have to account for the rare natural mutations by chance fluctuations of the heat motion, we must not be very much astonished that Nature has succeeded in making such a subtle choice of threshold values as is necessary to make mutation rare. For we have, earlier in these lectures, arrived at the conclusion that frequent mutations are detrimental to evolution. Individuals which, by mutation, acquire a gene configuration of insufficient stability, will have little chance of seeing their 'ultra-radical', rapidly mutating descendancy survive long. The species will be freed of them and will thus collect stable genes by natural selection.

49. *The sometimes lower stability of mutants*

But, of course, as regards the mutants which occur in our breeding experiments and which we select, *qua* mutants, for studying their offspring, there is no reason to expect that they should all show that very high stability. For they have not yet been 'tried out' — or, if they have, they have been 'rejected' in the wild breeds — possibly for too high mutability. At any rate, we are not at all astonished to learn that actually some of these mutants do show a much higher mutability than the normal 'wild' genes.

50. *Temperature influences unstable genes less than stable ones*

This enables us to test our mutability formula, which was

$$t = \tau e^{W/kT}.$$

(It will be remembered that t is the time of expectation for a mutation with threshold energy W.) We ask: How does t change with the temperature? We easily find from the preceding formula in good approximation the ratio of the value of t at temperature $T + 10$, to that at temperature T

$$\frac{t_{T+10}}{t_T} = e^{-10W/kT^2}$$

The exponent being now negative, the ratio is, naturally, smaller than 1. The time of expectation is diminished by raising the temperature, the mutability is increased. Now that can be tested and has been tested with the fly *Drosophila* in the range of temperature which the insects will stand. The result was, at first sight, surprising. The *low* mutability of wild genes was distinctly increased, but the comparatively *high* mutability occurring with some of the already mutated genes was not, or at any rate was much less, increased. That is just what we expect on comparing our two formulae. A large value of W/kT, which according to the first formula is required to make t large (stable gene), will, according to the second one, make for a small value of the ratio computed there, that is to say for a considerable increase of mutability with temperature. (The actual values of the ratio seem to lie between about $\frac{1}{2}$ and $\frac{1}{5}$. The reciprocal, $2 \cdot 5$, is what in an ordinary chemical reaction we call the van 't Hoff factor.)

51. *How X-rays produce mutation*

Turning now to the X-ray-induced mutation rate, we have already inferred from the breeding experiments, first (from the proportionality of mutation rate, and dosage), that some single event produces the mutation; secondly (from quantitative results and from the fact that the mutation rate is determined by the integrated ionization density and independent of the wave-length), this single event must be an ionization, or similar process, which has to take place inside a certain volume of only about 10 atomic-distances-cubed, in order to produce a specified mutation. According to our picture, the energy for overcoming the threshold must obviously be furnished by that explosion-like process, ionization or excitation. I call it explosion-like, because the energy spent in one ionization (spent, incidentally, not by the X-ray itself, but by a secondary electron it produces) is well known and has the comparatively enormous amount of 30 electron-volts. It is bound to be turned into enormously increased heat motion around the point where it is discharged and to spread from there in the form of a 'heat wave', a wave of intense oscillations of the atoms. That this heat wave should still be able to furnish the required threshold energy of 1 or 2 electron-volts at an average 'range of action' of about ten atomic distances, is not inconceivable, though it may well be that an unprejudiced physicist might have anticipated a slightly lower range of action. That in many cases the effect of the explosion will not be an orderly isomeric transition but a lesion of the chromosome, a lesion that becomes lethal when, by ingenious crossings, the uninjured partner (the corresponding chromosome of the second set) is removed and replaced by a partner whose corresponding gene is known to be itself morbid — all that is absolutely to be expected and it is exactly what is observed.

52. *Their efficiency does not depend on spontaneous mutability*

Quite a few other features are, if not predictable from the picture, easily understood from it. For example, an unstable mutant does not on the average show a much higher X-ray mutation rate than a stable one. Now, with an explosion furnishing an energy of 30 electron-volts you would certainly not expect that it makes a lot of difference whether the required threshold energy is a little larger or a little smaller, say 1 or 1·3 volts.

53. *Reversible mutations*

In some cases a transition was studied in both directions, say from a certain 'wild' gene to a specified mutant and back from that mutant to the wild gene. In such cases the natural mutation rate is sometimes nearly the same, sometimes very different. At first sight one is puzzled, because the threshold to be overcome seems to be the same in both cases. But, of course, it need not be, because it has to be measured from the energy level of the starting configuration, and that may be different for the wild and the mutated gene. (See Fig. 7 on p. 88, where '1' might refer to the wild allele, '2' to the mutant, whose lower stability would be indicated by the shorter arrow.)

On the whole, I think, Delbrück's 'model' stands the tests fairly well and we are justified in using it in further considerations.

Chapter VI
ORDER, DISORDER AND ENTROPY

> Nec corpus mentem ad cogitandum nec mens corpus ad motum, neque ad quietem nec ad aliquid (si quid est) aliud determinare potest.[18]
>
> *Spinoza*, ETHICS, P. III, Prop. 2

54. *A remarkable general conclusion from the model*

Let me refer to the last phrase in § 46, in which I tried to explain that the molecular picture of the gene made it at least conceivable 'that the miniature code should be in one-to-one correspondence with a highly complicated and specified plan of development and should somehow contain the means of putting it into operation'. Very well then, but how does it do this? How are we going to turn 'conceivability' into true understanding?

Delbrück's molecular model, in its complete generality, seems to contain no hint as to how the hereditary substance works. Indeed, I do not expect that any detailed information on this question is likely to come from physics in the near future. The advance is proceeding and

---

18. Neither can the body determine the mind to think, nor the mind the body to move or to rest nor to anything else, if such there be.

will, I am sure, continue to do so, from biochemistry under the guidance of physiology and genetics.

No detailed information about the functioning of the genetical mechanism can emerge from a description of its structure so general as has been given above. That is obvious. But, strangely enough, there is just one general conclusion to be obtained from it, and that, I confess, was my only motive for writing this book.

From Delbrück's general picture of the hereditary substance it emerges that living matter, while not eluding the 'laws of physics' as established up to date, is likely to involve 'other laws of physics' hitherto unknown, which, however, once they have been revealed, will form just as integral a part of this science as the former.

55. *Order based on order*

This is a rather subtle line of thought, open to misconception in more than one respect. All the remaining pages are concerned with making it clear. A preliminary insight, rough but not altogether erroneous, may be found in the following considerations:

It has been explained in Chapter I that the laws of physics, as we know them, are statistical laws.[19] They have a lot to do with the natural tendency of things to go over into disorder.

But, to reconcile the high durability of the hereditary substance with its minute size, we had to evade the tendency to disorder by 'inventing the molecule', in fact, an unusually large molecule which has to be a masterpiece of highly differentiated order, safeguarded by the conjuring rod of quantum theory. The laws of chance are not invalidated by this 'invention', but their outcome is modified. The physicist is familiar with the fact that the classical laws of physics are modified by quantum theory, especially at low temperature. There are many instances of this. Life seems to be one of them, a particularly striking one. Life seems to be orderly and lawful behaviour of matter, not based exclusively on its tendency to go over from order to disorder, but based partly on existing order that is kept up.

To the physicist — but only to him — I could hope to make my view clearer by saying: The living organism seems to be a macroscopic system which in part of its behaviour approaches to that purely mechanical (as contrasted with thermodynamical) conduct to which all systems tend, as the temperature approaches the absolute zero and the molecular disorder is removed.

The non-physicist finds it hard to believe that really the ordinary laws of physics, which he regards as the prototype of inviolable precision, should be based on the statistical tendency of matter to go over into disorder. I have given examples in Chapter I. The general principle involved is the famous Second Law of Thermodynamics (entropy principle) and its equally famous statistical foundation. In §§ 56–60 I will try to sketch the bearing of the entropy principle on the large-

---

19. To state this in complete generality about 'the laws of physics' is perhaps challengeable. The point will be discussed in Chapter VII.

scale behaviour of a living organism – forgetting at the moment all that is known about chromosomes, inheritance, and so on.

56. *Living matter evades the decay to equilibrium*

What is the characteristic feature of life? When is a piece of matter said to be alive? When it goes on 'doing something', moving, exchanging material with its environment, and so forth, and that for a much longer period than we would expect an inanimate piece of matter to 'keep going' under similar circumstances. When a system that is not alive is isolated or placed in a uniform environment, all motion usually comes to a standstill very soon as a result of various kinds of friction; differences of electric or chemical potential are equalized, substances which tend to form a chemical compound do so, temperature becomes uniform by heat conduction. After that the whole system fades away into a dead, inert lump of matter. A permanent state is reached, in which no observable events occur. The physicist calls this the state of thermodynamical equilibrium, or of 'maximum entropy'.

Practically, a state of this kind is usually reached very rapidly. Theoretically, it is very often not yet an absolute equilibrium, not yet the true maximum of entropy. But then the final approach to equilibrium is very slow. It could take anything between hours, years, centuries, ... To give an example – one in which the approach is still fairly rapid: if a glass filled with pure water and a second one filled with sugared water are placed together in a hermetically closed case at constant temperature, it appears at first that nothing happens, and the impression of complete equilibrium is created. But after a day or so it is noticed that the pure water, owing to its higher vapour pressure, slowly evaporates and condenses on the solution. The latter overflows. Only after the pure water has totally evaporated has the sugar reached its aim of being equally distributed among all the liquid water available.

These ultimate slow approaches to equilibrium could never be mistaken for life, and we may disregard them here. I have referred to them in order to clear myself of a charge of inaccuracy.

57. *It feeds on 'negative entropy'*

It is by avoiding the rapid decay into the inert state of 'equilibrium', that an organism appears so enigmatic; so much so, that from the earliest times of human thought some special non-physical or supernatural force (*vis viva*, entelechy) was claimed to be operative in the organism, and in some quarters is still claimed.

How does the living organism avoid decay? The obvious answer is: By eating, drinking, breathing and (in the case of plants) assimilating. The technical term is *metabolism*. The Greek word ($\mu\epsilon\tau\alpha\beta\acute{\alpha}\lambda\lambda\epsilon\iota\nu$) means change or exchange. Exchange of what? Originally the underlying idea is, no doubt, exchange of material. (E.g. the German for metabolism is Stoffwechsel.) That the exchange of material should be the essential thing is absurd. Any atom of nitrogen, oxygen, sulphur, etc., is as good as any other of its kind; what could be gained by exchanging them? For a while in the past our curiosity was silenced by being told that we feed upon energy. In some very advanced country (I don't remember whether it was Germany or the U.S.A. or both) you could find menu cards in restaurants indicating, in addition to the price, the energy content of every dish. Needless to say, taken literally, this is just as absurd. For an adult organism the energy content is as stationary as the material content. Since, surely, any calorie is worth as much as any other calorie, one cannot see how a mere exchange could help.

What then is that precious something contained in our food which keeps us from death? That is easily answered. Every process, event, happening — call it what you will; in a word, everything that is going on in Nature means an increase of the entropy of the part of the world where it is going on. Thus a living organism continually increases its entropy — or, as you may say, produces positive entropy — and thus tends to approach the dangerous state of maximum entropy, which is death. It can only keep aloof from it, i.e. alive, by continually drawing from its environment negative entropy — which is something very positive as we shall immediately see. What an organism feeds upon is negative entropy. Or, to put it less paradoxically, the essential thing in metabolism is that the organism succeeds in freeing itself from all the entropy it cannot help producing while alive.

58. *What is entropy?*

What is entropy? Let me first emphasize that it is not a hazy concept or idea, but a measurable physical quantity just like the length of a rod, the temperature at any point of a body, the heat of fusion of a given crystal or the specific heat of any given substance. At the absolute zero point of temperature (roughly $-273°$ C.) the entropy of any substance is zero. When you bring the substance into any other state by slow, reversible little steps (even if thereby the substance changes its physical or chemical nature or splits up into two or more parts of different physical or chemical nature) the entropy increases by an amount which is computed by dividing every little portion of heat you had to supply in that procedure by the absolute temperature at which it was supplied — and by summing up all these small contributions. To give an example, when you melt a solid, its entropy increases by the amount of the heat of fusion divided by the temperature at the melting-point. You see from this, that the unit in which entropy is measured is cal./°C. (just as the calorie is the unit of heat or the centimetre the unit of length).

59. *The statistical meaning of entropy*

I have mentioned this technical definition simply in order to remove entropy from the atmosphere of hazy mystery that frequently veils it. Much more important for us here is the bearing on the statistical concept of order and disorder, a connection that was revealed by the investigations of Boltzmann and Gibbs in statistical physics. This too is an exact quantitative connection, and is expressed by

$$\text{entropy} = k \log D,$$

where k is the so-called Boltzmann constant ($= 3 \cdot 2983.10^{-24}$ cal./$^\circ$ C.), and D a quantitative measure of the atomistic disorder of the body in question. To give an exact explanation of this quantity D in brief non-technical terms is well-nigh impossible. The disorder it indicates is partly that of heat motion, partly that which consists in different kinds of atoms or molecules being mixed at random, instead of being neatly separated, e.g. the sugar and water molecules in the example quoted above. Boltzmann's equation is well illustrated by that example. The gradual 'spreading out' of the sugar over all the water available increases the disorder D, and hence (since the logarithm of D increases with D) the entropy. It is also pretty clear that any supply of heat increases the turmoil of heat motion, that is to say increases D and thus increases the entropy; it is particularly clear that this should be so when you melt a crystal, since you thereby destroy the neat and permanent arrangement of the atoms or molecules and turn the crystal lattice into a continually changing random distribution.

An isolated system or a system in a uniform environment (which for the present consideration we do best to include as a part of the system we contemplate) increases its entropy and more or less rapidly approaches the inert state of maximum entropy. We now recognize this fundamental law of physics to be just the natural tendency of things to approach the chaotic state (the same tendency that the books of a library or the piles of papers and manuscripts on a writing desk display) unless we obviate it. (The analogue of irregular heat motion, in this case, is our handling those objects now and again without troubling to put them back in their proper places.)

60. *Organization maintained by extracting 'order' from the environment*

How would we express in terms of the statistical theory the marvellous faculty of a living organism, by which it delays the decay into thermodynamical equilibrium (death)? We said before: 'It feeds upon negative entropy', attracting, as it were, a stream of negative entropy upon itself, to compensate the entropy increase it produces by living and thus to maintain itself on a stationary and fairly low entropy level.

If D is a measure of disorder, its reciprocal, $1/D$, can be regarded as a direct measure of order. Since the logarithm of $1/D$ is just minus the logarithm of D, we can write Boltzmann's equation thus:

$$-(\text{entropy}) = k \log (1/D).$$

Hence the awkward expression 'negative entropy' can be replaced by a better one: entropy, taken with the negative sign, is itself a measure of order. Thus the device by which an organism maintains itself stationary at a fairly high level of orderliness (=fairly low level of entropy) really consists in continually sucking orderliness from its environment. This conclusion is less paradoxical than it appears at first sight. Rather could it be blamed for triviality. Indeed, in the case of higher animals we know the kind of orderliness they feed upon well enough, viz. the extremely well-ordered state of matter in more or less complicated organic compounds, which serve them as foodstuffs. After utilizing it they return it in a very much degraded form — not entirely degraded, however, for plants can still make use of it. (These, of course, have their most powerful supply of 'negative entropy' in the sunlight.)[20]

Chapter VII
IS LIFE BASED ON THE LAWS OF PHYSICS?

> Si un hombre nunca se contradice, será porque
> nunca dice nada.[21]
>
> *Miguel de Unamuno*
> (quoted from conversation)

61. *New laws to be expected in the organism*

What I wish to make clear in this last chapter is, in short, that from all we have learnt about the structure of living matter, we must be prepared to find it working in a manner that cannot be reduced to the ordinary laws of physics. And that not on the ground that there is any 'new force' or what not, directing the behaviour of the single atoms within a living organism, but because the construction is different from anything we have yet tested in the physical laboratory. To put it crudely, an engineer, familiar with heat engines only, will, after inspecting the construction of an electric motor, be prepared to find it working along principles which he does not yet understand. He finds the copper familiar to him in kettles used here in the form of long, long wires wound in coils; the iron familiar to him in levers and bars and steam cylinders is here filling the interior of those coils of copper wire. He will be convinced that it is the same copper and the same iron, subject to the same laws of Nature, and he is right in that. The difference in construction is enough to prepare him for an entirely different way of functioning. He will not suspect that an electric motor is driven by a ghost because it is set spinning by the turn of a switch, without boiler and steam.

62. *Reviewing the biological situation*

The unfolding of events in the life cycle of an organism exhibits an admirable regularity and orderliness, unrivalled by anything we meet

---

20. See note to Chapter VI, p. 106.
21. If a man never contradicts himself, the reason must be that he virtually never says anything at all.

with in inanimate matter. We find it controlled by a supremely well-ordered group of atoms, which represent only a very small fraction of the sum total in every cell. Moreover, from the view we have formed of the mechanism of mutation we conclude that the dislocation of just a few atoms within the group of 'governing atoms' of the germ cell suffices to bring about a well-defined change in the large-scale hereditary characteristics of the organism.

These facts are easily the most interesting that science has revealed in our day. We may be inclined to find them, after all, not wholly unacceptable. An organism's astonishing gift of concentrating a 'stream of order' on itself and thus escaping the decay into atomic chaos – of 'drinking orderliness' from a suitable environment – seems to be connected with the presence of the 'aperiodic solids', the chromosome molecules, which doubtless represent the highest degree of well-ordered atomic association we know of – much higher than the ordinary periodic crystal – in virtue of the individual role every atom and every radical is playing here.

To put it briefly, we witness the event that existing order displays the power of maintaining itself and of producing orderly events. That sounds plausible enough, though in finding it plausible we, no doubt, draw on experience concerning social organization and other events which involve the activity of organisms. And so it might seem that something like a vicious circle is implied.

63. *Summarizing the physical situation*

However that may be, the point to emphasize again and again is that to the physicist the state of affairs is not only not plausible but most exciting, because it is unprecedented. Contrary to the common belief, the regular course of events, governed by the laws of physics, is never the consequence of one well-ordered configuration of atoms – not unless that configuration of atoms repeats itself a great number of times, either as in the periodic crystal or as in a liquid or in a gas composed of a great number of identical molecules.

Even when the chemist handles a very complicated molecule *in vitro* he is always faced with an enormous number of like molecules. To them his laws apply. He might tell you, for example, that one minute after he has started some particular reaction half of the molecules will have reacted, and after a second minute three-quarters of them will have done so. But whether any particular molecule, supposing you could follow its course, will be among those which have reacted or among those which are still untouched, he could not predict. That is a matter of pure chance.

This is not a purely theoretical conjecture. It is not that we can never observe the fate of a single small group of atoms or even of a single atom. We can, occasionally. But whenever we do, we find complete irregularity, co-operating to produce regularity only on the average. We have dealt with an example in Chapter I. The Brownian movement of a small particle suspended in a liquid is completely irregular. But if there are many similar particles, they will by their irregular movement give rise to the regular phenomenon of diffusion.

The disintegration of a single radioactive atom is observable (it emits a projectile which causes a visible scintillation on a fluorescent screen). But if you are given a single radioactive atom, its probable lifetime is much less certain than that of a healthy sparrow. Indeed, nothing more can be said about it than this: as long as it lives (and that may be for thousands of years) the chance of its blowing up within the next second, whether large or small, remains the same. This patent lack of individual determination nevertheless results in the exact exponential law of decay of a large number of radioactive atoms of the same kind.

64. *The striking contrast*

In biology we are faced with an entirely different situation. A single group of atoms existing only in one copy produces orderly events, marvellously tuned in with each other and with the environment according to most subtle laws. I said, existing only in one copy, for after all we have the example of the egg and of the unicellular organism. In the following stages of a higher organism the copies are multiplied, that is true. But to what extent? Something like 10^{14} in a grown mammal, I understand. What is that! Only a millionth of the number of molecules in one cubic inch of air. Though comparatively bulky, by coalescing they would form but a tiny drop of liquid. And look at the way they are actually distributed. Every cell harbours just one of them (or two, if we bear in mind diploidy). Since we know the power this tiny central office has in the isolated cell, do they not resemble stations of local government dispersed through the body, communicating with each other with great ease, thanks to the code that is common to all of them?

Well, this is a fantastic description, perhaps less becoming a scientist than a poet. However, it needs no poetical imagination but only clear and sober scientific reflection to recognize that we are here obviously faced with events whose regular and lawful unfolding is guided by a 'mechanism' entirely different from the 'probability mechanism' of physics. For it is simply a fact of observation that the guiding principle in every cell is embodied in a single atomic association existing only in one (or sometimes two) copy—and a fact of observation that it results in producing events which are a paragon of orderliness. Whether we find it astonishing or whether we find it quite plausible, that a small but highly organized group of atoms be capable of acting in this manner, the situation is unprecedented, it is unknown anywhere else except in living matter. The physicist and the chemist, investigating inanimate matter, have never witnessed phenomena which they had to interpret in this way. The case did not arise and so our theory does not cover it—our beautiful statistical theory of which we were so justly proud because it allowed us to look behind the curtain, to watch the magnificent order of exact physical law coming forth from atomic and molecular disorder; because it revealed that the most important, the most general, the all-embracing law of entropy increase could be understood without a special assumption *ad hoc*, for it is nothing but molecular disorder itself.

65. *Two ways of producing orderliness*

The orderliness encountered in the unfolding of life springs from a different source. It appears that there are two different 'mechanisms' by which orderly events can be produced: the 'statistical mechanism' which produces 'order from disorder' and the new one, producing 'order from order'. To the unprejudiced mind the second principle appears to be much simpler, much more plausible. No doubt it is. That is why physicists were so proud to have fallen in with the other one, the 'order-from-disorder' principle, which is actually followed in Nature and which alone conveys an understanding of the great line of natural events, in the first place of their irreversibility. But we cannot expect that the 'laws of physics' derived from it suffice straightaway to explain the behaviour of living matter, whose most striking features are visibly based to a large extent on the 'order-from-order' principle. You would not expect two entirely different mechanisms to bring about the same type of law — you would not expect your latch-key to open your neighbour's door as well.

We must therefore not be discouraged by the difficulty of interpreting life by the ordinary laws of physics. For that is just what is to be expected from the knowledge we have gained of the structure of living matter. We must be prepared to find a new type of physical law prevailing in it. Or are we to term it a non-physical, not to say a super-physical, law?

66. *The new principle is not alien to physics*

No. I do not think that. For the new principle that is involved is a genuinely physical one: it is, in my opinion, nothing else than the principle of quantum theory over again. To explain this, we have to go to some length, including a refinement, not to say an amendment, of the assertion previously made, namely, that all physical laws are based on statistics.

This assertion, made again and again, could not fail to arouse contradiction. For, indeed, there are phenomena whose conspicuous features are visibly based directly on the 'order-from-order' principle and appear to have nothing to do with statistics or molecular disorder.

The order of the solar system, the motion of the planets, is maintained for an almost indefinite time. The constellation of this moment is directly connected with the constellation at any particular moment in the times of the Pyramids; it can be traced back to it, or vice versa. Historical eclipses have been calculated and have been found in close agreement with historical records or have even in some cases served to correct the accepted chronology. These calculations do not imply any statistics, they are based solely on Newton's law of universal attraction.

Nor does the regular motion of a good clock or of any similar mechanism appear to have anything to do with statistics. In short, all purely mechanical events seem to follow distinctly and directly the 'order-from-order' principle. And if we say 'mechanical', the term must be taken in a wide sense. A very useful kind of clock is, as you know, based on the regular transmission of electric pulses from the power station.

I remember an interesting little paper by Max Planck on the topic 'The Dynamical and the Statistical Type of Law' ('Dynamische und Statistische Gesetzmässigkeit'). The distinction is precisely the one we have here labelled as 'order from order' and 'order from disorder'. The object of that paper was to show how the interesting statistical type of law, controlling large-scale events, is constituted from the 'dynamical' laws supposed to govern the small-scale events, the interaction of the single atoms and molecules. The latter type is illustrated by large-scale mechanical phenomena, as the motion of the planets or of a clock, etc.

Thus it would appear that the 'new principle', the order-from-order principle, to which we have pointed with great solemnity as being the real clue to the understanding of life, is not at all new to physics. Planck's attitude even vindicates priority for it. We seem to arrive at the ridiculous conclusion that the clue to the understanding of life is that it is based on a pure mechanism, a 'clock work' in the sense of Planck's paper. The conclusion is not ridiculous and is, in my opinion, not entirely wrong, but it has to be taken 'with a very big grain of salt'.

67. *The motion of a clock*

Let us analyse the motion of a real clock accurately. It is not at all a purely mechanical phenomenon. A purely mechanical clock would need no spring, no winding. Once set in motion, it would go on for ever. A real clock without a spring stops after a few beats of the pendulum, its mechanical energy is turned into heat. This is an infinitely complicated atomistic process. The general picture the physicist forms of it compels him to admit that the inverse process is not entirely impossible: A springless clock might suddenly begin to move, at the expense of the heat energy of its own cog wheels and of the environment. The physicist would have to say: The clock experiences an exceptionally intense fit of Brownian movement. We have seen in Chapter I (§ 9) that with a very sensitive torsional balance (electrometer or galvanometer) that sort of thing happens all the time. In the case of a clock it is, of course, infinitely unlikely.

Whether the motion of a clock is to be assigned to the dynamical or to the statistical type of lawful events (to use Planck's expressions) depends on our attitude. In calling it a dynamical phenomenon we fix attention on the regular going that can be secured by a comparatively weak spring, which overcomes the small disturbances by heat motion, so that we may disregard them. But if we remember that without a spring the clock is gradually slowed down by friction, we find that this process can only be understood as a statistical phenomenon.

However insignificant the frictional and heating effects in a clock may be from the practical point of view, there can be no doubt that the second attitude, which does not neglect them, is the more fundamental one, even when we are faced with the regular motion of a clock that is driven by a spring. For it must not be believed that the driving mechanism really does away with the statistical nature of the process. The true physical picture includes the possibility that even a regularly going clock should all at once invert its motion and, working backward, re-wind its own spring—at the expense of the heat of the environment. The event is just 'still a little less likely' than a 'Brownian fit' of a clock without driving mechanism.

68. *Clockwork after all statistical*

Let us now review the situation. The 'simple' case we have analysed is representative of many others—in fact of all such as appear to evade the all-embracing principle of molecular statistics. Clockworks made of real physical matter (in contrast to imagination) are not true 'clockworks'. The element of chance may be more or less reduced, the likelihood of the clock suddenly going altogether wrong may be infinitesimal, but it always remains in the background. Even in the motion of the celestial bodies irreversible frictional and thermal influences are not wanting. Thus the rotation of the earth is slowly diminished by tidal friction, and along with this reduction the moon gradually recedes from the earth, which would not happen if the earth were a completely rigid rotating sphere.

Nevertheless the fact remains that 'physical clock-works' visibly display very prominent 'order-from-order' features—the type that aroused the physicist's excitement when he encountered them in the organism. It seems likely that the two cases have after all something in common. It remains to be seen what this is and what is the striking difference which makes the case of the organism after all novel and unprecedented.

69. *Nernst's Theorem*

When does a physical system—any kind of association of atoms —display 'dynamical law' (in Planck's meaning) or 'clock-work features'? Quantum theory has a very short answer to this question, viz. at the absolute zero of temperature. As zero temperature is approached the molecular disorder ceases to have any bearing on physical events. This fact was, by the way, not discovered by theory, but by carefully investigating chemical reactions over a wide range of temperatures and extrapolating the results to zero temperature—which cannot actually be reached. This is Walther Nernst's famous 'Heat-Theorem', which is sometimes, and not unduly, given the proud name of the 'Third Law of Thermodynamics' (the first being the energy principle, the second the entropy principle).

Quantum theory provides the rational foundation of Nernst's empirical law, and also enables us to estimate how closely a system must approach to the absolute zero in order to display an approximately 'dynamical' behaviour. What temperature is in any particular case already practically equivalent to zero?

Now you must not believe that this always has to be a very low temperature. Indeed, Nernst's discovery was induced by the fact that even at room temperature entropy plays an astonishingly insignificant role in many chemical reactions. (Let me recall that entropy is a direct measure of molecular disorder, viz. its logarithm.)

70. *The pendulum clock is virtually at zero temperature*

What about a pendulum clock? For a pendulum clock room temperature is practically equivalent to zero. That is the reason why it works 'dynamically'. It will continue to work as it does if you cool it (provided that you have removed all traces of oil!). But it does not continue to work, if you heat it above room temperature, for it will eventually melt.

71. *The relation between clockwork and organism*

That seems very trivial but it does, I think, hit the cardinal point. Clockworks are capable of functioning 'dynamically', because they are built of solids, which are kept in shape by London-Heitler forces, strong enough to elude the disorderly tendency of heat motion at ordinary temperature.

Now, I think, few words more are needed to disclose the point of resemblance between a clockwork and an organism. It is simply and solely that the latter also hinges upon a solid — the aperiodic crystal forming the hereditary substance, largely withdrawn from the disorder of heat motion. But please do not accuse me of calling the chromosome fibres just the 'cogs of the organic machine' — at least not without a reference to the profound physical theories on which the simile is based.

For, indeed, it needs still less rhetoric to recall the fundamental difference between the two and to justify the epithets novel and unprecedented in the biological case.

The most striking features are: first, the curious distribution of the cogs in a many-celled organism, for which I may refer to the somewhat poetical description in § 64; and secondly, the fact that the single cog is not of coarse human make, but is the finest masterpiece ever achieved along the lines of the Lord's quantum mechanics.

NOTE TO CHAPTER VI

The remarks on *negative entropy* have met with doubt and opposition from physicist colleagues. Let me say first, that if I had been catering for them alone I should have let the discussion turn on *free energy* instead. It is the more familiar notion in this context. But this highly technical term seemed linguistically too near to *energy* for making the average reader alive to the contrast between the two things. He is likely to take *free* as more or less an *epitheton ornans* without much relevance, while actually the concept is a rather intricate one, whose relation to Boltzmann's order-disorder principle is less easy to trace than for entropy and 'entropy taken with a negative sign', which by the way is not my invention. It happens to be precisely the thing on which Boltzmann's original argument turned.

But F. Simon has very pertinently pointed out to me that my simple thermo-dynamical considerations cannot account for our having to feed on matter 'in the extremely well ordered state of more or less complicated organic compounds' rather than on charcoal or diamond pulp. He is right. But to the lay reader I must explain, that a piece of un-burnt coal or diamond, together with the amount of oxygen needed for its combustion, is also in an extremely well ordered state, as the physicist understands it. Witness to this: if you allow the reaction, the burning of the coal, to take place, a great amount of heat is produced. By giving it off to the surroundings, the system disposes of the very considerable entropy increase entailed by the reaction, and reaches a state in which it has, in point of fact, roughly the same entropy as before.

Yet we could not feed on the carbon dioxide that results from the reaction. And so Simon is quite right in pointing out to me, as he did, that actually the energy content of our food *does* matter; so my mocking at the menu cards that indicate it was out of place. Energy is needed to replace not only the mechanical energy of our bodily exertions, but also the heat we continually give off to the environment. And that we give off heat is not accidental, but essential. For this is precisely the manner in which we dispose of the surplus entropy we continually produce in our physical life process.

This seems to suggest that the higher temperature of the warm-blooded animal includes the advantage of enabling it to get rid of its entropy at a quicker rate, so that it can afford a more intense life process. I am not sure how much truth there is in this argument (for which I am responsible, not Simon). One may hold against it, that on the other hand many warm-blooders are *protected* against the rapid loss of heat by coats of fur or feathers. So the parallelism between body temperature and 'intensity of life', which I believe to exist, may have to be accounted for more directly by van't Hoff's law, mentioned at the end of Sect. 50: the higher temperature itself speeds up the chemical reactions involved in living. (That it actually does, has been confirmed experimentally in species which take the temperature of the surrounding.)

LIGHT AND LIFE

Niels Bohr

As a physicist whose studies are limited to the properties of inanimate bodies, it is not without hesitation that I have accepted the kind invitation to address this assembly of scientific men met together to forward our knowledge of the beneficial effects of light in the cure of diseases. Unable as I am to contribute to this beautiful branch of science that is so important for the welfare of mankind, I could at most comment on the purely inorganic light phenomena which have exerted a special attraction for physicists throughout the ages, not least owing to the fact that light is our principal tool of observation. I have thought, however, that on this occasion it might perhaps be of interest, in connexion with such comments, to enter on the problem of what significance the results reached in the limited domain of physics may have for our views on the position of living organisms in the realm of natural science.

Notwithstanding the subtle character of the riddles of life, this problem has presented itself at every stage of science, since any scientific explanation necessarily must consist in reducing the description of more complex phenomena to that of simpler ones. At the moment, however, the unsuspected discovery of an essential limitation of the mechanical description of natural phenomena, revealed by the recent development of the atomic theory, has lent new interest to the old problem. This limitation was, in fact, first recognised through a thorough study of the interaction between light and material bodies,

"Light and Life," an address delivered at the opening meeting of the International Congress on Light Therapy, Copenhagen, on August 15, 1932. Reprinted from *Nature,* CXXXI (1933), 421 –423, 457 –459.

which disclosed features that cannot be brought into conformity with the demands hitherto made to a physical explanation. As I shall endeavour to show, the efforts of physicists to master this situation resemble in some way the attitude which biologists more or less intuitively have taken towards the aspects of life. Still, I wish to stress at once that it is only in this formal respect that light, which is perhaps the least complex of all physical phenomena, exhibits an analogy to life, the diversity of which is far beyond the grasp of scientific analysis.

From a physical point of view, light may be defined as the transmission of energy between material bodies at a distance. As is well known, such an energy transfer finds a simple explanation in the electromagnetic theory, which may be regarded as a direct extension of classical mechanics compromising between action at a distance and contact forces. According to this theory, light is described as coupled electric and magnetic oscillations which differ from the ordinary electromagnetic waves used in radio transmission only by their greater frequency of vibration and smaller wave-length. In fact, the practically rectilinear propagation of light, on which rests our location of bodies by direct vision or by suitable optical instruments, depends entirely on the smallness of the wave-length compared with the dimensions of the bodies concerned, and of the instruments.

The idea of the wave nature of light, however, not only forms the basis for our explanation of the colour phenomena, which in spectroscopy have yielded such important information of the inner constitution of matter, but is also of essential importance for every detailed analysis of optical phenomena. As a typical example, I need only mention the interference patterns which appear when light from one source can travel to a screen along two different paths. In such a case, we find that the effects which would be produced by the separate light beams are strengthened at those points on the screen where the phases of the two wave trains coincide, that is, where the electric and magnetic oscillations in the two beams have the same directions, while the effects are weakened and may even disappear at points where these oscillations have opposite directions, and where the two wave trains are said to be out of phase with one another. These interference patterns have made possible such a thorough test of the wave nature of the propagation of light, that this conception can no longer be considered as a hypothesis in the usual sense of this word, but may rather be regarded as an indispensable element in the description of the phenomena observed.

As is well known, the problem of the nature of light has, nevertheless, been subjected to renewed discussion in recent years, as a result of the discovery of a peculiar atomistic feature in the energy transmission which is quite unintelligible from the point of view of the electromagnetic theory. It has turned out, in fact, that all effects of light may be traced down to individual processes, in each of which a so-called light quantum is exchanged, the energy of which is equal to the product of the frequency of the electromagnetic oscillations and the universal quantum of action, or Planck's constant. The striking contrast between this atomicity of the light phenomena and the continuity of the energy transfer according to the electromagnetic theory places us before a dilemma of a character hitherto unknown in physics. For, in spite of the obvious insufficiency of the wave picture, there can be no question of replacing it by any other picture of light propagation depending on ordinary mechanical ideas.

Especially, it should be emphasised that the introduction of the concept of light quanta in no way means a return to the old idea of material particles with well-defined paths as the carriers of the light energy. In fact, it is characteristic of all the phenomena of light, in the description of which the wave picture plays an essential rôle, that any attempt to trace the paths of the individual light quanta would disturb the very phenomenon under investigation; just as an interference pattern would completely disappear, if, in order to make sure that the light energy travelled only along one of the two paths between the source and the screen, we should introduce a non-transparent body into one of the paths. The spatial continuity of light propagation, on one hand, and the atomicity of the light effects, on the other hand, must, therefore, be considered as complementary aspects of one reality, in the sense that each expresses an important feature of the phenomena of light, which, although irreconcilable from a mechanical point of view, can never be in direct contradiction, since a closer analysis of one or the other feature in mechanical terms would demand mutually exclusive experimental arrangements.

At the same time, this very situation forces us to renounce a complete causal description of the phenomena of light and to be content with probability calculations, based on the fact that the electromagnetic description of energy transfer by light remains valid in a statistical sense. Such calculations form a typical application of the so-called correspondence argument, which expresses our endeavour, by means of a suitably limited use of mechanical and electromagnetic concepts, to obtain a statistical description of the atomic phenomena that appears as a rational generalisation of the classical physical theories, in spite of the fact that the quantum of action from their point of view must be considered as an irrationality.

At first sight, this situation might appear very deplorable; but, as has often happened in the history of science, when new discoveries have revealed an essential limitation of ideas the universal applicability of which had never been disputed, we have been rewarded by getting a wider view and a greater power of correlating phenomena which before might even have appeared as contradictory. Thus, the strange limitation of classical mechanics, symbolised by the quantum of action, has given us a clue to an understanding of the peculiar stability of atoms which forms a basic assumption in the mechanical description of any natural phenomenon. The recognition that the indivisibility of atoms cannot be understood in mechanical terms has always characterised the atomic theory, to be sure; and this fact is not essentially altered, although the development of physics has replaced the indivisible atoms by the elementary electric particles, electrons and atomic nuclei, of which the atoms of the elements as well as the molecules of the chemical compounds are now supposed to consist.

However, it is not to the question of the intrinsic stability of these elementary particles that I am here referring, but to the problem of the required stability of the structures composed of them. As a matter of fact, the very possibility of a continuous transfer of energy, which marks both the classical mechanics and the electromagnetic theory, cannot be reconciled with an explanation of the characteristic properties of the elements and the compounds. Indeed, the classical theories do not even allow us to explain the existence of rigid bodies, on which all measurements made for the purpose of ordering phenomena in space and time ultimately rest. However, in connexion with the discovery of the quantum of action, we have learned that every change in the energy of an atom or a molecule must be considered as an individual process, in which the atom goes over from one of its so-called stationary states to another. Moreover, since just one light quantum appears or disappears in a transition process by which light is emitted or absorbed by an atom, we are able by means of spectroscopic observations to measure directly the energy of each of these stationary states. The information thus derived has been most instructively corroborated also by the study of the energy exchanges which take place in atomic collisions and in chemical reactions.

In recent years, a remarkable development of the atomic theory has taken place, which has given us such adequate methods of computing the energy values for the stationary states, and also the probabilities of the transition processes, that our account, on the lines of the correspondence argument, of the properties of atoms as regards completeness and self-consistency scarcely falls short of the explanation of astronomical observations offered by Newtonian mechanics. Although the rational treatment of the problems of atomic mechanics was possible only after the introduction of new symbolic artifices, the lesson taught us by the analysis of the phenomena of light is still of decisive importance for our estimation of this development. Thus, an unambiguous use of the concept of a stationary state is complementary to a mechanical analysis of intra-atomic motions; in a similar way the idea of light quanta is complementary to the electromagnetic theory of radiation. Indeed, any attempt to trace the detailed course of the transition process would involve an uncontrollable exchange of energy between the atom and the measuring instruments, which would completely disturb the very energy transfer we set out to investigate.

A causal description in the classical sense is possible only in such cases where the action involved is large compared with the quantum of action, and where, therefore, a subdivision of the phenomena is possible without disturbing them essentially. If this condition is not fulfilled, we cannot disregard the interaction between the measuring instruments and the object under investigation, and we must especially take into consideration that the various measurements required for a complete mechanical description may only be made with mutually exclusive experimental arrangements. In order fully to understand this fundamental limitation of the mechanical analysis of atomic phenomena, one must realise clearly, further, that in a physical measurement it is never possible to take the interaction between object and measuring instruments directly into account. For the instruments cannot be included in the investigation while they are serving as means of observation. As the concept of general relativity expresses the essential dependence of physical phenomena on the frame of reference used for their co-ordination in space and time, so does the notion of complementarity serve to symbolise the fundamental limitation, met with in atomic physics, of our ingrained idea of phenomena as existing independently of the means by which they are observed.

This revision of the foundations of mechanics, extending to the very question of what may be meant by a physical explanation, has not only been essential, however, for the elucidation of the situation in atomic theory, but has also created a new background for the discussion of the relation of physics to the problems of biology. This must certainly not be taken to mean that in actual atomic phenomena we meet with features which show a closer resemblance to the properties of living organisms than do ordinary physical effects. At first sight, the essentially statistical character of atomic mechanics might even seem difficult to reconcile with an explanation of the marvellously refined organisation, which every living being possesses, and which permits it to implant all the characteristics of its species into a minute germ cell.

We must not forget, however, that the regularities peculiar to atomic processes, which are foreign to causal mechanics and find their place only within the complementary mode of description, are at least as important for the account of the behaviour of living organisms as for the explanation of the specific properties of inorganic matter. Thus, in the carbon assimilation of plants, on which depends largely also the nourishment of animals, we are dealing with a phenomenon for the understanding of which the individuality of photo-chemical processes must undoubtedly be taken into consideration. Likewise, the peculiar stability of atomic structures is clearly exhibited in the characteristic properties of such highly complicated chemical compounds as chlorophyll or hæmoglobin, which play fundamental rôles in plant assimilation and animal respiration.

However, analogies from chemical experience will not, of course, any more than the ancient comparison of life with fire, give a better explanation of living organisms than will the resemblance, often mentioned, between living organisms and such purely mechanical contrivances as clockworks. An understanding of the essential characteristics of living beings must be sought, no doubt, in their peculiar organisation, in which features that may be analysed by the usual mechanics are interwoven with typically atomistic traits in a manner having no counterpart in inorganic matter.

An instructive illustration of the refinement to which this organisation is developed has been obtained through the study of the construction and function of the eye, for which the simplicity of the phenomena of light has again been most helpful. I need not go into details here, but shall just recall how ophthalmology has revealed to us the ideal properties of the human eye as an optical instrument. Indeed, the dimensions of the interference patterns, which on account of the wave nature of light set the limit for the image formation in the eye, practically coincide with the size of such partitions of the retina which have separate nervous connexion with the brain. Moreover, since the absorption of a few light quanta, or perhaps of only a single quantum, on such a retinal partition is sufficient to produce a sight impression, the sensitiveness of the eye may even be said to have reached the limit imposed by the atomic character of the light effects. In both respects, the efficiency of the eye is the same as that of a good telescope or microscope, connected with a suitable amplifier so as to make the individual processes observable. It is true that it is possible by such instruments essentially to increase our powers of observation, but, owing to the very limits imposed by the properties of light, no instrument is imaginable which is more efficient for its purpose than the eye. Now, this ideal refinement of the eye, fully recognised only through the recent development of physics, suggests that other organs also, whether they serve for the reception of information from the surroundings or for the reaction to sense impressions, will exhibit a similar adaptation to their purpose, and that also in these cases the feature of individuality symbolised by the quantum of action, together with some amplifying mechanism, is of decisive importance. That it has not yet been possible to trace the limit in organs other than the eye, depends solely upon the simplicity of light as compared with other physical phenomena.

The recognition of the essential importance of fundamentally atomistic features in the functions of living organisms is by no means sufficient, however, for a comprehensive explanation of biological phenomena. The question at issue, therefore, is whether some fundamental traits are still missing in the analysis of natural phenomena, before we can reach an understanding of life on the basis of physical experience. Quite apart from the practically inexhaustible abundance of biological phenomena, an answer to this question can scarcely be given without an examination of what we may understand by a physical explanation, still more penetrating than that to which the discovery of the quantum of action has already forced us. On one hand, the wonderful features which are constantly revealed in physiological investigations and differ so strikingly from what is known of inorganic matter, have led many biologists to doubt that a real understanding of the nature of life is possible on a purely physical basis. On the other hand, this view, often known as vitalism, scarcely finds its proper expression in the old supposition that a peculiar vital force, quite unknown to physics, governs all organic life. I agree with Newton that the real basis of science is the conviction that Nature under the same conditions will always exhibit the same regularities. Therefore, if we were able to push the analysis of the mechanism of living organisms as far as that of atomic phenomena, we should scarcely expect to find any features differing from the properties of inorganic matter.

With this dilemma before us, we must keep in mind, however, that the conditions holding for biological and physical researches are not directly comparable, since the necessity of keeping the object of investigation alive imposes a restriction on the former, which finds no counterpart in the latter. Thus, we should doubtless kill an animal if we tried to carry the investigation of its organs so far that we could describe the rôle played by single atoms in vital functions. In every experiment on living organisms, there must remain an uncertainty as regards the physical conditions to which they are subjected, and the idea suggests itself that the minimal freedom we must allow the organism in this respect is just large enough to permit it, so to say, to hide its ultimate secrets from us. On this view, the existence of life must be considered as an elementary fact that cannot be explained, but must be taken as a starting point in biology, in a similar way as the quantum of action, which appears as an irrational element from the point of view of classical mechanical physics, taken together with the existence of the elementary particles, forms the foundation of atomic physics. The asserted impossibility of a physical or chemical explanation of the function peculiar to life would in this sense be analogous to the insufficiency of the mechanical analysis for the understanding of the stability of atoms.

In tracing this analogy further, however, we must not forget that the problems present essentially different aspects in physics and in biology. While in atomic physics we are primarily interested in the properties of matter in its simplest forms, the complexity of the material systems with which we are concerned in biology is of fundamental significance, since even the most primitive organisms contain a large number of atoms. It is true that the wide field of application of classical mechanics, including our account of the measuring instruments used in atomic physics, depends on the possibility of disregarding largely the complementarity, entailed by the quantum of action, in the description of bodies containing very many atoms. It is typical of biological researches, however, that the external conditions to which any separate atom is subjected can never be controlled in the same manner as in the fundamental experiments of atomic physics. In fact, we cannot even tell which atoms really belong to a living organism, since any vital function is accompanied by an exchange of material, whereby atoms are constantly taken up into and expelled from the organisation which constitutes the living being.

This fundamental difference between physical and biological investigations implies that no well-defined limit can be drawn for the applicability of physical ideas to the phenomena of life, which would correspond to the distinction between the field of causal mechanical description and the proper quantum phenomena in atomic mechanics. However, the limitation which this fact would seem to impose upon the analogy considered will depend essentially upon how we choose to use such words as physics and mechanics. On one hand, the question of the limitation of physics within biology would, of course, lose any meaning, if, in accordance with the original meaning of the word physics, we should understand by it any description of natural phenomena. On the other hand, such a term as atomic mechanics would be misleading, if, as in common language, we should apply the word mechanics only to denote an unambiguous causal description of the phenomena.

I shall not here enter further into these purely logical points, but will only add that the essence of the analogy considered is the typical relation of complementarity existing between the subdivision required by a physical analysis and such characteristic biological phenomena as the self-preservation and the propagation of individuals. It is due to this situation, in fact, that the concept of purpose, which is foreign to mechanical analysis, finds a certain field of application in problems where regard must be taken of the nature of life. In this respect, the rôle which teleological arguments play in biology reminds one of the endeavours, formulated in the correspondence argument, to take the quantum of action into account in a rational manner in atomic physics.

In our discussion of the applicability of mechanical concepts in describing living organisms, we have considered these just as other material objects. I need scarcely emphasize, however, that this attitude, which is characteristic of physiological research, involves no disregard whatsoever of the psychological aspects of life. The recognition of the limitation of mechanical ideas in atomic physics would much rather seem suited to conciliate the apparently contrasting points of view which mark physiology and psychology. Indeed, the necessity of con-sidering the interaction between the measuring instruments and the object under investigation in atomic mechanics corresponds closely to the peculiar difficulties, met with in psychological analyses, which arise from the fact that the mental content is invariably altered when the attention is concentrated on any single feature of it.

It will carry us too far from our subject to enlarge upon this analogy which, when due regard is taken to the special character of biological problems, offers a new starting point for an elucidation of the so-called psycho-physical parallelism. However, in this connexion, I should like to emphasise that the considerations referred to here differ entirely from all attempts at viewing new possibilities for a direct spiritual influence on material phenomena in the limitation set for the causal mode of description in the analysis of atomic phenomena. For example, when it has been suggested that the will might have as its field of activity the regulation of certain atomic processes within the organism, for which on the atomic theory only probability calculations may be set up, we are dealing with a view that is incompatible with the inter-pretation of the psycho-physical parallelism here indicated. Indeed, from our point of view, the feeling of the freedom of the will must be considered as a trait peculiar to conscious life, the material parallel of which must be sought in organic functions, which permit neither a causal mechanical description nor a physical investigation sufficiently thorough-going for a well-defined application of the statistical laws of atomic mechanics. Without entering into metaphysical speculations, I may perhaps add that any analysis of the very concept of an explanation would, naturally, begin and end with a renunciation as to explaining our own conscious activity.

In conclusion, I wish to emphasise that in none of my remarks have I intended to express any kind of scepticism as to the future develop-ment of physical and biological sciences. Such scepticism would, indeed, be far from the mind of a physicist at a time when the very recognition of the limited character of our most fundamental concepts has resulted in such far-reaching developments of our science. Neither has the necessary renunciation as regards an explanation of life itself been a hindrance to the wonderful advances which have been made in recent times in all branches of biology and have, not least, proved so beneficial in the art of medicine. Even if we cannot make a sharp distinction on a physical basis between health and disease, there is, in particular, no room for scepticism as regards the solution of the important problems which occupy this Congress, as long as one does not leave the highroad of progress, that has been followed with so great success ever since the pioneer work of Finsen, and which has as its distinguishing mark the most intimate combination of the study of the medical effects of light treatment with the investigation of its physical aspects.

A PHYSICIST
LOOKS AT BIOLOGY

Max Delbrück

A mature physicist, acquainting himself for the first time with the problems of biology, is puzzled by the circumstance that there are no "absolute phenomena" in biology. Everything is time bound and space bound. The animal or plant or micro-organism he is working with is but a link in an evolutionary chain of changing forms, none of which has any permanent validity. Even the molecular species and the chemical reactions which he encounters are the fashions of today to be replaced by others as evolution goes on. The organism he is working with is not a particular expression of an ideal organism, but one thread in the infinite web of all living forms, all interrelated and all interdependent. The physicist has been reared in a different atmosphere. The materials and the phenomena he works with are the same here and now as they were at all times and as they are on the most distant stars. He deals with accurately measured quantities and their causal interrelations and in terms of sophisticated conceptual schemes. The outstanding feature of the history of his science is unification: two seemingly separate areas of experience are revealed, from a deeper point of view, to be two different aspects of one and the same thing. Thus, terrestrial and celestial mechanics, for thousands of years totally separate sciences, were reduced to one science by Newton, at a price, it is true — that of introducing the abstract notion of force acting at a distance and the notions of calculus. Thus, also, thermodynamics and mechanics were shown to be one and the same thing through the

"A Physicist Looks at Biology," an address delivered at the thousandth meeting of the Connecticut Academy of Arts and Sciences. Reprinted from *Transactions of the Connecticut Academy of Arts and Sciences*, XXXVIII (1949), 175–190, by permission of Max Delbrück.

discovery of statistical mechanics, as were chemistry and electricity through the discovery of the proportionality between charge transport and mass transport in electrolysis, at a price,—that of introducing atomicity into the concept of electric charge. Thus, optics and electromagnetism turned out to be two aspects of one theory, Maxwell's theory of the electro-magnetic field, at the price of introducing further abstract concepts, those of the field vectors. Thus, above all, chemistry and atomic physics were unified through the conceptual scheme of quantum mechanics, at the highest price of all—that of renouncing the ideal of a causal description in space and time.

The history of biology records discoveries of great generality, like those of the occurrence of sexual reproduction in all living forms, of the cellular structure of organisms, of the ubiquitous presence of closely similar oxidative mechanisms, and many others of lesser generality. It records one great unifying theory, bringing together separate fields: the theory of evolution. To a physicist this is a strange kind of theory. It states, in the first place, that all living forms are interrelated by common descent. This statement is not one that is proved by decisive experiments but one that has become more and more inescapable through centuries of accumulated evidence. At the same time, it is the principle which serves to bring to order vast masses of descriptive taxonomy and geographical distribution. The theory states, further, that evolution has progressed through natural selection of the fittest and the most prolific. The assumption here involved is not whether or not selection occurs. On the contrary, in this respect the theory is tautological, since the organisms best fitted are defined as those which are selected. Rather, the assumption here involved is that the things selected for carry genetic permanence. At the time the theory was proposed this assumption was not proved, in fact in Darwin's time it could not even be stated in clear terms. It gave rise to the basic questions of the new science of genetics: how does heritable variability originate and how is it transmitted? Eventually it gave rise to the new abstractions: genotype and gene. It is most remarkable how late and how slowly these abstractions were established. Actually, today the tendency is to say "genes are just molecules, or hereditary particles," and thus to do away with the abstractions. This, as we shall endeavour to show later on, may be an overstatement of the legitimate claim of molecular physics. On the whole, the successful theories of biology always have been and are still today simple and concrete. Presumably this is not accidental, but is bound up with the fact that every biological phenomenon is essentially an historical one, one unique situation in the infinite total complex of life.

Such a situation from the outset diminishes the hope of understanding any one living thing by itself and the hope of discovering universal laws, the pride and ambition of physicists. The curiosity remains, though, to grasp more clearly how the same matter, which in physics and in chemistry displays orderly and reproducible and relatively simple properties, arranges itself in the most astounding fashions as soon as it is drawn into the orbit of the living organism. The closer one looks at these performances of matter in living organisms the more impressive the show becomes. The meanest living cell becomes a magic puzzle box full of elaborate and changing molecules, and far outstrips all chemical laboratories of man in the skill of organic synthesis performed with ease, expedition and good judgment of balance. The complex accomplishment of any one living cell is part and parcel of the first-mentioned feature, that any one cell represents more an historical than a physical event. These complex things do not rise every day by spontaneous generation from the non-living matter — if they did, they would really be reproducible and timeless phenomena, comparable to the crystalization of a solution, and would belong to the subject matter of physics proper. No, any living cell carries with it the experiences of a billion years of experimentation by its ancestors. You cannot expect to explain so wise an old bird in a few simple words.

Perhaps one can hope to understand some of its features — how oxygen is transported, how food is digested, how muscles contract, how nerves conduct, how the senses perceive, etc. One hopes to fix one's attention on features of the greatest generality, features that are an expression of the organization of matter as it is peculiar to all living matter, and to living matter only, to living protoplasm. Do such features really exist? Take, for example, the so-called excitability of living cells. Text books of physiology assure us that excitability is a peculiarity of all living cells. From a physicist's point of view this feature may perhaps best be expressed in the following terms: a living cell is a system in flux equilibrium, matter and energy are taken in from the environment, are metabolized and partly assimilated, partly degenerated, and waste products are given back to the environment. To a first approximation, that in which growth is neglected, this represents a steady state. As long as the environment does not change, the cell does not change even though matter and energy flow through it. If the environment does change slowly, the state of the cell will also change slowly and continuously, but if the environment changes sufficiently rapidly the state of the cell will change abruptly. It will become excited. Thus, upon excitation a nerve cell will discharge an action current, a muscle fiber will contract, a sensory cell will discharge, and similarly all other kinds of cells under proper conditions of stimulation will produce a disproportionately large response to a relatively slight but rapid change in the environment. Do we here deal with a truly general feature of the organization of matter in living cells? More than a hundred years ago Weber went one step further and formulated quantitatively a general law relating the threshold of stimulation with the parameters characterizing the environment. The law can be most easily formulated for situations in which one external parameter, say, the light intensity, changes abruptly from one level to another. Weber's law then states that the threshold change of this parameter which will produce excitation is proportional to the initial value of the parameter. For instance, if at an illumination of 100 foot candles, a change of 5 foot candles to 105 foot candles is necessary to produce excitation, then at a 10 times greater intensity of illumination of 1000 foot candles, a ten times greater change of 50 foot candles to 1050 foot candles will be necessary to cause excitation. The rating which this law of

Weber has received in the biological literature has fluctuated from generation to generation, and has reached a very low level in recent times, so low in fact that it is barely mentioned in many of the current text books of physiology. The reasons for this decline furnish an instructive example of our perplexities regarding biological theory. In the first place it is quite clear that the law as stated experimentally can only be expected to hold over a limited range. It must fail at exceedingly low stimulus levels where the proportionate changes in stimulus fall below the size of individual quanta of action, and it must fail at exceedingly high stimulus levels where secondary effects of the stimulus become damaging to the cell. Experimentally, therefore, the validity of the law can only be apparent in a middle region of varying extent. In an ordinary physical law such limitations would not detract from its intrinsic value as a structural unit in the general theoretical edifice. Thus Boyle's law relating pressure and density of a gas fails at high density, where the molecules get crowded for space. Yet Boyle's law has been one of the chief clues to the kinetic theory of gases, and thus to atomic theory. A physicist would not be tempted to belittle a law merely because it is valid only over a limited range. Not so in biology. The biologist is tempted to discard the law altogether and say that it is an artefact. The threshold for stimulation, as a function of stimulus, may not really be proportional to the stimulus, with deviations from this law due to secondary causes at very low and at very high stimulus levels, but may be represented by an ill defined curve, running straight for a shorter or longer stretch. In fact, one can explain even a rather extended straight portion of this curve by appealing to the adaptive value that such a shape of the curve might have. It is perhaps reasonable to say that a proportionality of threshold with stimulus represents an advantageous situation for a cell that has to adjust to a very wide range of stimulus level, and thus to make natural selection responsible for simulating something that looks like a physical law, natural selection acting like the overly faithful assistant of a credulous professor, the assistant being so anxious to please that he discards all those data which conflict with his master's theory. Arguments of this kind, combined with our total lack of a proper theory of excitation and the fact that perception in higher organisms anyhow is known to be a very complex business, have led to the present decline in the rating of Weber's law. It remains to be seen whether closer quantitative studies of the law, particularly as displayed by the simplest organisms, will justify this low rating, or whether it will turn out that we have overlooked a powerful clue to the nature of the organization of the living cell. The situation just described is one frequently met with in biology.

If it be true that the essence of life is the accumulation of experience through the generations, then one may perhaps suspect that the key problem of biology, from the physicist's point of view, is how living matter manages to record and perpetuate its experiences. Look at a single bacterium in a large volume of fluid of suitable chemical composition. It assimilates substance, grows in length, divides in two. The two daughters do the same, like the broomstick of the Sorcerer's apprentice. Occasionally the replica will be slightly faulty and an individual arises with somewhat different properties, and it perpetuates itself in this modified form. It is quite easy to believe that the game of evolution is on once the trick of reproduction, covariant on mutation, has been discovered, and that the variety of types will be multiplied indefinitely.

Higher organisms manage the matter of reproduction in a slightly more sophisticated manner, insisting on biparental reproduction, giving each new individual something from each parent, namely, one half of what the parent itself received from its parents, the half selected by an elaborate lottery. The student of evolution appreciates this game of segregation and recombination as a clever trick for trying out heredity in new combinations; it is not the basic thing but a refinement and elaboration of the *really* marvelous accomplishment: ordinary, uniparental reproduction.

A physicist would like to know how this ordinary reproduction is done. This seems to be the elementary phenomenon of living matter. What sort of a thing is it, from the molecular point of view? What is the most elementary level upon which it can be observed? The answer to this question is that the cellular level is the most elementary level. There is a variety of approaches to this question, but none of these leads essentially below the cellular level.

Take for instance, ordinary classical genetics of some higher organism. We find that heredity is controlled by genes linearly arranged in chromosomes, and it might seem that the problem of reproduction has been reduced to that of the reproduction of the genes, but this is not true because no gene has been observed to reproduce except within the intact functional cell. We have every reason to believe that this dependence on the intactness of the cell is an essential one. The fact that there are many different genes in each cell, and that we have learned to combine different sets of genes in hybridization experiments, teaches us that the thing that is reproduced is a complex thing, but does not teach us how to break down the problem into simpler problems. Or, for instance, take the reproduction of a virus particle, that of a bacterial virus. A single virus particle will enter a bacterial cell and twenty minutes later several hundred virus particles identical with the one which infected the cell may be liberated. At first sight this may seem simpler than cellular reproduction because the individual virus particle is a very much smaller unit than the individual cell and may be analogous to an individual gene or to a small group of genes. In some respects, however, this case is really more complex than that of the reproduction of a cell. In the first place, it, too, requires the presence of a living and functional cell, and in the second place, what is observed is not a reproduction from one to two elements, but from one to several hundred. This feature makes it more complex than an ordinary cell division. Moreover, the complexities of sexual reproduction and of recombination are not eliminated by going to this seemingly elementary level. We have learned recently that when a bacterium is simultaneously infected with two similar but different virus particles, the progeny will contain recombinants in high proportions.[1] From this we draw two conclusions: that the virus particles themselves are complex, and that their reproduction must involve manoeuvers analogous to those occurring in meiosis and conjugation of higher organisms. This is news that is exciting principally by the blow it deals to our fond hope of analyzing a simple situation. Perhaps one might think that it would help to break up the bacterium prematurely, before the end of its natural term. An ingenious technique to do this has actually been developed by Doermann.[2] He finds that up to about half time there are no active virus particles, thereafter they increase rapidly in number up to the end of the natural term. Since no active virus particles are found before half time, although at least one was necessary to initiate virus reproduction in the bacterium, the infecting particles must be greatly modified if not actually broken down into subunits. It seems that the real reproduction and recombination has already occurred during the first dark period when no active particle can be detected, because when the first complete particles appear they contain as high a proportion of recombinants as will be found in the ultimate total crop of a full term liberation.[3] Thus, the technique of early inspection did not bring us an essential simplification of the problem.

The hopes associated with the study of bacterial viruses are based on one other feature, the ability to control and vary the experimental conditions under which reproduction occurs, and indeed in this respect we have learned something. We have learned that the reproduction of the virus particles in the bacterial cell requires that the cell be very actively assimilating. In fact, it seems that this is what happens: the virus particle which enters the bacterium commandeers the assimilatory apparatus of the bacterium. The primary products of assimilation, instead of being used to make bacterial substance, are used largely or exclusively to make virus particles of the type that enter.[4] We have no clue whatsoever as to how the virus particle manages to shunt the utilization of assimilatory products into its own channels nor how the reproduction proper is done. Presumably this situation can be analysed from the biochemical point of view in considerably more detail. Since we know that the virus substance comes largely from assimilates after infection, we could ask more specifically in what order the assimilates acquired are incorporated. In principle this can be done with radio-active tracer experiments by adding or removing labelled compounds at given times after infection of the bacterium. Moreover, by using bacterial strains unable to synthesize one or another major component of the virus particle, say, an amino acid or a purine, one might hope to analyse the pathway by which these constituents are incorporated into the virus particle. It is however not clear to me how experiments of this kind could give a clue to the key problem, the chemical mechanism of replication.

Another way to approach the problem of reproduction is to center one's attention on some of the cellular constituents outside of the chromosomes which seem to have genetic continuity. To this class belong the plastids of green plants and a number of specific structures in protozoa. Here too, however, the genetic continuity is strictly dependent upon the functioning of the whole cell, and since these bodies can only be identified with assurance if they are large enough to be visible under the microscope they do not offer any simplification of the basic problem. There is reason to suspect that genetic continuity is also involved in the production of the enzymes elaborated by the living cells. If this is so, enzymes may be the best material for the study of this key problem but at present the mechanisms involved in enzyme synthesis are not clearly understood. There seem to be four factors involved in the production of any particular enzyme.[5] The first is the external metabolism supplying energy and assimilates. The second is a genetic control of the following kind: one finds that a very specific and limited genetic change, a mutation of a single gene, can be responsible for whether or not a cell can manufacture a given enzyme. A third factor is the substrate upon which this enzyme is supposed to act. In many cases a cell which is genetically able to produce a certain enzyme and is well supplied with nutrients, will not produce this enzyme except in the presence of the particular substance upon which this enzyme can act. One says that the cell responds adaptively to the presence of the substance. It is even possible that every enzyme requires for its formation the presence of its specific substance, only we do not become aware of this necessity because the substance in question may be present within the cell as a normal intermediary metabolite at all times. This adaptive mechanism is obviously of enormous value to the economy of the cell. The cell can thus shift its limited manufacturing capacity into a great variety of channels according to what is offered by a changing chemical environment. While we can readily understand the usefulness of this mechanism, we do not in the least understand its chemical nature. Is it that any substance merely stabilizes corresponding enzyme molecules that are continuously formed even in its absence but would be quickly destroyed if it were not for the stabilization? This notion has been urged by several authors, but it is an unlikely one. An enzyme molecule that is stable only as long as it is held in the claws of its substrate would be pretty useless. It would vanish too quickly if the concentration of the substance is reduced below the level at which the enzyme is saturated with it. Arguments of this kind cannot yet be very well evaluated quantitatively because of the intervention of the fourth factor involved in enzyme synthesis. This factor becomes apparent in experiments in which a cell is offered simultaneously two different substances, for each of which it can form adaptive enzymes which differ from each other. It is then found that these two adaptations compete and interfere with each other. This could not happen if the adaptation merely consisted in the stabilization of enzymes. The phenomenon of interference between different adaptations indicates a power on the part of any enzyme forming process to commandeer supplies into its own channel. In other words, the enzyme forming process, too, involves some kind of self-accelerating mechanism. As yet, however, we are not able to pin down the element responsible for this power. Is it the enzyme itself, an unspecific precursor, a specific region of the enzyme, or any one of these combined with substrate? I believe a great deal of light could be shed on this situation by a much closer analysis than has hitherto been attempted of the adaptation interference phenomenon.

I have been trying to give you an impression of the intellectual uncertainties confronting a physicist entering biology. These are of two kinds. On the one hand, when he thinks he has discovered a law of nature as pertaining to living matter, like Weber's law, he must beware lest he be fooled by natural selection simulating such a law. On the other hand, when he has found a really fine phenomenon universal in the living world and specific to it, like reproduction, he finds that it is indissolubly tied into the enormously complex organization of a living cell. Baffled by these barriers to his usual approach, a physicist may well stop and consider what he may reasonably expect by way of theoretical progress in the application of physical principles to living matter. It is true that physics and chemistry have a firm hold over biology by virtue of two great generalizations: living matter is made up of the same elements as those of the inanimate world, and conservation of energy is valid for processes occurring in living matter, just as it is for all processes in the inanimate world. To the men who first established the validity of these generalizations for living matter, like Helmholtz, for instance, it seemed clear that the processes of living matter must be essentially the same as those of the inorganic world and that there could not possibly exist a biological science ruled by its own laws. For these men the phenomena of life presented essentially mechanical problems. They should be deducible from the laws of Newton's mechanics as movements of particles due to forces originating in other particles. Such a view, more recently slightly modified to incorporate a few quantum concepts, has been the driving force of several generations of bio-chemists. We may quote J. Loeb as fairly representative of this attitude: "The ultimate aim of the physical sciences is the visualization of all phenomena in terms of groupings and displacements of ultimate particles, and since there is no discontinuity between the matter constituting the living and the non-living world the goal of biology can be expressed in the same way." One should add at this point that some of the contemporaries of Newton took quite a different view of the Newtonian principles. To describe motions in terms of forces acting at a distance seemed to them like introducing magic. Moreover, to correlate forces with accelerations, that is, with the second derivative of the function describing the motion, seemed to them the height of abstraction, going beyond what should be permitted to occur in any science, and threatening to remove it from the realm of rational pursuit. Between the times of Newton and Helmholtz, then, a strange inversion took place. What had seemed magical and extravagant at the earlier period, after a century of success had become the *only* way in which one could hope to account rationally and visualizably for the phenomena of nature. Actually, most branches of biology manage to flourish without any recourse to this ideal. All of natural history operates with a system of concepts which has very little contact with the physical and chemical sciences. The habits of animals and plants, their reproduction and development, their relations to their symbionts and to their enemies, can all be described and analysed with very little reference to the concepts of physics and chemistry. Perhaps the most notable of these independent branches of biology is genetics, which in its pure form operates with "hereditary factors" and "phenotypic characters" in a perfectly logical system, as an exact science without ever having to refer to the processes by which the characters originate from the factors. The root of this science lies in the existence of natural units of observation, the individual living organisms, which in genetics play somewhat the same role as the atoms and molecules in chemistry.

This analogy of the individual living organism with the molecules of chemistry may be valid in more than one sense. In the first place the notion of the individual organism brings into biology discreteness, and number, and identity of type, as the concept of molecule does in chemistry. In the second place, the stability and reproducibility of type in biology we think is a result of the stability and reproducibility of the genes and this stability we think is based upon the stability of certain complex molecular structures. The third and perhaps the most interesting aspect of the analogy is the fact that the individual organism presents an indissoluble unit, barring us, at least at present, from a reduction to the terms of molecular physics. It may turn out that this bar is not really an essential one, but a physicist is well prepared to find that it is essential. This would be similar to the lesson the physicist had to learn most recently in the attempts to develop a proper approach to an understanding of the properties of molecules in terms of their constituent elements. To make this point clearer I want to illustrate it with an historical example. At the beginning of this century enough was known about the existence of atoms and molecules to make the question of their structure a real one. The analysis of the interaction of atoms with light had begun before the constituent elements of the atoms, electron and nucleus had been discovered. It was known that atoms emit radiations of characteristic frequencies which could be determined with high accuracy. The attitude of the physicists of those days was that these characteristic frequencies represent frequencies of vibration of the atoms themselves and as such are expressions of certain properties of the atoms as mechanical systems. Examples of solid objects having characteristic frequencies of vibration had been well worked out and understood in terms of classical physics. The vibrations of the atoms were presumed to be vibrations of electrical matter within the atoms and it was considered the task of future analysis to infer the structure of the atom from a close inspection of the frequencies of vibration and of the conditions under which atoms could be excited in their various modes of vibration. Nothing could have seemed more sane and reasonable a program of research. In fact, many interesting regularities in the system of frequencies characteristic for a given atom were discovered. As long as nothing definite was known of the parts of which atoms are made up, these findings may have seemed a little strange but by no means suggestive that a suitable description in terms of a mechanical model could not be obtained. The situation was changed suddenly when it became clear that every atom is made up of one nucleus and a number of electrons. Very simple and general arguments could be brought forward showing that no system consisting of these elements could possibly have the properties that atoms were known to have. Here was a clear paradox. In Bohr's paper of 1913 this paradox was met by introducing the notions of stable orbits and jumps between these orbits. The frequencies of revolution of electrons in these orbits were unrelated to the frequencies of the light waves emitted. These were very irrational assumptions which shocked and in fact disgusted many physicists of that time.

The crucial point in this abbreviated account of an historical episode is the appearance of a conflict between separate areas of experience, which gradually sharpens into a paradox and must then be resolved by a radically new approach.

As is well known, the resolution of the paradoxes of atomic structure necessitated a revision of our ideals (or prejudices) regarding the description of nature. It was necessary to replace the classical conceptual scheme of particles moving in well defined orbits by the new scheme of quantum states and transition probabilities. Let us consider, for instance, a hydrogen atom in an excited state. Quantum mechanics permits us to calculate the probability that the atom will make a transition to the ground state in a definite time interval, with emission of a light quantum which carries off the difference in energy between the two states. Suppose we wanted to improve the statistical prediction and find out exactly at what moment the transition will take place. To make such a prediction we would need more precise information regarding the state of the atom, beyond the fact that it is in this excited state. We might try to obtain this more precise information by finding out at what point within the atom the electron is located at a certain moment. Such information can be obtained, in principle at least, by using an ideal microscope employing a radiation of very short wave length. Observation with light of such very short wave lengths, however, necessitates the use of an experimental arrangement in which we cannot control the exchange of energy between the atom and the measuring instrument, the light in this case. This uncontrolled exchange of energy will be of such a magnitude that the atom thereafter will be in any one of the excited states. If the first aim, that of obtaining the precise location of the electron, is not to be sacrificed, the microscope has to be used in a fashion which is mutually exclusive with any arrangement designed to give us information about the excited state. While, therefore, obtaining exact information regarding the position of the electron at this particular moment, the uncontrolled interaction between the tool of observation, the short wave light, and the atom introduces an uncertainty in the energy of the atom and we are not better off than before. We have just swapped the knowledge of a stationary state for the knowledge of the location of the electron at one particular moment, and our primary aim of additional information, beyond that of knowing that the atom is in the first excited state, has been frustrated. This state of affairs is at the root of all quantum phenomena. Each process of observation has an individuality which cannot be broken down beyond a certain limit and different types of observation stand to each other in a mutually exclusive, complementary relationship. Different observations will therefore lead to a variety of optimal informations regarding an atomic system, and each such optimal information we describe by the abstract notion of the state of that system. From such knowledge we can make precise statistical predictions regarding the future of the system. The different optimal informations are obtained from mutually exclusive experimental arrangements, and the quantum mechanical formalism is designed to embody this particular feature of complementariness. We believe that quantum mechanics is the final word as regards the behavior of atoms and we base this belief upon the analysis by Bohr and Heisenberg of the possibilities of observation, which shows that the renunciation of the ideal of classical physics for the description of Nature eliminates nothing that could be defined operationally. Therefore this renunciation should not be considered as a loss but as a liberation from unnecessary restrictions and thus as the essential element of our advance which opened the widest possibilities for future developments.

Let us now go back to the situation as it appeared to Helmholtz in the 1870's. For him it seemed that the behavior of living cells should be accountable in terms of motions of molecules acting under certain fixed force laws. How far we have wandered from this ideal! We now know that if we tried to adhere to this ideal we could not even account for the behavior of a single hydrogen atom. In fact, we account for the stationary state of the hydrogen atom precisely at the price of not describing the motion of the electron. But how about the living cell? Should we now perhaps consider it as a super molecule and ideally calculate its stationary states and transition probabilities? Would it be sufficient to modify Helmholtz's views to this slight extent?

Such a view might seem reasonable to the structural chemist, who applies the general concepts of quantum mechanics successfully to more and more complex molecules. Even though his efforts have not yet been successful with any structures of molecular weight higher than a few thousand, a limitation in principle can hardly be expected. However, the experimental analysis of the structural chemist always presupposes the availability of a practically infinite number of molecules of the same kind, and of a practically infinite stability of the molecules if not disturbed.

In the living cell we know that a great deal depends on very fine features of structure. By structure we mean relevant inhomogeneities in the make-up of the cell. These relevant inhomogeneities go right down to the atomic scale. It would certainly not be possible, even in an ideal experiment, from observation of an *individual* living cell to gain knowledge of these details sufficient to make quantum mechanical calculations of the development of the cell. To make structural observations of such extreme finesse again a practically infinite number of cells in *identical quantum states* would be required. Such a requirement can certainly not be met in practice and it seems likely to me that also it cannot be met in principle. This leads to the point of the third analogy between individual living organisms and molecules. It may turn out that certain features of the living cell, including perhaps even replication, stand in a mutually exclusive relationship to the strict application of quantum mechanics, and that a new conceptual language has to be developed to embrace this situation. The limitation in the applicability of present day physics may then prove to be, not the dead end of our search, but the open door to the admission of fresh views of the matter. Just as we find features of the atom, its stability, for instance, which are not reducible to mechanics, we may find features of the living cell which are not reducible to atomic physics but whose appearance stands in a complementary relationship to those of atomic physics.

This idea, which is due to Bohr, puts the relation between physics and biology on a new footing. Instead of aiming from the molecular physics end at the whole of the phenomena exhibited by the living cell, we now expect to find natural limits to this approach, and thereby implicitly new virgin territories on which laws may hold which involve new concepts and which are only loosely related to those of physics, by virtue of the fact that they apply to phenomena whose appearance is conditioned on *not* making observations of the type needed for a consistent interpretation in terms of atomic physics.

I would like to explain this point of view a little further by a brief reference to the problem of spontaneous generation.[6] We know that life originated on earth within less than a billion years after conditions had become reasonable, perhaps in much less time and perhaps not once but repeatedly. We do not know the chemical environment of those days, but it can hardly have been anything that could not be reproduced today nor is it likely to have been anything very specific. Therefore, spontaneous generation should be an experimentally reproducible phenomenon. Imagine that we knew these conditions. We could then prescribe a certain synthetic medium and temperature and predict that spontaneous generation should occur with a certain probability per time unit, and it would seem that this would bring life completely into the domain of chemistry. Or would it? Conceivably spontaneous generation would be a very gradual thing, going through lengthy stages of inaccurate and poorly defined replications, perhaps evolving from something like crystallization from supersaturated solutions. In that event the algebra of natural selection and of statistical fluctuations would enter decisively into the kinetics of spontaneous generation and would limit the predictability of the outcome, just as it does in the later stages of evolution. The creatures emerging in such a test tube experiment presumably would be extremely different, biochemically, from those of our world, and not being adapted to our world would have no chance of survival in it. This implies that we could not tell the precise chemical make-up of a living thing from its mode of chemical origin. Nor can we tell it, as pointed out before, from a structural analysis of its actual state. The detailed chemical structure of a living cell is thus operationally undefinable and the concept therefore meaningless. It remains to be seen whether a retrenchment in the demand for a detailed chemical description for such phenomena as replication, chromosome movements, excitation, active transport, etc., will facilitate giving a coherent account of these phenomena.

Perhaps you will think that such speculations and arguments as here presented are very dangerous: they seem to encourage defeatism before it is necessary, and to open the door to wild and unreasonable speculations of a vitalistic kind. I sympathize with this criticism and want to justify the presentation I have given by saying that Bohr's suggestion of a complementarity situation in biology, analogous to that in physics, has been the prime motive for the interest in biology of at least one physicist and may possibly play a similar role for other physicists who come into the field of biology. Biology is a very interesting field to enter for anyone, by the vastness of its structure and the extraordinary variety of strange facts it has collected, but to the physicist it is also a depressing subject, because, insofar as physical explanations of seemingly physical phenomena go, like excitation, or chromosome movements, or replication, the analysis seems to have stalled around in a semidescriptive manner without noticeably progressing towards a radical physical explanation. He may be told that the only real access of atomic physics to biology is through biochemistry. Listening to the story of modern biochemistry he might become persuaded that the cell is a sack full of enzymes acting on substrates converting them through various intermediate stages either into cell substance or into waste products. The enzymes must be situated in their proper strategic positions to perform their duties in a well regulated fashion. They in turn must be synthesized and must be brought into position by manoeuvers which are not yet understood, but which, at first sight at least, do not necessarily seem to differ in nature from the rest of biochemistry. Indeed, the vista of the biochemist is one with an infinite horizon. And yet, this program of explaining the simple through the complex smacks suspiciously of the program of explaining atoms in terms of complex mechanical models. It looks sane until the paradoxes crop up and come into sharper focus. In biology we are not yet at the point where we are presented with clear paradoxes and this will not happen until the analysis of the behaviour of living cells has been carried into far greater detail. This analysis should be done on the living cell's own terms and the theories should be formulated without fear of contradicting molecular physics. I believe that it is in this direction that physicists will show the greatest zeal and will create a new intellectual approach to biology which would lend meaning to the ill-used term biophysics.

References

1. Delbrück, M., 1949. Internat. Symposium of the Centre Natl. de la Recherche Scientifique, 8: 91–104. .

2. Doermann, A. H., 1948. Carnegie Institution of Washington Yearbook, 47, 176–185.

3. _____. *Personal communication.*

4. Cohen, S. S., 1949. Bacteriological Reviews, 13: 1–24.

5. Monod, J., 1949. Internat. Symposium of the Centre Natl. de la Recherche Scientifique, 8: 181–199.

6. Pirie, N. W., 1948. Modern Quarterly, 3 (new series): 82–93.

IN DEFENSE OF BIOLOGY

Barry Commoner

A great deal has been said of late about the flourishing state of biology and its exciting progress toward the solution of basic problems. There would appear to be little need for a defense of biology, zoology, botany, or any other part of the sciences of life.

Certainly much of this is true. Remarkable progress has been made in our understanding of important biological processes: metabolism, photosynthesis, the biosynthesis of macromolecules, the structure of viruses. Yet certain equally fundamental questions that have long been of concern to biologists have firmly resisted the recent winds of progress. We still have but inadequate answers to the questions: What is the cause of speciation? How do cells differentiate? What processes dictate their division, growth, and cessation of growth? How does inheritance control these developmental processes? Obviously, some areas of biology are still making relatively slow progress.

A divided science

What distinguishes the slower areas of biology from those which seem to grow by startling jumps ("breakthroughs" in newspaper parlance) and which surround themselves with glamor? The fast-growing fields, which appear to represent the cutting edge of progress in biology, are those in which the biological problem has been reduced to chemical or physical terms. The slower-paced areas are those which have thus far largely resisted this advance. When a biological problem

---

"In Defense of Biology," *Science*, CXXXIII (June 2, 1961), 1745–1748. Reprinted by permission of the publisher and Barry Commoner.

can be restated in molecular terms the enormously powerful insights and instruments of modern chemistry, physics, and engineering can be brought to bear on it. Under such a massive attack, quite rapid and sometimes spectacular discoveries are made.

Of course, there is a more homely way to distinguish between the two types of studies. In the fast-moving fields the laboratories are large and densely packed with expensive electromechanical apparatus, students, and postdoctoral fellows. In the other areas of biology, we see some microscopes (optical, that is), herbarium sheets, and fewer people.

From almost any viewpoint there seems to be a widening gap between the more traditional areas of biology and those which are closely related to modern chemistry and physics.

It is true, of course, that chemistry and physics have come to occupy an increasingly important place in *all* areas of biological research, including the traditional ones. But the levels of application current in the two segments of biology are vastly different. While investigations of the more traditional sort may concern themselves with pH or oxygen consumption, really modern biological studies feature semiconductors, charge-transfer complexes, radioisotopes, and information theory.

How well can such a divided science work? Will the very problems that attract the more glamorous laboratories be advanced, in the long run, in circumstances which preclude a close contact with taxonomy, evolution, and morphogenesis?

One view is that this separation is inevitable and healthy—that traditional biology has served its purpose and must now give way to biochemistry and biophysics. A recent review of Isaac Asimov's new book about modern biology states that "For him . . . biology is a system that proceeds from biochemistry to the associated subjects of neurophysiology and genetics. All else, as they used to say of the nonphysical sciences, is stamp collecting." "I happen to agree firmly with Asimov about what is central in science and what is not," the reviewer writes, "and I will defend him to the death against traditionalists who might deplore his not starting with 'Heat, Light, and Sound' or his giving short shrift to 'Natural History'" (1).

Having rarely been accused of being a traditionalist, perhaps I may be permitted to disagree with this view.

I believe that the increasing separation between "traditional" and "modern" biology is regrettable. In the narrow view, this process may have unfortunate effects on the number and competence of students in traditional departments of biology, zoology, and botany, and may be reflected in the level of support these departments command both within and without the university. But what is a far more serious matter is the harmful effect on science itself.

Process of alienation

The view that biology is only an unresolved form of chemistry and physics is not new. Biology has always produced adventitious areas of investigation which quickly lose their contact with the mother science. So long as the chemistry of rubber was poorly understood, the problem of the role of latex in the plant, of its composition and properties, belonged to biology. As soon as chemistry had advanced sufficiently to deal with such a complex substance, the problem was taken over by biochemists, physical chemists, and engineers. Certainly we have gained from this process and our knowledge of rubber is vastly increased. But how much of this new knowledge has been reflected back upon plant biology?

A similar estrangement characterizes the history of research on starch. Classical plant morphologists have produced monumental works on starch grains, which have unique structural organization closely correlated with the plant's specific character. In more recent years an equally impressive body of knowledge about the chemical substances extractable from the starch grain—amylose and amylopectin—has accumulated. Moreover, enzymes that synthesize these substances have been isolated. Yet an analysis of the information available from studies of extracts shows that we do not understand how the enzymes could possibly account for the presence together in the starch grain of both amylose and amylopectin in proportions which are under genetic control. Clearly, our attention must now return to the developing starch grain, and we must learn how the enzymes are disposed within it, and how the cellular environment can give rise to a precise correlation between the two paths of biosynthesis that cannot be accounted for in terms of test-tube chemistry. The stage is set for a fascinating marriage between the classical studies of the starch grain and modern starch biochemistry and biophysics. But to my knowledge no proposals have been made, consummation is a distant prospect, and fruitful results are even more remote. Why? I believe that we can blame the unfortunate separation between the classical and the more modern aspects of biology.

I believe that there is some justification for a generalization: as soon as an interesting and important biological problem becomes susceptible to chemical or physical attack, a process of alienation begins, and the question becomes, in the end, lost to biology. But in each case, the purely chemical—or physical—studies run their course and come to the blank wall that still surrounds the intimate events which occur within the *living* cell. The obvious need is to return home to biology. But now the errant science has long forgotten its home, and the mother is too bewildered by its fast-talking offspring to be very happy about welcoming it back into the family.

Clearly, such a course of events cannot go on indefinitely, for there are, after all, only a limited number of substances and processes that can be removed without finally leaving nothing at all behind. So long as this process of alienation affected only the end products of metabolism (such as starch, rubber, or pigments), the parent science suffered some damage but no really lethal blow. But now biochemistry and biophysics have reached deep into the core of biology—to reproduction and inheritance—and the question arises as to how biology will sustain this more penetrating attack.

Biology under attack

One view of the result of this latest event is readily obtained from the new volume that has already been referred to. The book is a summary of the present state of the biological sciences written for "the intelligent man." It opens with the following sentence: "Modern science has all but wiped out the borderline between life and non-life" (2).

Since biology is the science of life, any successful obliteration of the distinction between living things and other forms of matter ends forever the usefulness of biology as a separate science. If the foregoing sentence is even remotely correct, biology is not only under attack; it has been annihilated.

An explanation of the basis for this remarkable assertion is of course necessary, and it will, I believe, reveal that this statement is the crowning and wholly logical conclusion of a series of ideas which have attained considerable approval among scientists.

What evidence is offered in support of this statement? We can begin with Asimov's consideration of that marvelously meaningful problem that has for so long intrigued biologists: At what moment in the history of matter did life appear? The answer given is this: "Then, eventually, must have come the key step—the formation, through chance combinations, of a nucleic acid molecule, capable of inducing replication. That moment marked the beginning of life" (2, p. 542).

Why is this so? Because "All of the substances of living matter— enzymes and all the others, whose production is catalyzed by enzymes— depend in the last analysis on DNA" (2, p. 535).

Deoxyribonucleic acid

This story is, of course, well known. The DNA molecule is a code which contains all the information required to specify the inheritable characteristics of the organism. The information is translated into protein structure by a process in which DNA dictates the specificity of protein synthesis. Once the information has been so translated, all of the chemical reactions of the cell—which are wholly determined by the structure of enzyme proteins—have also been specified. Moreover, the genes, which according to biological evidence regulate the inherited characteristics of a species, consist of DNA, and the self-duplication of DNA is the basis of genetics. In sum, DNA is the vehicle for the continuity of life.

All of us have heard this story told at every level of the ladder of scientific discourse, from research papers, through review articles to textbooks and the latest issues of the news magazines. The basic ideas are attractive and widely accepted in the scientific community. Many of us have heard them in the classroom—sometimes from our own lips. And so I must apologize—and hereby do—to our helpful author whom I have rudely represented as leader of an attack in which so many others participate.

But can it be true that the familiar "DNA story" is really an attack on biology? Let us return for a moment to the assertion that "the boundary between life and non-life has all but disappeared," for most of us will agree that, if this statement is not an attack on biology, it is at least a pretty fair insult.

If we agree both that nucleic acid is an encoded form of life, capable of self-duplication, and that it can bring about the translation of its own code into the remaining aspects of life, then it follows that, given a reasonably healthy environment, nucleic acid can indeed create life and perpetuate it. Since it is also indisputable that nucleic acid is a chemical substance, then we must agree (if all this is true) that life is essentially nothing more than an expression of the chemistry of nucleic acid. Following this closely reasoned logic, we end inevitably with the conversion of biology into the chemistry of nucleic acid and its creations.

Is biology worth saving?

Now the problem is more evident. Biology *does* appear to be dwindling, and in need of defense. I believe that in the last decade every academic biologist has begun to feel the realistic effects of the atrophy of biology on the life of his laboratory, his classroom, and his institution. Twenty-five years ago, bright young people eager to conquer the world of science were proud to become biologists, to study *Drosophila* genetics, plant taxonomy, or embryology. Nowadays, a student with a budding interest in genetics often ends up mating strands of DNA rather than fruit flies, and greenhouses are built to grow plants for the purpose of producing viruses. Bright young biologists, if they are good enough, become biochemists and biophysicists.

Biology does seem to be in some need of a defense. But is it worth saving? To be explicit, what I mean is this: Is there any good reason why we should resist the progressive isolation of taxonomy, morphology, physiology, and the rest of the "less exciting" fields from the areas that have apparently been won over to modern chemistry and physics?

I believe that this process should be resisted, not because the traditional fields of biology ought to be protected from the effects of chemistry and physics, but because unless biology itself survives, the great powers of these modern sciences cannot be fully used. I believe, for example, that the proper correlation of physics and biology requires that *the integrity of both sciences* be maintained in the collaborative process.

Part of the argument in support of this view has already been made: that in many instances the pursuit of a purely physical or chemical line of attack runs out of momentum and needs to return to the truly living system.

But the chief argument that I should like to propose is this: Analysis of living systems, based on modern physical and chemical theory, leads to the conclusion that life is unique and that it cannot be reduced to the property of a single substance or of a system less complex than a living cell. I propose to cite several examples of such analyses in order to show that fundamental theories of physics and chemistry support the view that there is, in modern science, no justification for the "obliteration of the boundary between life and non-life."

An interesting case in point is the matter of information theory, which now plays such an important role in proposals regarding the genetic function of DNA. The basic notion is well known: The DNA in the germ cell is supposed to contain in an encoded form all the information required to specify in detail the inheritable features of the adult organism.

Elsasser

Now this question has been given a searching examination by a distinguished physicist, W. M. Elsasser, in his book *The Physical Foundation of Biology* and in a subsequent article (3). While space does not permit even an approximate description of Elsasser's work, certain aspects of it can be simply stated. Elsasser points out that from recent advances in computer theory one can set certain fairly precise requirements on the above hypothesis. Two critical requirements are (i) The information content of the amount of DNA present in the germ cell of a complex organism, such as a horse, should greatly exceed that present in the cell of a more simple organism, such as an ameba. (ii) Cells should contain a device for translating the code library contained in the DNA into the biological characters which it determines; computer experience indicates that the translation device ought to be considerably more massive than the library.

The available facts suggest that living things do not meet these requirements: (i) Organisms which must differ considerably in their genetic complexity often have similar cellular DNA contents (4), and there is no evidence that the discrepancy can be accounted for by differences in genetic redundancy or in the inertness of some chromosome sections. Conversely, organisms which are nearly identical in genetic complexity may differ considerably in cellular DNA content (5). The available evidence does not support the idea of a one-to-one correspondence between genetic information and the information represented by the structure of DNA, or for that matter of any other molecular component of the cell. (ii) No cytologist has discovered a ubiquitous structure, considerably larger than the chromosomes (the code library) which shows evidence of serving as a translator. While recent biochemical evidence suggests possible means whereby DNA-borne information may be translated into genetically effective protein specificity, there is still no sign of a device capable of translating the DNA code into the numerous anatomical features (fingerprints, for example) that are also inherited.

Thus, a strict analysis of the problem of inheritance in accordance with modern information theory leads to the remarkable result that the organism's specificity must be determined, at least in part, by agencies not present in the initial germ cell and certainly not in the DNA alone. Elsasser points out that this view, which can be derived directly from modern physical theory, is identical with a principle already well established in biology—*epigenesis*. This view holds that the fertilized egg begins with a limited amount of specificity, which develops into more detail in progressive, superimposed, stages. Strong evidence from embryology supports this conclusion, and recently some investigators have suggested that certain specific types of inheritance, especially in protozoa, are epigenetic in character (6).

These results have an important bearing on the customary ideas about DNA, for they call into question the basic assumption that DNA (or for that matter any other single component of the germ cell) can possibly serve, by itself, as the final arbiter of biological specificity. There are many fascinating questions that arise from these considerations, but these will need to be taken up at another time.

Bohr

Another notable defense of life as something unique and distinct from non-life comes from one of the great physicists of our time, Niels Bohr. Bohr has written several remarkable papers (7) about the relation between biology and physics, which have for too long been neglected by biologists and biophysicists alike. One of Bohr's contributions to physics is the theory of complementarity, which holds, for example, that the electron is characterized by both particulate and wave properties, which are nevertheless mutually contradictory (the more precisely the wavelength is defined the less certain we become of the electron's position).

According to Bohr this relationship is an example of a *general* law of complementarity which applies as well to biology. Bohr suggests that complementarity regulates the relationship between two coeval aspects of biological systems: the existence of life in the whole intact cell, and the separate physicochemical events that occur within it. The more precisely we try to determine the internal events of a cell the more likely we are to destroy its life. Bohr concludes: "On this view, the very existence of life must in biology be considered an elementary fact, just as in atomic physics the existence of a quantum of action has to be taken as a basic fact that cannot be derived from ordinary mechanical physics."

Now, no one should conclude from this statement that the property of life is somehow nonmaterial and innately mysterious. Bohr is not a vitalist. On the contrary, Bohr's principle simply serves as a warning that we cannot study the property of life without retaining it in our experiments. Again, this view raises a host of fascinating questions that we cannot go into here. It is pertinent here only to show that the penetrating insight of modern physical theory reveals certain inconsistencies in the notion that life can be reduced to the chemistry of some special substance.

Hinshelwood

An equally cogent analysis of the problem, this time from the viewpoint of the kinetics of complex chemical systems has been made by one of the founders of that field, Sir Cyril Hinshelwood. He points out that "the view that nucleoproteins are the basis of genes which could ever be self-replicating in isolation and merely in virtue of their structure is probably a dangerous over-simplification. . . . The picture presented is essentially static. The phenomena of growth, adaptation and reproduction need a dynamic one." From a straightforward analysis of the kinetic behavior of the complex metabolic processes of bacterial cells, Hinshelwood suggests an alternative source for the self-regulation of living cells. "The building blocks of the cells, wonderful as they may be as structures, are useless by themselves. Cell function depends upon the rhythm and harmony of their reciprocal actions: the mutual dependence of protein and nucleic acid; the spatial and temporal relations of a host of elementary processes which with their sequences and bifurcations make up the reaction pattern of the cell. A system of mutually dependent parts, each of which performs something like enzymatic functions in relation to another, will, as can easily be shown, in the steady state appear as a whole to be autosynthetic. No individual part need be credited with a new and mysterious virtue by which to duplicate itself" (8). In effect, it is Hinshelwood's view that nothing less complex than an entire cell is capable of *self*-duplication.

A true alliance

These brief descriptions of the views of life developed by Elsasser, Bohr, and Hinshelwood reveal a considerable unanimity, and — what is perhaps more surprising — a remarkable agreement with the biologist's long-held opinion that life is inherently complex and unique. How can we explain this unexpected convergence of conclusions reached, separately, by such different routes as information theory, the theory of complementarity, the physical chemistry of complex systems, and the manifest properties of living things? I believe that what is common — and to some degree unusual — in these physical and chemical views of life is that they are profound. They apply modern physical and chemical theory to the problem of life with the same standards of depth and rigor that are required in the treatment of purely physical and chemical problems. Perhaps I am permitted to generalize: Whether the approach to the problem of life is through physics, through chemistry, or through biology itself, the results are consistent — provided that the analysis is fundamental and thorough.

Perhaps the remedy for the declining fortunes of biology is now clear. Biologists should not regard chemistry or physics as a nemesis but as an ally. If modern physical theory requires that epigenesis govern biological development, and if the cell theory can be deduced from physical chemistry, then physics and chemistry must be regarded as biology's most powerful friends.

If this mutual relationship is to bear fruit there must be a true alliance between real sciences rather than the creation of rootless hybrids. If we allow classical biology to decline, the full powers of modern physics and chemistry cannot be brought to bear on the study of life. I believe that in our university organization we must discover how to combine biology, chemistry, and physics in ways that will retain the integrity of each discipline.

A final point is in order, for the problem of the future of biology, however important to us, does not exist apart from the society in which we live. It appears to me that in the recent applications of science to social problems, there has been an increasing tendency to ignore the facts of life. Too often, we are prepared to expose miles of countryside to substances known chiefly for their power to kill. By the time we have dispersed insecticides, herbicides, fungicides, nematocides, pesticides, and other assorted agents, the adaptive latitude of the ecological environment, which is so vital to the success of plant, beast, and man, may have been fatally restricted. I sometimes think that the difficulties we now face in controlling water, air, and soil pollution, and the undue dissemination of radioactive materials, are the result of a common impression that "the boundary between life and non-life has all but disappeared." In fact, if we do not mend our ways, the statement may, after all, turn out to be true.

I believe that the time has come to restore the science of life. We need to do this for the sake of the science, and for the sake of that which is the goal of all science — the welfare of man (9).

References and Notes

1. D. J. de Solla Price, *Science*, 132, 1830 (1960), review of (2).

2. I. Asimov, *The Intelligent Man's Guide to Modern Science*, vol. 2, "The Biological Sciences" (Basic Books, New York, 1960).

3. W. M. Elsasser, *The Physical Foundation of Biology* (Pergamon Press, New York, 1958). See also W. M. Elsasser, *J. Theoretical Biol.*, 1, 27 (1961). I am indebted to Dr. Elsasser for illuminating discussions of these matters.

4. A. E. Mirsky and H. Ris, *J. Gen. Physiol.*, 34, 451 (1951); R. Vendrely and C. Vendrely, *Compt. rend.*, 235, 444 (1952).

5. F. Schrader and S. Hughes-Schrader, *Chromosoma,* 7, 469 (1956).

6. D. L. Nanney, *Cold Spring Harbor Symposia Quant. Biol.*, 23, 327 (1958).

7. N. Bohr, *Atomic Physics and Human Knowledge* (Wiley, New York, 1958).

8. C. Hinshelwood, *Proc. Roy. Soc. London,* B146, 155 (1956).

9. In the development of the views put forward in this paper, I have had the benefit of research grants from the National Foundation, the National Science Foundation, and the Rockefeller Foundation.

CAUSE AND EFFECT IN BIOLOGY

Ernst Mayr

Being a practicing biologist I feel that I cannot attempt the kind of analysis of cause and effect in biological phenomena that a logician would undertake. I would instead like to concentrate on the special difficulties presented by the classical concept of causality in biology. From the first attempts to achieve a unitary concept of cause, the student of causality has been bedeviled by these difficulties. Descartes's grossly mechanistic interpretation of life, and the logical extreme to which his ideas were carried by Holbach and de la Mettrie, inevitably provoked a reaction leading to vitalistic theories which have been in vogue, off and on, to the present day. I have only to mention names like Driesch (entelechy), Bergson (élan vital), and Lecomte du Noüy, among the more prominent authors of the recent past. Though these authors may differ in particulars, they all agree in claiming that living beings and life processes cannot be causally explained in terms of physical and chemical phenomena. It is our task to ask whether this assertion is justified, and if we answer this question with "no," to determine the source of the misunderstanding.

Causality, no matter how it is defined in terms of logic, is believed to contain three elements: (i) an explanation of past events ("a posteriori causality"); (ii) prediction of future events; and (iii) interpretation of teleological — that is, "goal-directed" — phenomena.

The three aspects of causality (explanation, prediction, and teleology) must be the cardinal points in any discussion of causality and were

---

"Cause and Effect in Biology," *Science*, CXXXIV (November 10, 1961), 1501–1506. This article was adapted from one of the annual series of Hayden lectures presented at Massachusetts Institute of Technology. Reprinted by permission of Ernst Mayr.

quite rightly singled out as such by Nagel (1). Biology can make a significant contribution to all three of them. But before I can discuss this contribution in detail, I must say a few words about biology as a science.

Biology

The word *biology* suggests a uniform and unified science. Yet recent developments have made it increasingly clear that biology is a most complex area—indeed, that the word *biology* is a label for two largely separate fields which differ greatly in method, *Fragestellung*, and basic concepts. As soon as one goes beyond the level of purely descriptive structural biology, one finds two very different areas, which may be designated functional biology and evolutionary biology. To be sure, the two fields have many points of contact and overlap. Any biologist working in one of these fields must have a knowledge and appreciation of the other field if he wants to avoid the label of a narrow-minded specialist. Yet in his own research he will be occupied with problems of either one or the other field. We cannot discuss cause and effect in biology without first having characterized these two fields.

Functional biology. The functional biologist is vitally concerned with the operation and interaction of structural elements, from molecules up to organs and whole individuals. His ever-repeated question is "How?" How does something operate, how does it function? The functional anatomist who studies an articulation shares this method and approach with the molecular biologist who studies the function of a DNA molecule in the transfer of genetic information. The functional biologist attempts to isolate the particular component he studies, and in any given study he usually deals with a single individual, a single organ, a single cell, or a single part of a cell. He attempts to eliminate, or control, all variables, and he repeats his experiments under constant or varying conditions until he believes he has clarified the function of the element he studies. The chief technique of the functional biologist is the experiment, and his approach is essentially the same as that of the physicist and the chemist. Indeed, by isolating the studied phenomenon sufficiently from the complexities of the organism, he may achieve the ideal of a purely physical or chemical experiment. In spite of certain limitations of this method, one must agree with the functional biologist that such a simplified approach is an absolute necessity for achieving his particular objectives. The spectacular success of biochemical and biophysical research justifies this direct, although distinctly simplistic, approach.

Evolutionary biology. The evolutionary biologist differs in his method and in the problems in which he is interested. His basic question is "Why?" When we say "why" we must always be aware of the ambiguity of this term. It may mean "how come?," but it may also mean the finalistic "what for?" It is obvious that the evolutionist has in mind the historical "how come?" when he asks "why?" Every organism, whether individual or species, is the product of a long history, a history which indeed dates back more than 2000 million years. As Max Delbrück (2) has said, "a mature physicist, acquainting himself for the first time with the problems of biology, is puzzled by the circumstance that there are no 'absolute phenomena' in biology. Everything is time-bound and space-bound. The animal or plant or micro-organism he is working with is but a link in an evolutionary chain of changing forms, none of which has any permanent validity." There is hardly any structure or function in an organism that can be fully understood unless it is studied against this historical background. To find the causes for the existing characteristics, and particularly adaptations, of organisms is the main preoccupation of the evolutionary biologist. He is impressed by the enormous diversity of the organic world. He wants to know the reasons for this diversity as well as the pathway by which it has been achieved. He studies the forces that bring about changes in faunas and floras (as in part documented by paleontology), and he studies the steps by which have evolved the miraculous adaptations so characteristic of every aspect of the organic world.

We can use the language of information theory to attempt still another characterization of these two fields of biology. The functional biologist deals with all aspects of the decoding of the programmed information contained in the DNA code of the fertilized zygote. The evolutionary biologist, on the other hand, is interested in the history of these codes of information and in the laws that control the changes of these codes from generation to generation. In other words, he is interested in the causes of these changes.

Many of the old arguments of biological philosophy can be stated far more precisely in terms of these genetic codes. For instance, as Schmalhausen, in Russia, and I have pointed out independently, the inheritance of acquired characteristics becomes quite unthinkable when applied to the model of the transfer of genetic information from a peripheral phenotype to the DNA of the germ cells.

But let us not have an erroneous concept of these codes. It is characteristic of these genetic codes that the programming is only in part rigid. Such phenomena as learning, memory, nongenetic structural modification, and regeneration show how "open" these programs are. Yet, even here there is great specificity, for instance with respect to what can be "learned," at what stage in the life cycle "learning" takes place, and how long a memory engram is retained. The program, then, may be in part quite unspecific, and yet the range of possible variation is itself included in the specifications of the code. The codes, therefore, are in some respects highly specific; in other respects they merely specify "reaction norms" or general capacities and potentialities.

Let me illustrate this duality of codes by the difference between two kinds of birds with respect to "species recognition." The young cowbird is raised by foster parents—let us say, in the nest of a song sparrow or warbler. As soon as it becomes independent of its foster parents it seeks the company of other young cowbirds, even though it has never seen a cowbird before! In contrast, after hatching from the egg, a young goose will accept as its parent the first moving (and preferably also calling) object it can follow and become "imprinted" to. What is programmed is, in one case, a definite "gestalt," in the other, merely the capacity to become imprinted to a "gestalt." Similar differences in the specificity of the inherited program are universal throughout the organic world.

Let us now get back to our main topic and ask: Is *cause* the same thing in functional and evolutionary biology?

Max Delbrück, again, has reminded us (2) that as recently as 1870 Helmholtz postulated "that the behavior of living cells should be accountable in terms of motions of molecules acting under certain fixed force laws." Now, says Delbrück correctly, we cannot even account for the behavior of a single hydrogen atom. As he also says, "any living cell carries with it the experiences of a billion years of experimentation by its ancestors."

Let me illustrate the difficulties of the concept of causality in biology by an example. Let us ask: What is the cause of bird migration? Or more specifically: Why did the warbler on my summer place in New Hampshire start his southward migration on the night of the 25th of August?

I can list four equally legitimate causes for this migration.

1. *An ecological cause.* The warbler, being an insect eater, must migrate, because it would starve to death if it should try to winter in New Hampshire.

2. *A genetic cause.* The warbler has acquired a genetic constitution in the course of the evolutionary history of its species which induces it to respond appropriately to the proper stimuli from the environment. On the other hand, the screech owl, nesting right next to it, lacks this constitution and does not respond to these stimuli. As a result, it is sedentary.

3. *An intrinsic physiological cause.* The warbler flew south because its migration is tied in with photoperiodicity. It responds to the decrease in day length and is ready to migrate as soon as the number of hours of daylight have dropped below a certain level.

4. *An extrinsic physiological cause.* Finally, the warbler migrated on the 25th of August because a cold air mass, with northerly winds, passed over our area on that day. The sudden drop in temperature and the associated weather conditions affected the bird, already in a general physiological readiness for migration, so that it actually took off on that particular day.

Now, if we look over the four causations of the migration of this bird once more we can readily see that there is an immediate set of causes of the migration, consisting of the physiological condition of the bird interacting with photoperiodicity and drop in temperature. We might call these the *proximate* causes of migration. The other two causes, the lack of food during winter and the genetic disposition of the bird, are the *ultimate* causes. These are causes that have a history and that have been incorporated into the system through many thousands of generations of natural selection. It is evident that the functional biologist would be concerned with analysis of the proximate causes, while the evolutionary biologist would be concerned with analysis of the ultimate causes. This is the case with almost any biological phenomenon we might want to study. There is always a proximate set of causes and an ultimate set of causes; both have to be explained and interpreted for a complete understanding of the given phenomenon.

Still another way to express these differences would be to say that proximate causes govern the responses of the individual (and his organs) to immediate factors of the environment while ultimate causes are responsible for the evolution of the particular DNA code of information with which every individual of every species is endowed. The logician will, presumably, be little concerned with these distinctions. Yet, the biologist knows that many heated arguments about the "cause" of a certain biological phenomenon could have been avoided if the two opponents had realized that one of them was concerned with proximate and the other with ultimate causes. I might illustrate this by a quotation from Loeb (3): "The earlier writers explained the growth of the legs in the tadpole of the frog or toad as a case of adaptation to life on land. We know through Gudernatsch that the growth of the legs can be produced at any time even in the youngest tadpole, which is unable to live on land, by feeding the animal with the thyroid gland."

Let us now get back to the definition of "cause" in formal philosophy and see how it fits with the usual explanatory "cause" of functional and evolutionary biology. We might, for instance, define cause as "a nonsufficient condition without which an event would not have happened," or as "a member of a set of jointly sufficient reasons without which the event would not happen" [after Scriven (4)]. Definitions such as these describe causal relations quite adequately in certain branches of biology, particularly in those which deal with chemical and physical unit phenomena. In a strictly formal sense they are also applicable to more complex phenomena, and yet they seem to have little operational value in those branches of biology that deal with complex systems. I doubt that there is a scientist who would question the ultimate causality of all biological phenomena—that is, that a causal explanation can be given for past biological events. Yet such an explanation will often have to be so unspecific and so purely formal that its explanatory value can certainly be challenged. In dealing with a complex system, an explanation can hardly be considered very illuminating that states: "Phenomenon A is caused by a complex set of interacting factors, one of which is b." Yet often this is about all one can say. We will have to come back to this difficulty in connection with the problem of prediction. However, let us first consider the problem of teleology.

Teleology

No discussion of causality is complete which does not come to grips with the problem of teleology. This problem had its beginning with Aristotle's classification of causes, one of the categories being the "final" causes. This category is based on the observation of the orderly and purposive development of the individual from the egg to the "final" stage of the adult, and of the development of the whole world from its beginnings (chaos?) to its present order. Final cause has been defined as "the cause responsible for the orderly reaching of a preconceived ultimate goal." All goal-seeking behavior has been classified as "teleological," but so have many other phenomena that are not necessarily goal-seeking in nature.

Aristotelian scholars have rightly emphasized that Aristotle—by training and interest—was first and foremost a biologist, and that it was his preoccupation with biological phenomena which dominated his ideas on causes and induced him to postulate final causes in addition to the material, formal, and efficient causes. Thinkers from Aristotle to the present have been challenged by the apparent contradiction between a mechanistic interpretation of natural processes and the seemingly purposive sequence of events in organic growth, in reproduction, and in animal behavior. Such a rational thinker as Bernard (5) has stated the paradox in these words.

> There is, so to speak, a preestablished design of each being and of each organ of such a kind that each phenomenon by itself depends upon the general forces of nature, but when taken in connection with the others it seems directed by some invisible guide on the road it follows and led to the place it occupies.
>
> We admit that the life phenomena are attached to physico-chemical manifestations, but it is true that the essential is not explained thereby; for no fortuitous coming together of physico-chemical phenomena constructs each organism after a plan and a fixed design (which are foreseen in advance) and arouses the admirable subordination and harmonious agreement of the acts of life. . . . Determinism can never be [anything] but physico-chemical determinism. The vital force and life belong to the metaphysical world.

What is the *x*, this seemingly purposive agent, this "vital force," in organic phenomena? It is only in our lifetime that explanations have been advanced which deal adequately with this paradox.

The many dualistic, finalistic, and vitalistic philosophies of the past merely replaced the unknown *x* by a different unknown, *y* or *z*, for calling an unknown factor *entelechia* or *élan vital* is not an explanation. I shall not waste time showing how wrong most of these past attempts were. Even though some of the underlying observations of these conceptual schemes are quite correct, the supernaturalistic conclusions drawn from these observations are altogether misleading.

Where, then, is it legitimate to speak of purpose and purposiveness in nature, and where is it not? To this question we can now give a firm and unambiguous answer. An individual who—to use the language of the computer—has been "programmed" can act purposefully. Historical processes, however, can *not* act purposefully. A bird that starts its migration, an insect that selects its host plant, an animal that avoids a predator, a male that displays to a female—they all act purposefully because they have been programmed to do so. When I speak of the programmed "individual," I do so in a broad sense. A programmed computer itself is an "individual" in this sense, but so is, during reproduction, a pair of birds whose instinctive and learned actions and interactions obey, so to speak, a single program.

The completely individualistic and yet also species-specific DNA code of every zygote (fertilized egg cell), which controls the development of the central and peripheral nervous systems, of the sense organs, of the hormones, of physiology and morphology, is the *program* for the behavior computer of this individual.

Natural selection does its best to favor the production of codes guaranteeing behavior that increases fitness. A behavior program that guarantees instantaneous correct reaction to a potential food source, to a potential enemy, or to a potential mate will certainly give greater fitness in the Darwinian sense than a program that lacks these properties. Again, a behavior program that allows for appropriate learning and the improvement of behavior reactions by various types of feedbacks gives greater likelihood of survival than a program that lacks these properties.

The purposive action of an individual, insofar as it is based on the properties of its genetic code, therefore is no more nor less purposive than the actions of a computer that has been programmed to respond appropriately to various inputs. It is, if I may say so, a purely mechanistic purposiveness.

We biologists have long felt that it is ambiguous to designate such programmed, goal-directed behavior "teleological," because the word *teleological* has also been used in a very different sense, for the final stage in evolutionary adaptive processes. When Aristotle spoke of final causes he was particularly concerned with the marvelous adaptations found throughout the plant and animal kingdom. He was concerned with what later authors have called design or plan in nature. He ascribed to final causes not only mimicry or symbiosis but all the other adaptations of animals and plants to each other and to their physical environment. The Aristotelians and their successors asked themselves what goal-directed process could have produced such a well-ordered design in nature.

It is now evident that the terms *teleology* and *teleological* have been applied to two entirely different sets of phenomena. On one hand is the production and perfecting throughout the history of the animal and plant kingdoms of ever-new programs and of ever-improved DNA codes of information. On the other hand there is the testing of these programs and the decoding of these codes throughout the lifetime of each individual. There is a fundamental difference between, on the one hand, end-directed behavioral activities or developmental processes of an individual or system, which are controlled by a program, and, on the other hand, the steady improvement of genetic codes. This genetic improvement is evolutionary adaptation controlled by natural selection.

In order to avoid confusion between the two entirely different types of end direction, Pittendrigh (6) has introduced the term *teleonomic* as a descriptive term for all end-directed systems "not committed to Aristotelian teleology." Not only does this negative definition place the entire burden on the word *system*, but it makes no clear distinction between the two teleologies of Aristotle. It would seem useful to restrict the term *teleonomic* rigidly to systems operating on the basis of a program, a code of information. Teleonomy in biology designates "the apparent purposefulness of organisms and their characteristics," as Julian Huxley expressed it (7).

Such a clear-cut separation of teleonomy, which has an analyzable physicochemical basis, from teleology, which deals more broadly with the over-all harmony of the organic world, is most useful because these two entirely different phenomena have so often been confused with each other.

The development or behavior of an individual is purposive, natural selection is definitely not. When MacLeod (8) stated, "What is most challenging about Darwin, however, is his re-introduction of purpose into the natural world," he chose the wrong word. The word *purpose* is singularly inapplicable to evolutionary change, which is, after all, what Darwin was considering. If an organism is well adapted, if it shows superior fitness, this is not due to any purpose of its ancestors or of an outside agency, such as "Nature" or "God," who created a superior design or plan. Darwin "has swept out such finalistic teleology by the front door," as Simpson (9) has rightly said.

We can summarize this discussion by stating that there is no conflict between causality and teleonomy, but that scientific biology has not found any evidence that would support teleology in the sense of various vitalistic or finalistic theories (9, 10). All the so-called teleological systems which Nagel discusses (11) are actually illustrations of teleonomy.

The problem of prediction

The third great problem of causality in biology is that of prediction. In the classical theory of causality the touchstone of the goodness of a causal explanation was its predictive value. This view is still maintained in Bunge's modern classic (12): "A theory can predict to the extent to which it can describe and explain." It is evident that Bunge is a physicist; no biologist would have made such a statement. The theory of natural selection can describe and explain phenomena with considerable precision, but it cannot make reliable predictions, except through such trivial and meaningless circular statements as, for instance: "the fitter individuals will on the average leave more offspring." Scriven (13) has emphasized quite correctly that one of the most important contributions to philosophy made by the evolutionary theory is that it has demonstrated the independence of explanation and prediction.

Although prediction is not an inseparable concomitant of causality, every scientist is nevertheless happy if his causal explanations simultaneously have high predictive value. We can distinguish many categories of prediction in biological explanation. Indeed, it is even doubtful how to define "prediction" in biology. A competent zoogeographer can predict with high accuracy what animals will be found on a previously unexplored mountain range or island. A paleontologist likewise can predict with high probability what kind of fossils can be expected in a newly accessible geological horizon. Is such correct guessing of the results of past events genuine prediction? A similar doubt pertains to taxonomic predictions, as discussed in the next paragraph. The term *prediction* is, however, surely legitimately used for future events. Let me give you four examples to illustrate the range of predictability.

1. *Prediction in classification.* If I have identified a fruit fly as an individual of *Drosophila melanogaster* on the basis of bristle pattern and the proportions of face and eye, I can "predict" numerous structural and behavioral characteristics which I will find if I study other aspects of this individual. If I find a new species with the diagnostic key characters of the genus *Drosophila*, I can at once "predict" a whole set of biological properties.

2. *Prediction of most physicochemical phenomena on the molecular level.* Predictions of very high accuracy can be made with respect to most biochemical unit processes in organisms, such as metabolic pathways, and with respect to biophysical phenomena in simple systems, such as the action of light, heat, and electricity in physiology.

In examples 1 and 2 the predictive value of causal statements is usually very high. Yet there are numerous other generalizations or causal statements in biology that have low predictive values. The following examples are of this kind.

3. *Prediction of the outcome of complex ecological interactions.* The statement, "An abandoned pasture in southern New England will be replaced by a stand of grey birch (*Betula populifolia*) and white pine (*Pinus strobus*)" is often correct. Even more often, however, the replacement may be an almost solid stand of *P. strobus*, or *P. strobus* may be missing altogether and in its stead will be cherry (*Prunus*), red cedar (*Juniperus virginianus*), maples, sumac, and several other species.

Another example also illustrates this unpredictability. When two species of flour beetles (*Tribolium confusum* and *T. castaneum*) are brought together in a uniform environment (sifted wheat flour), one of the two species will always displace the other. At high temperatures and humidities, *T. castaneum* will win out; at low temperatures and humidities, *T. confusum* will be the victor. Under intermediate conditions the outcome is indeterminate and hence unpredictable (Table 1) (14).

4. *Prediction of evolutionary events.* Probably nothing in biology is less predictable than the future course of evolution. Looking at the Permian reptiles, who would have predicted that most of the more flourishing groups would become extinct (many rather rapidly), and that one of the most undistinguished branches would give rise to the mammals? Which student of the Cambrian fauna would have predicted the revolutionary changes in the marine life of the subsequent geological eras? Unpredictability also characterizes small-scale evolution. Breeders and students of natural selection have discovered again and again that independent parallel lines exposed to the same selection pressure will respond at different rates and with different correlated effects, none of them predictable.

As is true in many other branches of science, the validity of pre-

TABLE 1. Two species of Tribolium in competition [from Park (14)].

CONDITION		Replicas (No.)	VICTORIOUS SPECIES (NO. OF TRIALS)	
Temp. (°C)	Humidity (%)		*T. confusum*	*T. castaneum*
34	70	30		30
29	70	66	11	55
24	70	30	21	9
34, 29	30	60	53	7
24	30	20	20	

dictions for biological phenomena (except for a few chemical or physical unit processes) is nearly always statistical. We can predict with high accuracy that slightly more than 500 of the next 1000 newborns will be boys. We cannot predict the sex of a particular unborn child.

Reasons for indeterminacy in biology

Without claiming to exhaust all the possible reasons for indeterminacy, I can list four classes. Although they somewhat overlap each other, each deserves to be treated separately.

1. *Randomness of an event with respect to the significance of the event.* Spontaneous mutation, caused by an "error" in DNA replication, illustrates this cause for indeterminacy very well. The occurrence of a given mutation is in no way related to the evolutionary needs of the particular organism or of the population to which it belongs. The precise results of a given selection pressure are unpredictable because mutation, recombination, and developmental homeostasis are making indeterminate contributions to the response to this pressure. All the steps in the determination of the genetic contents of a zygote contain a large component of this type of randomness. What we have described for mutation is also true for crossing over, chromosomal segregation, gametic selection, mate selection, and early survival of the zygotes. Neither underlying molecular phenomena nor the mechanical motions responsible for this randomness are related to their biological effects.

2. *Uniqueness of all entities at the higher levels of biological integration.* In the uniqueness of biological entities and phenomena lies one of the major differences between biology and the physical sciences. Physicists and chemists often have genuine difficulty in understanding the biologist's stress of the unique, although such an understanding has been greatly facilitated by the developments in modern physics. If a physicist says "ice floats on water," his statement is true for any piece of ice and any body of water. The members of a class usually lack the individuality that is so characteristic of the organic world, where all individuals are unique; all stages in the life cycle are unique; all populations are unique; all species and higher categories are unique;

all interindividual contacts are unique; all natural associations of species are unique; and all evolutionary events are unique. Where these statements are applicable to man, their validity is self-evident. However, they are equally valid for all sexually reproducing animals and plants. Uniqueness, of course, does not entirely preclude prediction. We can make many valid statements about the attributes and behavior of man, and the same is true for other organisms. But most of these statements (except for those pertaining to taxonomy) have purely statistical validity. Uniqueness is particularly characteristic for evolutionary biology. It is quite impossible to have for unique phenomena general laws like those that exist in classical mechanics.

3. *Extreme complexity.* The physicist Elsässer stated in a recent symposium: "[an] outstanding feature of all organisms is their well-nigh unlimited structural and dynamical complexity." This is true. Every organic system is so rich in feedbacks, homeostatic devices, and potential multiple pathways that a complete description is quite impossible. Furthermore, the analysis of such a system would require its destruction and would thus be futile.

4. *Emergence of new qualities at higher levels of integration.* It would lead too far to discuss in this context the thorny problem of "emergence." All I can do here is to state its principle dogmatically: "When two entities are combined at a higher level of integration, not all the properties of the new entity are necessarily a logical or predictable consequence of the properties of the components." This difficulty is by no means confined to biology, but it is certainly one of the major sources of indeterminacy in biology. Let us remember that indeterminacy does not mean lack of cause, but merely unpredictability.

All four causes of indeterminacy, individually and combined, reduce the precision of prediction.

One may raise the question at this point whether predictability in classical mechanics and unpredictability in biology are due to a difference of degree or of kind. There is much to suggest that the difference is, in considerable part, merely a matter of degree. Classical mechanics is, so to speak, at one end of a continuous spectrum, and biology is at the other. Let us take the classical example of the gas laws. Essentially they are only statistically true, but the population of molecules in a gas obeying the gas laws is so enormous that the actions of individual molecules become integrated into a predictable — one might say "absolute" — result. Samples of five or 20 molecules would show definite individuality. The difference in the size of the studied "populations" certainly contributes to the difference between the physical sciences and biology.

Conclusions

Let us now return to our initial question and try to summarize some of our conclusions on the nature of the cause-and-effect relations in biology.

1. Causality in biology is a far cry from causality in classical mechanics.

2. Explanations of all but the simplest biological phenomena usually consist of sets of causes. This is particularly true for those biological phenomena that can be understood only if their evolutionary history is also considered. Each set is like a pair of brackets which contains much that is unanalyzed and much that can presumably never be analyzed completely.

3. In view of the high number of multiple pathways possible for most biological processes (except for the purely physicochemical ones) and in view of the randomness of many of the biological processes, particularly on the molecular level (as well as for other reasons), causality in biological systems is not predictive, or at best is only statistically predictive.

4. The existence of complex codes of information in the DNA of the germ plasm permits teleonomic purposiveness. On the other hand, evolutionary research has found no evidence whatsoever for a "goal-seeking" of evolutionary lines, as postulated in that kind of teleology which sees "plan and design" in nature. The harmony of the living universe, so far as it exists, is an a posteriori product of natural selection.

Finally, causality in biology is not in real conflict with the causality of classical mechanics. As modern physics has also demonstrated, the causality of classical mechanics is only a very simple, special case of causality. Predictability, for instance, is not a necessary component of causality. The complexities of biological causality do not justify embracing nonscientific ideologies, such as vitalism or finalism, but should encourage all those who have been trying to give a broader basis to the concept of causality.

References and Notes

1. E. Nagel, lecture presented at the Massachusetts Institute of Technology in the 1960–61 Hayden Lectures series.
2. M. Delbrück, *Trans. Conn. Acad. Arts Sci.,* 38, 173 (1949).
3. J. Loeb, *The Organism as a Whole* (Putnam, New York, 1916).
4. M. Scriven, unpublished manuscript.
5. C. Bernard, *Leçons sur les phénomènes de la vie* (1885), vol 1.
6. C. S. Pittendrigh, in *Behavior and Evolution,* A. Roe and G. G. Simpson, Eds. (Yale Univ. Press, New Haven, Conn., 1958), p. 394.
7. J. Huxley, *Zool. Jahrb. Abt. Anat. u. Ontog. Tiere,* 88, 9 (1960).
8. R. B. MacLeod, *Science,* 125, 477 (1957).
9. G. G. Simpson, *ibid.,* 131, 966 (1960).
10. ———, *Sci. Monthly,* 71, 262 (1950); L. F. Koch, *ibid.,* 85, 245 (1957).
11. E. Nagel, *The Structure of Science* (Harcourt, Brace and World, Inc., New York, 1961).
12. M. Bunge, *Causality* (Harvard Univ. Press, Cambridge, Mass. 1959), p. 307.
13. M. Scriven, *Science,* 130, 477 (1959).
14. T. Park, *Physiol. Zoöl.,* 27, 177 (1954).

BIOLOGY AND THE NATURE OF SCIENCE

George Gaylord Simpson

. . . .

The straying physical sciences

. . . The first sciences, as we now strictly define science, were physical sciences. That was at a time when scientists considered themselves to be also, or even primarily, philosophers, and indeed "natural philosophy" was long synonymous with "physics." The tradition has persisted. It has been reinforced by the reductionist half-truth (of which more later) that all phenomena are ultimately explicable in strictly physical terms. Another factor has been the prestige accruing from the thorough and more obvious impingement of the physical sciences on daily life through technology. It is also possible that more of the most brilliant and thoughtful minds have gone into the physical sciences; I prefer not to think so, but I suspect there is some truth in that.

The point here is that most considerations of the history, methods, and nature of science have been heavily biased by concentration on physical science and not on science as a whole. That has been notably true of concepts of scientific laws, of predictability, of the testing of hypotheses, and of causality. Francis Bacon warned, "Though there are many things in nature which are singular and unmatched, yet it

Abridged from *This View of Life*, © 1963, 1964, by George Gaylord Simpson. Reprinted by permission of Harcourt, Brace & World, Inc.

[the human understanding] devises for them parallels and conjugates and relatives which do not exist." Nineteenth-century physicists did not heed his warning. They refused to consider the unique object or event and assumed that all phenomena could be reduced to supposedly invariable and universal laws such as the gas laws or the law of gravitation. It followed that, once a law was known, its consequences could be fully predicted. The consequences deduced from a hypothesis became predictions as to what would happen if an experiment were performed, and that is the pertinent test embodied in Pearson's, and still in Conant's (and many others'), descriptions of scientific method. It further followed—or the physical scientists thought it did—that when a law successfully predicted an event, the law explained the event as a result and specified its causes.

Here we in the 20th century have seen something curious and indeed almost comic happen. Physicists have found that some, at least, of their laws are not invariable; that their predictions are statistical and not precise; that some observations cannot in fact be made; and that absolute confirmation by testing of a hypothesis therefore cannot be obtained. Many have gone further and concluded that causality is meaningless and even that order in nature—the last *scientific* relic of our Greek heritage—has disappeared. That is, of course, the so-called scientific revolution wrought by quantum theory and the principle of indeterminacy. The physicists' reactions to this (even in my very limited knowledge of them) ran the gamut from reason to hysteria. Some—Bridgman is a sad example—found science coming apart in their hands, further scientific knowledge impossible, and the universe and existence itself left wholly meaningless. Others, such as Jeans, also accepted the whole idea of orderlessness and acausality but, with almost mystical glee, likened the release from physical law to release from prison. Still others, with Schrödinger, have had what seems both the most mature and the most scientific reaction: they have concluded that the physicists have failed somewhere and that there must be some rational way to get over the difficulty.

The aspect that I spoke of as almost comic is this: well before the "revolution" life scientists had observed that laws, in the rigid 19th-century conception of physics, do not apply to many phenomena in nature. Further, they knew that prediction (not the only way of testing hypotheses) is commonly statistical and no less scientific or confirmatory of a hypothesis for all that. They knew that this is no contradiction of the orderliness of nature, and they discerned that only an unnecessarily restricted concept of causality is affected. The "revolution" was a revolution only for those who had insisted that everything must be explained ultimately in terms of classical physics—and where were there ever any real grounds for such a narrow view of science? It is true that understanding of statistical law and polymodal causality had crept over the life scientists gradually, so that the impact of these concepts was not seen as revolutionary. It is also true that not many biologists are given to exploring the philosophical implications of their science. There was therefore little really clear discussion of causality in biology before that by Ernst Mayr in 1961.

Self-testing in science

A fundamental, though not a sufficient, criterion of the self-testability of science is repeatability. Norman Campbell's definition of science as "the study of those judgments concerning which universal agreement can be obtained" emphasizes this point. That is indeed not so much a definition of science as of its field and its connection with reality. Campbell's meaning is that the data of science are observations that can be repeated by any normal person. That is as true of, say, the observation of a fossil tooth under a microscope as it is of the height of mercury in a tube in Torricelli's famous experiment, or of more recent observations of protein separation by chromatography and electrophoresis. Illusion, even to the point of hallucination, is always a possibility, but it is one that can be eliminated for all practical purposes by repetition of observations, especially by different observers and different methods. It is also true that unique events occur, but evidence on them is acceptable if there is confidence that anyone in a position to observe them would have observed them.

In what used to be called the exact sciences, which have turned out not to be so exact, it was formerly assumed that uniform phenomena had absolute constants measurable to any degree of accuracy. As a very simple example, the length and period of a pendulum were assumed to have an infinitely exact and determinable value. It now appears that this is not necessarily true, and that is one of the discoveries that so upset the physical scientists. But in the actual practice of observation it has always been evident that infinitely exact measurement is impossible. All that repetition and instrumental refinement can do is to generate a degree of confidence that a measurement (at any given time and under given conditions) lies within a certain range. Inference from the observation takes into account the size of the range and the degree of confidence. The conclusion that even in principle the range cannot be infinitely small and confidence infinitely great makes no difference operationally, at least.

It is further true that with many phenomena the whole point of observation is not an exact measurement or determination of occurrence but establishment (again to some degree of confidence) of a probability. The classical example is the tossing of a coin, and here the biologists' point is that we do *not* expect the probability of throwing heads to be exactly one-half. As modern scientists and not ancient Greeks, we are examining real, objective coins and not the Platonic idea of a coin. By repeated observation of a real coin, we can establish a high degree of confidence that the probability is in a certain range. If the range is large, it is likely to include the probability of one-half, but if the range is made small it is likely to exclude that a priori ideal. Analogous phenomena are very common in biology. For example, we do not expect an expanding population of flies to spread according to an exact law. We expect only to achieve confidence that the rate will be within a certain range of probability, or to construct a frequency distribution of rates. Discovery that Boyle's "law" has the same probabilistic nature neither surprises nor upsets us. We would expect it, because the molecules of gas, like the flies, are real individuals which, however alike they are in other respects, have had different histories. The Greeks could, but a scientist cannot, be concerned with the ideal gas of classical physics. Perhaps the revolution in physics was only the final severing of the umbilical cord from ancient Greece.

The most widespread and conclusive process of self-testing in science is testing by multiplication of relevant observations. In the natural sciences it is impossible to prove anything in the absolute sense of, for example, a proof in mathematics. Multiplication of observations can only increase our confidence within a narrowing range of probability. If confidence becomes sufficiently great and the range is encompassed by the hypothesis, we begin to call the hypothesis a theory, and we accept it and go on from there. The test is, of course, whether the range of probability is in fact within the scope of the hypothesis — in other words, whether the observations are consistent with the hypothesis.

A key word in the expression "multiplication of relevant observations" is *relevant*. The simplest definition is that relevant observations are those that could *disprove* the hypothesis, for disproof is often possible even though absolute proof is not. The more observations fail to disprove a hypothesis, the greater the confidence in it. Prediction in the classical sense is a special case of that general procedure. From the hypothesis consequences are deduced such that their failure to occur would disprove the hypothesis. Of course their occurrence would not *prove* anything; it would only increase confidence. That this is in fact a special case and not the touchstone of scientific theory is easy to demonstrate. Again, examples are more familiar to biological than to physical scientists, although they occur in both fields. The most striking example is the most important of all biological theories: that of organic evolution. Although some quite limited predictions can be deduced from the theory, the theory was not in fact established by prediction and is not sufficiently tested by it. An enormous number of observations enormously varied in kind are all consistent with this theory, and many of them are consistent with no other theory that has been proposed. We therefore can and, if we are rational, must have an extremely high degree of confidence in the theory — higher than legitimate confidence in many things we call "facts" in daily life. That kind of nonpredictive testing most commonly occurs in fields that have a temporal or historical element, such as evolution among the biological sciences or the time-linked processes in geology among the physical sciences. In fact a neglected historical component also affects many physical laws, as in the example of the histories of the individual molecules in a gas.

Science and reality

. . . .

. . . The fact is that man originated by a slow process of evolution guided by natural selection. At every stage in this long progression our ancestors necessarily had adaptive reactions to the world around them. As behavior and sense organs became more complex, perception of sensations from those organs obviously maintained a realistic relationship to the environment. To put it crudely but graphically, the monkey who did not have a realistic perception of the tree branch he jumped for was soon a dead monkey — and therefore did not become one of our ancestors. Our perceptions do give true, even though not complete, representations of the outer world because that was and is a biological necessity, built into us by natural selection. If it were not so, we would not be here! We do now reach perceptions for which our ancestors had no need, for example, of x-rays or electrical potentials, but we do so by translating them into modalities that are evolution-tested.

Biological nature of science

That is one of the several senses in which science itself, as a whole, is fundamentally biological. A second sense in which that is true is involved in another point that has lately been bothering the physicists. The point is that whenever a scientist observes anything he is himself part of the system in which the observing takes place. He therefore should not assume that what he observes would be exactly the same if he were not observing it. But he cannot very well observe what happens when he is not observing! Therefore, the argument runs (but personally I do not run with it), there is no such thing as objective knowledge, and the goals of science are wholly delusive. Some atomic physicists say this does not matter as far as the man-sized world is concerned but matters only when you get down to their invisible, but all too obviously not imaginary, objects of study. Yet I really do not see why size matters in principle. In either case the system actually observed contains something alive — to wit (as a minimum), the observer. Surely it would never occur to anyone but an atomic physicist that because a system includes something alive it cannot be properly studied!

To suppose that study, to be objective, should exclude the observer is as unrealistic as Plato. Science is *man's* exploration of his universe, and to exclude himself even in principle is certainly not objective realism — unless you insist that his inclusion is subjective by definition, but that would be merely playing with words. And to say that we cannot learn anything materially factual about a situation if we ourselves are in it is utter and nonsensical negation of the very meaning of learning. The essential in objectivity is not the pretense of eliminating ourselves from a situation in which we are objectively present. It is that the situation should not be interpreted in terms of ourselves but that our roles should be interpreted realistically in terms of the situation. To a biologist the discovery (to call it such) that every system observed includes the observer has quite a simple meaning. It merely means that all systems in science have a biological component.

. . . .

Flight from teleology

. . . .

The doctrine of final cause, of the end's determining the means, was another essential element in Greek thought, which was anthropomorphic in a truly primitive way. This doctrine was probably an inevitable outcome of introspective and deductive philosophy. Rational human actions are largely explicable by their purpose, by the results they are expected to produce. It therefore seemed logical to conclude that the orderly intricacy of the world at large was in a similar way purposeful and governed by a foreseen end. Such concepts were particularly important to Aristotle, and through his works they came to be held as almost axiomatic in the western European milieu in which science finally arose. The broadly philosophical position was that things exist, or events occur, as prerequisites of their results, and that the result, as final cause, is the real principle of explanation. In more popular form, this view led to the belief that nature exists only for and in relation to man, considered as the ultimate purpose of creation or the overriding final cause.

As physical science became more objective, it was apparent that teleology, even if not rejected as a philosophy, had to be ignored as a means of scientific explanation. The scientist, as such, asked "What?" or "How?" about phenomena such as gravity or gas pressure, not "Why?" or "What for?" Description of how things fall, in terms of masses, distances, and gravitational constants, is clearly scientific, but the question, "What do things fall for?" seems unscientific. It elicits no objectively testable answers. It was thus inevitable that the strictest scientific attitude should endeavor to exclude any form of teleology, and in the physical sciences there seemed to be no great difficulty in excluding it. One could, at least, readily evade teleology by ascribing physical laws to a first rather than a final cause, although even here the usual philosophical or theological belief continued to be that natural laws exist in order to make the world a suitable habitat for man.

In the biological sciences the elimination or even the brushing aside of crude teleology was incomparably more difficult, and that is a principal reason why a fully scientific biology lagged so far behind a scientific physics. It is not necessary or perhaps even possible to see any immediate, inherent purpose in a stone's falling, but it is quite inevitable that an animal's seeking its food should be interpreted in terms of purpose or, at least, of an end served. All organisms are clearly adapted to live where and how they in fact live, and adapted in the most extraordinary, thoroughgoing, and complex ways. In fact they plainly have the adaptations in order to live as they do. The question, then, is how those key words *in order to* are to be interpreted. Until a century or so ago it occurred to very few naturalists to interpret them in any but the classical teleological way. For example, to Cuvier, high priest of natural history in the early 19th century, the validity of fully Aristotelian teleology seemed self-evident, and it was the heart of his theoretical system. Cuvier went all the way to a man-centered teleological conception of the universe. He could think of no better reason for the existence of fishes—which he considered poor things, even to the watery, unromantic nature of their *amours*—than that they provide food for man. That was also the period in England of Paley's *Natural Theology* and, later, of the Bridgewater *Treatises* "on the power, wisdom, and goodness of God, as manifested in the creation"—that is to say, on Christian teleology as a necessary and sufficient explanation of nature, and most particularly of animate nature.

The facts of adaptation *are* facts, and the purposeful aspect of organisms is incontrovertible. Even if the explanation offered by Aristotelian, and much later by what was then orthodox Christian, teleology were true, that would definitely be an article of faith and not of objectively testable science. Thus it was necessary either to conclude that there is no scientific explanation of organic adaptation or to provide an acceptable, testable hypothesis that was scientific. Before Darwin most biologists accepted the first alternative, which (although few of them realized this fact) meant quite simply that there could be no such thing as a fully scientific biology. It was Darwin, more than any other one person, who supplied the second alternative. In *The Origin of Species* he made no entirely clear distinction between establishing the fact that evolution has occurred and proposing a theory as to how natural processes could produce organic adaptation. He has therefore been accused of unnecessarily confusing two issues that should have been kept quite separate, but that was not really the case. Evolution itself becomes a nonscientific issue if the explanation of adaptation in the course of evolution is left in the field of metaphysics, philosophy, and theology. Darwin really went to the heart of the matter with unerring insight. Explanation of adaptation was the key point, and Darwin demonstrated, at the very least, that a natural, objective explanation of adaptation is a rational possibility and a legitimate scientific goal. That, at long last, made biology a true and complete science.

Darwin fully respected the appearances and made no attempt to save them by explaining them away. The hand of man, for example, *is* made for grasping. Darwin said so, and then provided a natural scientific explanation for the fact. He thus did not ignore the teleological aspects of nature but brought them into the domain of science. Some of Darwin's contemporaries and immediate successors recognized that fact by redefining teleology as the study of adaptation and by pointing out that Darwin had substituted a scientific teleology for a philosophical or theological one. The redefinition did not take. The older meanings of the word *teleology* were ineradicable, and they brought a certain scientific (although not necessarily philosophical) disrepute to the whole subject.

The physical scientists had earlier, and more completely, evaded the issues of classical teleology. By the end of the 19th century, if not before, it had become for them virtually a dogma that a scientist simply *must not* ask, "What for?" Physical scientists considered the question as applied to natural phenomena either completely meaningless or, at best, unanswerable in scientific terms. Such was the priority and primacy of the physical sciences that this position even came to be widely considered a necessary qualification of truly scientific endeavor, part of the definition of science. That led in turn to a very curious development that was at its height in the 1920's and is still exerting a strong but now more clandestine effect. Many biologists threw out the baby with the bath water. In seeking to get rid of nonscientific teleology they decided to throw out all the quite real and scientific problems that teleology had attempted to solve.

That took several different forms. One form in evolutionary studies was the mutationist belief that organisms do not become adapted to a way of life but simply adopt the way of life that their characteristics, originating at random, make possible. Another form was behaviorism, which also, in essence, sought to eliminate adaptation as a scientific problem by refusing to consider behavior as motivated, as goal-directed, or even as serving needs (and hence in some sense having purpose) in the organism as a whole. Behaviorism strove to be primarily descriptive, and what explanatory element was admitted was meant to be confined to consideration of the physiological substrates and concomitants of the behavior described. It is that latter aspect that still influences a considerable segment of opinion in biology, confining biological explanation to the physicist's question, "How?" and eschewing "What for?" This attitude, still strongly held in some quarters, involves the idea that scientific explanation must be reductionist, reducing all phenomena ultimately to the physical and the chemical. In application to biology, that leads to the quite extraordinary proposition that living organisms should be studied as test-tube reactions and that their being alive should enter into the matter as little as possible. As behaviorism omits the psyche from psychology, so this form of reductionism omits the bios from biology.

Explanation in biology

Those tendencies were unquestionably salutary in some respects. They have helped to elimate the last vestiges of pre-Darwinian teleology from biology. They have also helped to counteract vitalistic, metaphysical, and mystical ideas which, whatever one may think of them in their own sphere, are completely stultifying as principles of scientific explanation. Here, however, the reductionist tendency has been two-edged. By seeming to negate the very possibility of scientific explanation of purposive aspects of life, it has encouraged some biologists, who insist that such aspects nevertheless exist, to seek explanations quite outside the legitimate field of science. Naming of names is perhaps invidious, but to show that I am here setting up no straw man I will just mention Teilhard de Chardin in Europe and Sinnott in the United States.

The reaction went much too far. It went so far as to falsify the very nature of biology and of science through supine acceptance of a dictum that all science is in essence physical science. In fact, the life sciences are not only much more complicated than the physical sciences, they are also much broader in significance, and they penetrate much farther into the exploration of the universe that *is* science than do the physical sciences. They require and embrace the data and *all* the explanatory principles of the physical sciences and then go far beyond that to embody many other data and additional explanatory principles that are no less — that are, in a sense, even more — scientific.

This can be expressed, as Mayr, Pittendrigh, and others have expressed it, in terms of kinds of scientific explanations and kinds of questions that elicit them. "How?" is the typical question in the physical sciences. There it is often the only meaningful or allowable one. It must also always be asked in biology, and the answers can often be put in terms of the physical sciences. That is one kind of scientific explanation, a reductionist one as applied to biological problems: "How is heredity transmitted?" "How do muscles contract?" and so on through the whole enormous gamut of modern biophysics and biochemistry. But biology can and must go on from there. Here, "What for?" — the dreadful teleological question — not only is legitimate but also must eventually be asked about every vital phenomenon. In organisms, but not (in the same sense) in any nonliving matter, adaptation *does* occur. Heredity and muscle contraction do serve functions that are *useful* to organisms. They are not explained, in this aspect, by such answers to "How?" as that heredity is transmitted by DNA or that energy is released in the Krebs cycle.

In biology, then, a second kind of explanation must be added to the first or reductionist explanation made in terms of physical, chemical, and mechanical principles. This second form of explanation, which can be called compositionist in contrast with reductionist, is in terms of the adaptive usefulness of structures and processes to the whole organism and to the species of which it is a part, and still further, in terms of ecological function in the communities in which the species occurs. It is still scientifically meaningful to say that, for instance, a lion has its thoroughgoing adaptations to predation *because* they maintain the life of the lion, the continuity of its species, and the economy of its communities.

Such statements exclude the grosser, man-centered forms of teleology, but they still do not necessarily exclude a more impersonal philosophical teleology. A further question is necessary: "How does the lion happen to have these adaptive characteristics?" or, more generally and more colloquially, "How come?" This is another question that is usually inappropriate and does not necessarily elicit scientific answers as regards strictly physical phenomena. In biology it is both appropriate and necessary, and Darwin showed that it can here elicit truly scientific answers, which embody those that go before. The fact that the lion's characteristics are adaptive for lions has caused them to be favored by natural selection, and this in turn has caused them to be embodied in the DNA code of lion heredity. That statement, which of course summarizes a large body of more detailed information and principle, combines answers to all three questions: not only "How?" and "What for?" but also "How come?" Always in biology but not invariably in the physical sciences, a full explanation ultimately involves a historical — that is, an evolutionary — factor.

Here I should briefly clarify a point of possible confusion. Insistence that the study of organisms requires principles additional to those of the physical sciences does not imply a dualistic or vitalistic view of nature. Life, or the particular manifestation of it that we call mind, is not thereby necessarily considered as nonphysical or nonmaterial. It is just that living things have been affected for upward of 2 billion years by historical processes that are in themselves completely material but that do not affect nonliving matter, or at least do not affect it in the same way. Matter that was affected by these processes became, for that reason, living, and matter not so affected remained nonliving. The results of those processes are systems different in kind from any nonliving systems and almost incomparably more complicated. They are not for that reason necessarily any less material or less physical in nature. The point is that *all* known material processes and explanatory principles apply to organisms, while only a limited number of them apply to nonliving systems. And that leads to another point, my final one.

Unity of the sciences

. . . .

. . . In our own days, Einstein and others have sought unification of scientific concepts in the form of principles of increasing generality. The goal is a connected body of theory that might ultimately be *completely* general in the sense of applying to *all* material phenomena.

The goal is certainly a worthy one, and the search for it has been fruitful. Nevertheless, the tendency to think of it as *the* goal of science or *the* basis for unification of the sciences has been unfortunate. It is essentially a search for a least common denominator in science. It necessarily and purposely omits much the greatest part of science, hence can only falsify the nature of science and can hardly be the best basis for unifying the sciences. I suggest that both the characterization of science as a whole and the unification of the various sciences can be most meaningfully sought in quite the opposite direction, not through principles that apply to all phenomena but through phenomena to which all principles apply. Even in this necessarily summary discussion, I have, I believe, sufficiently indicated what those latter phenomena are: they are the phenomena of life.

Biology, then, is the science that stands at the center of all science. It is the science most directly aimed at science's major goal and most definitive of that goal. And it is here, in the field where all the principles of all the sciences are embodied, that science can truly become unified.

THE CONCEPT OF INTEGRATIVE LEVELS AND BIOLOGY

Alex B. Novikoff

The concept of integrative levels of organization is a general description of the evolution of matter through successive and higher orders of complexity and integration. It views the development of matter, from the cosmological changes resulting in the formation of the earth to the social changes in society, as continuous because it is never-ending, and as discontinuous because it passes through a series of different levels of organization—physical, chemical, biological and sociological.

In the continual evolution of matter, new levels of complexity are superimposed on the individual units by the organization and integration of these units into a single system. What were wholes on one level become parts on a higher one. Each level of organization possesses unique properties of structure and behavior which, though dependent on the properties of the constituent elements, appear only when these elements are combined in the new system. Knowledge of the laws of the lower level is necessary for a full understanding of the higher level; yet the unique properties of phenomena at the higher level can not be predicted, a priori, from the laws of the lower level. The laws describing the *unique* properties of each level are qualitatively distinct, and their discovery requires methods of research and analysis appropriate to the particular level. These laws express the new organizing relationships, *i.e.*, the reciprocal relationships of elementary units to each other and to the unit system as a whole.

The concept of integrative levels recognizes as equally essential

---

"The Concept of Integrative Levels and Biology," *Science*, CI (March 2, 1945), 209–215.

for the purpose of scientific analysis both the isolation of parts of a whole and their integration into the structure of the whole. It neither reduces phenomena of a higher level to those of a lower one, as in mechanism, nor describes the higher level in vague non-material terms which are but substitutes for understanding, as in vitalism. Unlike other "holistic" theories, it never leaves the firm ground of material reality. Integration does not imply, as Lillie has recently maintained, "special vital factors"[1] or "something of the mental or psychic."[2] Both parts and wholes are material entities, and integration results from the interaction of the parts, as a consequence of their properties. The concept points the need to study the organizational interrelationships of parts and whole. This full recognition of both units and whole leads to a more adequate understanding of the whole.

The different levels of matter, while distinct, are not completely delimited from each other. No boundary in nature is fixed and no category air-tight. "Mesoforms" are found at the transition point of one level of organization to the next. Between the highest level of organization of non-living, the crystal, and the lowest level of uni-cellular organisms are protein paracrystals, the viruses, with some of the internal structure and behavior of living substance. Between the single-cell organism and the multicellular organism are the colonial organisms. Yet the absence of rigid demarcation between two levels does not make the difference between them any less clear or fundamental. Mesoforms, "the more clearly we understand them, will all the more clearly serve to bring out the essentially new elements of (the) higher order."[3]

There is both continuity and discontinuity in the evolution of the universe; and consideration of one to the exclusion of the other acts to retard the development of biological and sociological sciences. Knowledge of the general qualities of development common to all levels of organization of matter will aid in the analysis and description of the concrete attributes of each level. But it can not be a substitute for such analysis or for the determination of the qualitative uniqueness of each level and the characteristic laws which govern it.

Physico-chemical and biological levels

The concept of integrative levels does not regard living organisms as machines made of a multitude of discrete parts (physico-chemical units), removable like pistons of an engine and capable of description without regard to the system from which they are removed. Its approach is one which biochemists are adopting more and more: living cells present problems not to be encountered in the test-tube or flask. The structural pattern of the cell plays a decisive role in many of the chemical reactions which constitute metabolism. The ordering, as well as speed, of the chemical reactions in the cell are largely the result of

1. Ralph S. Lillie, *The American Naturalist*, 72: 414, 1938.
2. Ralph S. Lillie, *Philosophy of Science*, 7: 327, 1940.
3. Joseph Needham, *The Modern Quarterly* (London), 1: 30, 1938.

the distribution and activity of colloidal enzymes. Korr[4] has indicated that even simple colloidal systems "represent a much higher level of integration . . . and that, because of the quantitative and qualitative modification which interfaces and their molecular groupings impose, there emerge new classes of phenomena for which there are no analogies in homogeneous systems, and which, therefore, require new sets of rules." Commoner[5] has discussed the increased dependence of enzyme function on structural factors in the living cell. The degree of dependence of a particular enzyme system on protoplasmic structure or physico-chemical organization can be revealed by changes in this structure, both natural and experimentally produced.

It has been the great contribution of the "organicists" that they have demonstrated the error of the mechanistic reduction of the biological organism to the physico-chemical. It is therefore unfortunate that "organicism" has been marred by non-material concepts. Organicists fail to picture the "whole" as developing through the integration of individual units of matter into a single system; they omit a discussion of the organizing relationships of the parts. They try to describe the behavior of the organism solely in terms of the higher level, the whole. As a result, the impression is created that no material basis exists for the part-whole relation.

Almost all the text-book definitions of physiology reduce phenomena of living matter, a highly complex and integrated system, to the level of free molecules and atoms. Certainly chemical and physical forces are operative in cells, yet defining physiology as "the physics and chemistry of life processes" overlooks the fact that the cell organization imposes a new and higher order on physico-chemical change, and that tissues, organs, organ-systems and organism impose a higher order on cell activity. Physiology rightly concerns itself also with the activities of the higher orders: cellular organization and function as well as chemistry and physics in the narrow sense; the tissue, organ, organ-system as well as the cell. No matter how complete our knowledge of the chemistry and physics of living systems becomes in the future, living substance must still be recognized as matter on a higher level, with new, unique properties which have emerged on combination of the lower-level units. When molecules become part of a highly integrated system, protoplasm, it is important to know the properties of the molecules, but protoplasmic behavior needs description in terms and laws which have no meaning for molecules, in specifically biological terms and laws.

Biological levels

Within the biological level, there are a series of other integrative levels.

In the multicellular organism there is a hierarchy of levels — cells, tissues, organs, organ-systems and organism. Viewed in terms of inte-

---

4. Irvin Korr, *Cold Spring Harbor Symposia*, 7: 74, 1939.
5. Barry Commoner, *Quarterly Review of Biology*, 17: 46, 1942.

grative levels, Heilbrunn's assertion that "general physiology thus becomes cellular physiology" and that "the ultimate mechanism responsible for any form of vital activity lies inherent in the individual cells"[6] is one-sided. A full understanding of the organism is not possible without complete knowledge of the activities of its cells. But knowledge of "the individual cells" does not exhaust the problems of organism physiology; the activity of the individual cell is greatly influenced by the products of activity of other cells in tissue, organ, organ-system and organism.

The inadequacy of a cell concept in which the cell is considered an independent unit of activity is clear from the work of experimental embryologists. The embryo is not a collection of unrelated portions developing independently of each other; on the contrary, the development of any cell is dependent not only on its own constitution but also on the nature of the surrounding materials outside the egg or produced in adjacent cells of the embryo. If ectoderm cells which normally form belly skin were removed from a salamander embryo and transplanted over the mouth organizer of a frog embryo, they would develop into salamander structures — of the mouth; they would form teeth and not belly skin.

Similarly, in the adult organism, plant or animal, the behavior of a cell is influenced by the activity of other cells of the body. Thus, the hormone, auxin, produced in the apical cells of a plant, will cause the elongation of stem cells, inhibit the growth of cells of lateral buds, influence the course of differentiation of root cells and stimulate the growth of cambium cells. Chiefly through such hormones, the cells of the plant body are integrated into an organism. In animals, the activity of cells is under the integrating influence of nerve impulses, hormones and other cell products like carbon dioxide. Activity of cells of the salivary glands is dependent upon stimulation by nerve impulses begun elsewhere in the body. The behavior of uterine cells depends not only on its own constitution, but also on hormones produced by cells of pituitary and ovary. Carbon dioxide produced by muscle cells in the legs will influence the behavior of the respiratory center cells in the medulla.

Just as cells do not exist in isolation in the organism, neither do organs or organ-systems. Thus, the functioning of the heart (the rate and force of its beat) is not unrelated to the pressure of the blood in the aorta and carotid arteries, the diameter of the arterioles or the amount of blood returning through the veins; nor is the circulatory system unaffected by or without effects on the nervous, endocrine, muscular or respiratory systems. Coghill,[7] using embryos, and Lashley[8] and Goldstein,[9] studying adult animals and men, have demonstrated the weakness of an atomistic approach to the activity of the nervous system and have emphasized that it functions as an integrated whole.

---

6. L. V. Heilbrunn, "An Outline of General Physiology," pp. 3, 4. Philadelphia, 1943.
7. G. E. Coghill, *Science*, 78: 131, 1933.
8. K. S. Lashley, "Brain Mechanisms and Intelligence." Chicago, 1929.
9. Kurt Goldstein, "The Organism." New York, 1939.

Populations constitute a distinct level of integration, higher than that of the individual organism. Schneirla, in his excellent studies on the interrelations between individual behavior of the army-ant and the population unit or colony, stresses this point. "Any social organization represents a qualitatively new emergent level not equivalent to that which might be attained through a mere summation of the properties of its constituent individuals."[10a] It is solely the reactions of the individual ant which are responsible for the highly organized mass behavior; yet "strictly speaking, the Eciton worker has no behavior pattern outside the social sphere."[10b]

Dobzhansky, in his authoritative work on population genetics, similarly describes populations as higher levels of integration. The fate of a newly-arisen genetic variant depends not alone on its effect on the individual organism but also upon the "dynamic regularities of the physiology of populations." Thus, it is the effective size of a population which may determine whether a useless or even deleterious mutant will, through chance recombinations, become incorporated into the constitution of the group. The smaller this population size the less effective is selective pressure in evolution. Dobzhansky emphasizes that evolutionary changes are changes in the genetic constitution of groups — of populations. Through natural selection, migration, and isolation, biological groups are produced whose genetic structure is molded in relation to the environment. The laws of population genetics which describe these evolutionary changes are on a higher level than those of the genetics of the individual. "The rules governing the genetic structure of a population are, nevertheless, distinct from those governing the genetics of individuals, just as rules of sociology are distinct from physiological ones, although they are in fact merely integrated forms of the latter."[10c]

The concept of integrative levels stresses the need to study living organisms at all levels — cells, tissues, organs, organ-systems, organisms and populations. It is not "organicist"; always the reciprocal relationship of elementary units to each other and to the unit system as a whole must be studied. It is not mechanistic; the detailed methods of study at higher levels will include not only some used at lower levels but new methods peculiar to the higher levels; the laws of one level will be expressed differently from those of the others.

Biological and social levels

According to the concept of integrative levels, man's social relationships represent a new level, higher than that of his biological make-up. Man's behavior differs from that of other animals because of his possession of body structures, notably, the highly developed nervous system, which make thought and speech possible and whose functioning

---

10. (a) T. C. Schneirla, *Psychological Review*, 48: 465, 1941; (b) *idem*, *The Journal of Comparative Psychology*, 29: 447, 1940; (c) Theodosius Dobzhansky, "Genetics and the Origin of Species," p. 11. New York, 1941; (d) Francis H. Bartlett, "Sigmund Freud," p. 80. London, 1938.

is profoundly affected by social or cultural influences. Man possesses a unique head and hand, and is able to confront nature not only with his body but with tools devised and wielded by him. The crude tools of primitives give way to the more complex technology characteristic of modern society. As the technological forces change, the social and economic relations of men change, and, with them, man's behavior. Socio-economic or cultural forces thus come to dominate biological factors in directing man's actions.

In a penetrating analysis of Sigmund Freud's failure to recognize the inseparability of the biological and the cultural forces which determine man's behavior, Bartlett writes,

> The biological organism, by its existence in society, has become a "new biological species." . . . The biological organism is transformed; it no longer exists as a biological phenomenon, strictly speaking. Under the influence of society, the biological has become the psychological. New laws of motion have come into being which are neither biological nor sociological, but the subject of study of a different science, psychology.[10d]

The concept of integrative levels, as it stresses the need to study the interrelationships between the biological and sociological, emphasizes the fact that the two constitute two distinct levels. Blurring this distinction leads to anthropomorphism and to mystical, often dangerous, statements about society.

Anthropomorphism — endowing animals, and even plants, with human attributes, psychical and social — transports the higher level (social) bodily into the lower level (biological). In doing so, it presents a wholly erroneous picture of the animal. The aspects of behavior common to man and animals are studied in comparative psychology, just as comparative cytology studies the uniformity of structure of diverse cells and comparative biochemistry the fundamental chemical changes common to all cells and organisms. Often, the significance of certain aspects of man's behavior (*e.g.,* instincts) can be illuminated by studies on lower animals where the problem may be analyzed more directly. And in the anthropoid apes, it is possible to investigate the beginning of reflective thought and of social influences on behavior.

Yet the study of animal behavior can not be a substitute for the study of man's behavior. As we establish the likenesses in behavior of animals and men, we must simultaneously investigate the fundamental qualitative differences between them. Except in certain pathological conditions, man's behavior is as unique as the organs which he, alone of all animals, possesses; thought, speech, labor are impossible without a highly developed brain and a hand. It is his unique biological constitution which makes possible the development of truly social relations among men. Many investigators studying the integrated animal populations, the so-called societies of animals, appear to have overlooked the fact that animal societies never rise above the biological level, that only man's society is truly sociological.

Any one who has tried to teach biological change to college students

knows the barriers to learning which have been created by the identification of animals with men throughout the student's lifetime. Every
phenomenon is approached by them in terms of human experience.
There is no time scale other than the clock, calendar or century. Yet
important biological change can be expressed only in a "non-human"
time scale. For each living organism travels at two enormously different
speeds of life.[11] The comparatively rapid one is easy to comprehend
because the changes can be observed; the birth, growth and death of
the body, the movement of the plant on the window sill, and even the
less obvious chemical changes of cells and organisms. But only the end
results of changes over many thousands of centuries can be seen in the
diverse plants and animals, each almost perfectly adapted to its environment. A species, in high-speed terms, is constant; but in low-speed
terms, it is changing.

Thinking in high-speed terms of these low-speed phenomena leads
almost inevitably to teleological conceptions, ascribing these phenomena to a divine purpose in nature. The terrestrial mammal has
no gills because the air, containing little water, would dry out the exposed soft tissues; the earthworm has no eyes because it has no need for
them, buried as it is in the ground. Such teleological reasoning is carried
over even to changes which are directly observable. The heart beats
in order to bring food-laden blood to all cells of the organism. The
leaf bends to the light in order to intercept more energy for photosynthesis. There is no awareness that ascribing such purposive behavior to
the heart or the plant imparts the ability to reason and to look into the
future, in one case to a small individual part of the organism, and, in
the other, to an organism which lacks a nervous system, let alone a brain!

The history of biology demonstrates that teleology explains nothing,
and, worse still, hampers the search for explanations and causes. You
do not study the causal development of eyes in worms if you believe
their absence in earthworms is explained by the statement that under-
ground worms need none. Nor do you trouble to analyze the causes of
cardiac muscle contraction or the distribution of plant growth hormones if it suffices to say that the heart beats to pump blood and the
leaf bends to get light. You do not study the causes of evolution or
the explanation of mutual adaptation of organism and environment
if you assert, as Gerard has recently, that the "selection or creation of
these particular mechanisms" is volitional or purposive.[12] Only when
purpose was excluded from descriptions of all biological activity
except rational behavior of human beings, could biological problems
be properly formulated and analyzed.

Critique of some biological literature on integrative levels

In a recent volume devoted to the concept of integrative levels,[13]

---

11. Henry Collier, "An Interpretation of Biology," Chapter 5. London, 1938.
12. Ralph W. Gerard, "Organic Freedom," p. 425, in "Freedom, Its Meaning," edited
by R. N. Anshen. New York, 1940, *Scientific Monthly*, 50: 349, 1940.
13. Biological Symposia, VIII. "Levels of Integration in Biological and Social
Sciences," edited by R. Redfield. Lancaster, 1942.

a number of serious errors occur. These errors stem from a tendency to concentrate exclusively on the continuity of development of matter from low to high levels. While the "organicists" concentrate their attention exclusively on the uniqueness of the biological level ("the organism as a whole") without relating it to the lower levels, this tendency is preoccupied with the general similarity of organizational development in evolution to the exclusion of any consideration of the uniqueness of each level. This overemphasis of the continuity of evolution leads to the confusion of biological and sociological levels.

A. E. Emerson acknowledges the distinction between biological and social sciences but then says, "Society is surely a manifestation of fundamental life attributes which are shared with other biological systems and the division between the social and non-social is not sharp."[14] Elsewhere, he maintains that "the evolution of human social and ethical characteristics is governed by the same forces which have been directing organismic evolution through the ages."[15] However, the material in Emerson's articles reveals the basic difference between the forces making for change in human society and those producing changes in "organismic evolution." There has apparently been no important change in the society of insects in the thirty-five million years since the Oligocene period. Since insects possess neither intelligence nor the ability to transmit the results of experience to others, change is dependent on the slow process of germinal change (mutation) and their society is therefore relatively fixed. On the other hand, in the seven or eight thousand years of recorded history, man's society has continually changed; because of the transmission of experience symbolized by tools, language, printing, photography, etc., there is social-cultural inheritance as well as biological inheritance. It is the plasticity of man's intelligence which brings ethics into being.

While man's social relations have undergone marked transformation, his biology has remained essentially unchanged. What small biological change has occurred (*e.g.,* increased mean length of life) has been the result and not the cause of social development. The "forces . . . governing . . . human social and ethical characteristics" have been not biological but social, the relation of man to changing technological and economic relations. The "forces . . . governing . . . organismic evolution through the ages" have been biological (mutation, etc.). That is why whatever similarities one notes in animal and human societies must be purely formal and therefore meaningless.

Gerard accepts the old analogy between society and the living organism and, by what Simpson has aptly described as the "most reckless, unjustified, and non-scientific extrapolation,"[16] he draws a great many parallels between aspects of society and organisms. Thus, he equates scientists with receptors,[17] the formation of an army by a nation with the fusion of slime molds in the face of "emergency

---

14. Alfred E. Emerson, "Basic Comparisons of Human and Insect Societies," p. 173, in Redfield, *op. cit.*

15. Alfred E. Emerson, Abstract 21423, in *Biological Abstracts*, vol. 16, 1942.

16. George G. Simpson, *Journal of the Washington Academy of Sciences*, 31: 18, 1941.

17. R. W. Gerard, "Higher Levels of Integration," p. 79, in Redfield, *op. cit.*

conditions,"[18] altruism of men with "service and mutual helpfulness seen in the interplay of cell nucleus and chloroplast,"[19] and so on. It is unnecessary to enumerate all the parallels. In every one of them, the social activities for which Gerard finds biological counterparts are not of biological origin but are the results of long processes of social development. We can not overlook the fact that the origin of social integrations of rational men in society is fundamentally distinct from that of biological integration of masses of protoplasm in the living organism. Aside from its refinement in terms of modern biological data, the organism-society analogy of Gerard is the same as that of Herbert Spencer in which, Needham has pointed out, instead of seeking the economic basis of social relations, he "elaborates to a degree sometimes almost fantastic the analogy between animal and social organisms."[20]

Just as the striking but fundamentally misleading analogy between living organisms and non-living engines has stimulated both mechanical and vitalistic biology, so this organism-society analogy leads to erroneous and dangerous social conclusions as well as to anthropomorphism.[21] Because he fails to distinguish the social from the biological, Gerard[22] is led to formulate a single principle to govern the entire historical process from the origin of molecules to the development of human society, the progressive growth of cooperation and altruism. By oversimplifying phenomena and divesting each level of organization, among organisms and in society, of its specific characteristic qualities, a metaphysical statement is produced, to the effect that society will inevitably—because it is an organism—progress toward a cooperative state. "The ultimate future of society, however dark it may look to the contemporary sociologist or even to the historian, appears in the eyes of the biologist, sighting down the long perspective of organic evolution, as bright with hope."

It should be remembered that even in the biological world, evolution is not always in the direction of progress—witness the "regression" of the tapeworm. We can not afford to take refuge in Gerard's idea of a mysteriously operating "organizing trend"[23] which will insure the steady march of progress for man's society. Such evolutionary fatalism is unsound science, and dangerous social advice for it leads only to inaction. Fortunately, the United Nations are not guided by such fatalism; they are relying not on any "trend," but on their armed might, in order to defeat fascism and keep society on the road of progress.

---

18. *Idem*, "Higher Levels of Integration," p. 81.

19. *Idem*, "A Biological Basis for Ethics," p. 108, *Philosophy of Science*, vol. 9, 1942.

20. Joseph Needham, *The Modern Quarterly* (London), 1: 38, 1938.

21. Needham, Huxley and Simpson have noted that even the formal aspect of the organism-society analogy is erroneous because it overlooks the fundamental differences between organism and society in: (1) the degree of concentration of consciousness in specialized parts, (2) the degree of differentiation arising during reproduction (of individuals in society and of cells in organisms), (3) the mode of reproduction and inheritance, and (4) the degree of subordination of individual parts to the whole.

22. R. W. Gerard, "Higher Levels of Integration," pp. 83–85.

23. *Idem*, "A Biological Basis for Ethics," p. 108.

Despite occasional backward movements and many blind alleys, biological evolution has moved in the direction of progress—towards more and more highly integrated and efficient organisms in which there is an increasing independence of and control over the external environment. This is to be explained on the basis of phenomena such as genetic mutations and natural selection. We may agree that, despite more or less temporary setbacks, society will develop eventually to a high level of cooperation. But it will do so not because of "organizing trends," mutations or natural selection. Discussion of social evolution in terms of natural selection as it applies in the biological world is no more meaningful than metaphysics, for, as we have indicated, without a study of man's socio-economic relations, it is impossible either to explain the past history or to indicate the prospects for the future development of society. Progress in social development is basically different from progress in organic evolution; the latter does not involve conscious activity, the former, depending on scientific and technological advance, is the result of conscious activity of men and is directed by experience of life and study of history. Progress in organic evolution occurs without a set plan or direction; social progress rests upon planned activity of men. As Huxley says, human progress "is not inevitable; man . . . must work and plan if he is to achieve further progress for himself and so for life."[24]

Needham[25] has demonstrated that the most dangerous aspect of the reduction of social phenomena to the biological level, at the present historical moment, is the basis it provides for fascist "philosophy." The central point in this "philosophy" is the thesis that man's biology decides his social behavior, and ruthless oppression of certain groups of people is justified because these groups are for all times fixed as "inferior" by their biology. Gerard's view gives indirect support to this thesis, by making biological principles the guide for social thought and action.

A sharp separation of the two levels—biological and social—must precede a fruitful discussion of how man's society can be kept free and democratic. That discussion must be based on a study, by means appropriate to the level, of the social forces making for change. Only a scientific analysis of these forces will enable man to speed social progress.

It is perhaps not surprising that Gerard's one-sided view of evolution —which ignores the qualitative differences of successive levels of integration and the specific part-whole relationships in each—should lead him to embrace the concept of purpose.[26] The retarding influence of teleological thinking on the advance of biological science has already been referred to. Here we add our agreement with Huxley that any "apparent purpose" in evolution is "just as much a product of blind forces as is the falling of a stone to earth or the ebb and flow of the tides. It is we who have read purpose into evolution, as earlier men projected will and emotion into inorganic phenomena like storm or earthquake.

---

24. Julian Huxley, "Evolution, The Modern Synthesis," p. 578. New York, 1942.
25. Joseph Needham, Foreword to Prenant, "Biology and Marxism." New York, 1938.
26. See references, note 13.

If we wish to work towards a purpose for the future of man, we must formulate that purpose ourselves. Purposes in life are made, not found."[27]

Conclusion

The concept of integrative levels describes the progress of evolution of the inanimate, animate and social worlds. It maintains that such progress is the result of forces which differ in each level and which can properly be described only by laws which are unique for each level. Since higher level phenomena always include phenomena at lower levels, one can not fully understand the higher levels without an understanding of the lower level phenomena as well. But a knowledge of the lower levels does not enable us to predict, *a priori*, what will occur at a higher level. Although some may have validity for the higher level, laws of a lower level are inadequate to describe the higher level. The laws unique to the higher level can be discovered by approaches appropriate to the particular level; to do otherwise is invalid scientifically and, in some instances, dangerous socially.

By stressing the material interrelationships of parts and whole and the qualitative uniqueness of each level of integration, the concept is of genuine help to biologists. Its dialectical approach avoids "organicism," "fatalism" and mechanical "atomism," and helps attain a fuller understanding of such problems as the interrelations of cellular structure and metabolism, of cell and organism in ontogeny and in adult physiology, of individual and population biologies, of biological and social factors in the development of man's behavior; and the mechanisms responsible for organic evolution. By avoiding teleology, the concept aids the search for causes of biological phenomena.

The concept of integrative levels indicates to research biologists the crucial aspects of their problems, the solution of which puts the known facts into proper perspective by revealing the decisive element, the element imparting the uniqueness to the phenomena under study. It emphasizes the importance of studying the "mesoforms," matter at the point of transition from one level of organization to the next, so as to deepen our understanding of the unique qualities of the higher level. For example, it would indicate that an intensive study of the transition region between the chemical and biological levels, between protein and protoplasm, will help reveal the organizing relations unique to living matter and fundamental to vital activities.

As biologists become more familiar with the concept, a greater number will recognize its value both as an aid in the understanding of biological data already accumulated and as a reliable guide for research. Such recognition of its value will, however, be delayed by any presentation which creates the erroneous impression that it is metaphysical, teleological or mystical. This article has pointed to shortcomings in the presentation of the concept in some recent biological literature, with the hope that this may help make future references to the concept more reliable.

---

27. Julian Huxley, *op. cit.*, p. 576.

MAN AND SCIENCE

W. Heitler

Newton versus Kepler

In writing the history of physics it is usual to start by mentioning a few great names such as Kepler, Galileo and others, culminating finally in Isaac Newton, the chief founder of physics — as though a straight line of development led from Kepler to Newton. It is of course true to say that our science began about the turn of the sixteenth-seventeenth century, if we disregard isolated precursors in antiquity whose tradition was interrupted. It is also true that Kepler's three laws[1] were one of the foundation stones on which Newton built. Galileo, a contemporary of Kepler, is as regards attitude of mind Newton's immediate predecessor, but he has practically nothing in common with Kepler. When we compare Kepler's great work[2] (his last) with Newton's,[3] a great gulf is evident between completely different intellectual orientations. Almost the only modern feature in Kepler is that he used Tycho Brahe's accurate observational material and insisted that a correct conception of the planetary system must be consistent with it. (In earlier times this had not been regarded as of much importance.) In other ways however Kepler was still the complete mediaeval mystic; he was above all part Platonist, part Pythagorean. For instance we find in his writings detailed

---

From *Man and Science* by W. Heitler, tr. Robert Schlapp (New York: Basic Books, Inc., and Edinburgh: Oliver & Boyd, Ltd., 1963), pp. 6–14, 54–55, 61–68, 96–98.

1. They are (1) The planets move in ellipses with the sun in one focus. (2) The line joining sun and planet describes equal areas in equal times. (3) The squares of the periodic times are as the cubes of the major axes.
2. Johannes Kepler, *Harmonices mundi*, 1619.
3. Isaac Newton, *Principia*, 1687.

astrological considerations, such as how the aspects of the planets influence the "earth soul". The validity of astrology was for him a fact,[4] notwithstanding his vigorous denunciation – doubtless justified – of the astrological quacks of his day. His first attempt to understand the planetary system consisted in establishing a connection between the six planetary orbits and the five regular Platonic solids.[5] After prolonged efforts he had perforce to abandon the attempt, in view of the observational material. His next aim was to discover the Pythagorean harmony of the spheres in the planetary system. This aim he pursued tenaciously for many years – until he succeeded. Pythagoras had made the important discovery that musical concords are associated with simple whole-number relationships, for instance the lengths of sounding strings. We now know that it is in general a question of the ratios of frequencies of oscillation. The Pythagoreans also had a notion – call it a theory or an intuition – that the motion of the planets is accompanied by musical sounds harmonically related, so that the heavens resound with harmonies. The exact origin of this idea is unknown. It is reported of Pythagoras himself that he was able to apprehend these harmonies by extrasensory means. However this may be, the next step, already implicit in the Pythagorean intuition, was obviously to assign whole-number relationships to the planetary orbits; to reveal these relationships in detail was Kepler's aim. Of the existence of these harmonies he was absolutely convinced. God the Creator, so his argument ran, could have created the heavens only as a perfect structure, even although the earth, for well-known reasons, is no such thing. But harmony was completion. So Kepler divines the Creator's aim, and this aim was so to create the planetary system *in order that* the harmonies might resound in heaven, for ears that can hear them.

So the question was where in the planetary orbits these whole-number relationships were to be found. Was it for instance in the distances from the sun, or in some other feature? To this single purpose his laborious year-long study of planetary motion was devoted. In the course of it Kepler also discovered – as a by-product – his three laws, i.e. the elliptical form of the orbits and so on. For him this was, however, an intermediate step. He never set much store by this discovery, for which he is famed today. In the end, when he was nearly fifty years old, he found what he was looking for. He found that the angular velocities of each individual planet at perihelion and aphelion are, to a close approximation, in the ratio of simple integers, and thus correspond to a musical interval. The system of the six planets gives the whole major or minor scale, depending on whether one starts with the perihelion or aphelion of Saturn. This was Kepler's triumph; his life-work was completed.

---

4. He asserts for instance that he has established the influence of the aspects on the weather.

5. As Plato showed, there are only five regular solids, i.e. symmetrical bodies bounded by identical equilateral polygons, while in the plane there are arbitrarily many kinds of equilateral polygons. The five regular solids are: tetrahedron, cube, octahedron, dodecahedron, icosahedron. They are bounded respectively by 4 triangles, 6 squares, 8 triangles, 12 pentagons, 20 triangles, all equilateral in each case.

Let us try to analyse the course of Kepler's thought. It is clear that his guiding principle is markedly metaphysical and theological. But this is not its most surprising feature. Whether he is aware of it or not, the modern theoretical physicist also allows himself to be guided by at least one metaphysical principle. In his search for new laws of nature he uses the idea that they must be capable of formulation in a mathematically simple and perspicuous manner. Without this guiding principle scarcely a single general physical law could ever have been discovered. No law is discovered from experience alone, although empirical material plays an important part. In the first place there is no such thing as *exact* agreement between the law and experience, because there are always disturbances, such as friction etc. and secondly there are no exact facts of experience, for every measurement is inexact. But why should physical nature be mathematically simple? There is no logical reason; it is a metaphysical conviction, and we could amplify it by saying that we are convinced that the Creator can have made the laws of nature only in simple and mathematically elegant form. But unlike Kepler we no longer openly maintain this (or something like it), though Newton and some of his successors still said it explicitly. At all events the physicist has made successful use of this guiding idea.

The fundamental distinction between Kepler and later science lies in the structure of the laws for which he is looking. The Keplerian type of law has to do with the planetary orbit as a whole. Motion and orbit are considered in combination, and these orbits, as Kepler found, are arranged on harmonic principles. They are such as they are *in order that* the harmony of the spheres may exist and resound (for the adornment of the world, he says). Thus we have to do with teleological arguments, i.e., with purposive considerations that concern the world as a whole. The world is what it is *in order that* something else may be so, and not because it is necessarily so or because there is a reason for it. Kepler's research is directed to finding the purpose and understanding it. We shall frequently come back to teleological considerations.

Quite a different course was taken by science in the hands of Galileo and Newton, and in a tremendous crescendo since their time. Newton is the true discoverer of laws that are differential, causal and deterministic. Consider Newton's fundamental second law—a body moves in such a way that at each instant its acceleration (i.e. change of velocity in unit time) is equal to the force acting on it, divided by its mass. The motion is thus determined only from one instant to the next. So the law is differential. For every change in speed there is a compelling cause, force. So the law is causal. The whole motion of the body in its path is obtained by integrating all these instantaneous actions. The orbit can be worked out in advance with complete precision if (1) the force is known, and (2) the position and velocity of the body have prescribed values at a certain initial instant. We call these the initial conditions. In this case the future is completely predetermined. So the law is deterministic. It is in this deterministic property that the immense power of the law resides. No wonder that the whole of later physics—up to 1925—followed the pattern of causal deterministic laws.

Let us now compare Newton's law and its consequences with Kepler's type of law. In the first place it follows as a mathematical consequence from Newton's law, together with the law of gravitation (also due to Newton) that the planets move in ellipses, with the further properties expressed by Kepler's three laws. The latter are thus a consequence of the Newtonian laws. The actual planetary orbits however do not by any means follow. What does follow is merely a series of *possible* orbits, small, large, nearly circular or elongated ellipses. The actual orbits of our planets are a particular selection from among these possibilities. The harmonic relations of Kepler are therefore not a consequence of Newtonian mechanics. For this reason Kepler's three laws have become a part of present-day science, while the harmonic relations have been eliminated. The former can be derived from causal mechanics, but not the latter. It will not do to argue that the harmonic relations are not exactly fulfilled. No physical law is exactly fulfilled in nature. The planetary orbit is not exactly an ellipse because there are always small perturbations, e.g. by a third body, such as another planet. To fix the actual planetary orbits according to Newton it is necessary to know the initial conditions. To determine them in the sense of a causal science we would have to go back to the origin of the planetary system some thousands of millions of years in the past. At present we know nothing definite about this. At all events the initial conditions seem to be determined more by chance than by any obvious regularity. So the actual planetary orbits become a chance selection from among all possible orbits.

Thus Kepler's aim was considerably more far-reaching. He wanted to fix the actual orbit by his teleology. Had he known the Newtonian laws he could quite readily have accepted them (and probably would have done so with his characteristic enthusiasm): but they would not have solved his particular problem. He could still have discovered and upheld his harmonic relations. He only needed to say that what appears to Newton as chance is the purposeful work of the Creator. Whether we speak of "the origin of the universe" which is probably beyond the range of scientific treatment, or of an "act of creation" depends largely on our metaphysical attitude.

At first sight causality and teleology appear to be completely opposed to each other. The mental attitudes involved in setting up and considering the two types of law are wholly distinct. Perhaps this is the reason why Galileo took scarcely any notice of Kepler. Nevertheless it is important to bear in mind that the two ways of looking at the matter are not necessarily contradictory. In many cases they are mutually complementary. In physics there are indeed cases where a causal law is identical with a teleological one. If a ray of light passes through a medium of variable refractive index, its path is no longer a straight line. A ray of light traverses the atmosphere in a slightly curved path (as a result of which the setting sun appears slightly oval in shape). There is a causal law for the path of the ray, similar to the Newtonian law of motion. But we can also determine the path by a teleological law: the ray of light travels by such a path that the time it takes between two fixed points is a minimum. The two laws are mathematically equivalent.

Again a machine naturally obeys strictly causal laws: but we can understand it properly only if we know and have investigated the purpose of its constructor. In this case teleology supplements the causal law.

Again, in our example of the planetary system causality and teleology could be mutually complementary. The causal laws provide a broad framework (the possible ellipses) leaving room for the chance initial conditions necessary to determine the actual orbits. *A priori* it is quite conceivable that for a complete understanding of the planetary system this vacant place might have to be filled by teleological laws of Kepler's type, which actually fix the planetary orbits. Here a teleological law would supplement a causal law, by substituting a kind of over-all plan for the unknown and chance initial conditions. It is to be understood that nothing is thereby said about the real truth-content of Kepler's harmonic relations, either for or against. Our considerations were intended solely to clarify the relation between causality and teleology. But we shall see that we have every reason to admit or to introduce teleological considerations into other fields of natural science.

Here and throughout the sequel the word causal is used in the narrow sense of the exact sciences. From the data at an instant of time the course of events immediately afterwards follows of necessity. Thus causal does not mean simply that there is a reason or a motive (in this latter sense an action with an aim in view would be causal; the aim would be the motive. But that is not the sense in which causality is meant here). Causal and teleological are fundamentally different attributes, although it may happen that both are necessary for the understanding of any particular phenomenon, as we have seen.

From Newton's time on the causal idea takes over the whole of science, gradually at first, and then at a breath-taking pace. Science moves towards an unparalleled blossoming—and mankind at the same time towards the danger of a catastrophe, in more senses than one. First the exact sciences celebrate their triumph. Almost all the achievements of physics, chemistry and astronomy up to 1925 and to a great extent till later follow the pattern of Newtonian causal and deterministic laws. It is not necessary to elaborate this. Physics itself was compelled, from 1925 on, to depart from this strict pattern—but more of this later.

The causal idea then encroaches on other sciences, on biology and psychology and, from the nineteenth century onwards, even on other fields of learning. This may be illustrated by a few examples. Primitive views of nature have always made use of teleological arguments. The frog is green in order that it may not be seen in the grass by its enemies. The reader can find hundreds of other examples. The genius of Darwin converted this explanation into a causal one. The frog is green because red, yellow and blue frogs have long since been devoured by their enemies, or would be devoured, so that only frogs that "happen" to have the appropriate protective coloration have been able to survive. Karl Marx introduces the causal argument into his view of history. The course of history is the consequence of the interplay of mutually opposing economic forces. He or his successors go so far as to conclude that history follows an inexorable and deterministic course, just like mechanical motions in physics. Examples could be multiplied at will.

Not everything of this sort, however, merits the name of science. It has almost come to this, that anything that is not causal (and quantitative) is unfit for polite scientific society.

The reasons for this growing trend towards the causal are at least in part easily recognisable. It is above all the unparalleled success of the exact sciences that has carried conviction. For there is nothing so persuasive as success. This began the process of "re-educating" the thought of scientifically thinking persons in the new direction. Secondly a metaphysical reason undoubtedly plays an important part. Let us again consider teleology, as a counter-example to the idea of causality. A teleological argument pre-supposes, outside the object of scientific study, some being endowed with intelligence which has determined the purpose. The question of such a being is too obvious to be simply evaded. In the age of rationalism (which science itself brought in its train) such a question was inappropriate. In investigating causal laws we could rather be content simply to discover the laws without bringing up the question of the origin and meaning of these laws. This does not of course dispose of the question, but it can be ignored (and is ignored by science) or relegated to philosophy. . . .

. . . .

The science of living things

The author is a physicist and not a biologist. Perhaps some readers will say he is not entitled to write on a subject in which he is not an "expert". But the questions to be dealt with here are concerned with the borderline between the exact sciences of physics and chemistry on one hand and of biology on the other, above all the question of how far physical and chemical laws are capable of explaining vital processes. And here the physicist must have his say.

Modern biology is also tending strongly in the direction of the causal and quantitative. This is unmistakably shown by the birth of two new sciences, biochemistry and biophysics. The attempt is being made, not without considerable success, to investigate physical and chemical processes in living bodies, and then to reduce typical vital processes to a physico-chemical mechanism.

But is this all? Can a basic understanding of vital processes be reached through physical laws? Far be it from us — let there be no mistake — to minimise the great achievements of this causally and quantitatively orientated biology, achievements which will doubtless be even greater in the future. All the same we must put the question as one of principle, and try to answer it.

We shall consider three typical vital phenomena and test the possibility of reducing them to purely physical and chemical facts. (1) Form and size of the living body and of its separate organs; (2) evolution, the historical development of higher organisms out of lower; (3) the existence of consciousness in animals and in man.

. . . .

In the second place let us consider evolution. We take it as basic that living organisms have in course of time developed from lower, that is, relatively simply constructed forms into higher, more complex forms. The period of time for this development from the most primitive living organisms to man is given as roughly as 100 to 1000 million years. The development certainly did not follow a steadily rising line; there were mistakes, Nature made false steps; and also retrograde development, phenomena of degeneration. Whole species, at one time masters of the earth, have become extinct in their turn. We shall not discuss in any detail that part of the Darwinian thesis which states that "better" developed species are more efficient in the struggle for existence, and so suppress other less efficient species. How great a part this principle of selection plays in evolution is a question which we shall leave entirely open.

We shall not discuss at all the problem of the origin of the first living cell — perhaps from non-living matter. Absolutely nothing is known about this; there is not even a useful hypothesis. The one question we shall ask and discuss is how do higher organisms develop from lower organisms? It is probable that this development took place by more or less discontinuous stages. There are indeed intermediate steps between different species now extant, but no really continuous transition. The development must therefore have involved a more or less discontinuous element.[6]

It will be well to link our discussion with a theory held by many biologists. This theory rests on the existence of mutations in a particular species. Mutations are more or less essential changes occurring suddenly in the body structure of the species, whose chief property is that they are transmissible. For instance it might be a matter of colour change in the wings of insects, or small changes in the shape of limbs, etc. Some gross defects are also of this nature, such as missing limbs, etc. In the case of man, haemophilia and colour blindness are relatively frequent mutations, which are transmitted according to perfectly definite laws.

Mutations often occur spontaneously, in which case they first appear in the progeny of a particular pair of parents. But they can also be produced artificially by irradiation of the germ cells with X-rays or rays from radioactive bodies, and also by chemical influences. This is one of the reasons why radioactivity is so extraordinarily dangerous, not only for the organisms exposed to it but also for their progeny. It is quite possible that spontaneous mutations are due, at least in part, to the same causes as artificially induced mutations, since even without human intervention we are exposed to weak radioactivity from the earth's crust as well as to cosmic radiation.

All these mutations are harmful or at best — as in the case of insignificant colour changes — neutral. In many cases severe damage is

---

6. It is possible that while there is a continuous transition between different stable species, the intermediate stages are traversed relatively rapidly, so that they do not survive into the present. Or it is possible that present species are branches of a common unobserved stock; but in this case too a more or less discontinuous element must enter at some point. However this may be, the matter is not essential for the following discussion.

involved, leading even to stillbirth.[7] It is fairly certain that these mutations are due to structural changes in the chromosomes. A change of this kind under the influence of e.g. a quantum of X-rays on a macro-molecule of a gene would not be difficult to understand with the help of quantum theory. Mutations arising in this way are governed largely by chance. Whether a mutation will occur, and what mutation, depends on what particular microscopic point of the chromosome is hit by the X-ray and what change it induces in the gene. As molecular changes are involved, the indeterminism of quantum mechanics comes in. The physical changes that an X-ray quantum causes in a molecule are also determined by laws of probability. This is an additional chance element in the origin of mutations.

The theory we are speaking of assumes that among the numerous mutations that occur, most of which are harmful, there will occasionally, even though very rarely, be favourable ones which imply development of the living organism to a higher form. Since the mutation is trans-missible, these more highly developed organisms will spread and succeed in the struggle for existence. According to the Darwinian principle of selection harmful mutations are of course immediately eliminated. This hypothesis is called Neo-Darwinism.

This theory follows the main stream of the idea of causality, with chance playing a part, as always in complex processes. The random element is due (if we accept the above detailed picture) in part to the essentially random element in quantum mechanics, but also in part to our inability to tell precisely when and where an X-ray quantum registers a hit. The latter is not randomness in principle, but is random to the same extent as the place where the first raindrop falls from a cloud.

It is certainly a very plausible theory — until we consider all that is involved in a "chance" of this sort. A higher mammal is determined by an enormous number of factors. All the bones, muscles, tendons, nerves and other organs are fairly accurately determined as to position, size and shape. We are for the moment disregarding completely the refine-ment and complexity of internal structure of these parts of the body. How many factors alone (relating to muscles, limbs, nerves) are needed merely to enable the squirrel to carry out its incredibly surefooted climbing feats? We shall leave instinctive aptitude entirely out of account. If even one of the essential determining factors in the mutation had "come out wrong" the whole thing would not work. The probability that all this does come out right by chance is so fantastically small that we could not expect to find a squirrel once in the whole course of the evolution of life. It scarcely matters whether the mutations leading to the squirrel took place in one large step in which several determining factors changed at the same time, or in a large number of small steps.

---

7. Reports from Japan on human mutations induced by the radioactivity of the atomic bombs are contradictory. One report (Midwives' Conference, 1954) asserts that about fifteen per cent of the offspring of parents who had been exposed to the radiation exhibit severe damage. Other reports, issued by special research stations, on the consequences of irradiation, do not mention mutations at all.

This recalls examples such as the well-known puzzle whether even the first line of Hamlet's soliloquy could arise by a chance arrangement of letters. It is desirable that we should get a clear picture of the improbability of such a chance. The first line of Hamlet's soliloquy consists of thirty letters, of which a, q, r, u, each occur once, b, h, i, n, s, each twice, e four times, o five times and t seven times. Let us take these letters out of a type-case (the letters themselves are already determined) and arrange them repeatedly according to blind chance until we obtain the right arrangement. We would have to make nearly 10^{24}, that is, nearly a billion billion trials before having a single chance of finding the correct arrangement. (We use the European billion, not the American billion; 1 European billion = 1 million million.) Of course this example has no direct connection with mutations. But consider the DNA molecule described above, the main constituent of the chromosomes, with its 10,000 links, in which four different types occur in various arrangements. If it is the case (which is scarcely certain as yet) that hereditary properties are located in the DNA molecules, these properties can be expressed only in different arrangements. And if for instance we assume that the mutation requisite for an upward step in evolution needs a particular re-arrangement of only 32 links in a single DNA molecule — this is certainly not asking too much — then we have just about arrived at the above example. Assuming that the 32 links of the chain contain 8 of each type we get for the odds of a particular arrangement $1:10^{17}$, that is, one to a hundred thousand billion (a few zeros more or less really hardly matter).

However we look at it — we shall discuss another comparison later on — the extraordinary complexity of the body-structure of the higher animals absolutely excludes chance evolution. And the more closely we study the structure of the body, the more complex it turns out to be and the more unlikely does "chance" become.

So evolution does not depend on chance. Hence the possibility of understanding evolution solely on the basis of physico-chemical laws falls to the ground; for these laws always contain, in the case of so complex a structure, at least the essential but chance element of the initial conditions. As we have already said this does not mean that causal laws lose their validity. But if evolution is not governed by chance there must have been or must be some kind of plan. It is after all obvious that the squirrel is constructed in the way it is in order that it may perform its climbing feats. Evolution, even more than morphology, forces us to invoke teleological considerations. This is not to say that teleology combined with causal laws will suffice for an understanding of life. Much more will certainly be involved, but meanwhile let us keep to teleology, which is in any case scarcely to be avoided. We have repeatedly referred to the possibility of teleological arguments as a constituent part of exact science. They have in fact been used constantly and in various ways. Leaving aside primitive views of nature ("the lion has strong teeth in order that . . .") the biologist uses them in the first place when he wants to know the function of an organ. He must enquire what purpose the organ serves. But the modern tendency is to regard this merely as an intermediate step which will lead by degrees to the causal mechanism which explains the function of the organ.

As we have already remarked, the chief objection to a teleologically oriented science lies in the metaphysical implications. In testing the possibility of teleology taking a fundamental place in science it will be well to distinguish two separate groups of problems, namely the purely teleological situations and regularities (if we may use this expression here too), and the more metaphysical implications connected with them. Archaeology affords a good illustration of these two problems.

The archaeologist investigating a prehistoric structure and wanting to reconstruct it makes use — as a matter of course — of teleological arguments. First of all he asks what was the purpose of the chamber, or portion of a ditch, whose ground-plan is before him. His task is easy, for he can take it that the building was used by men to some extent like ourselves. Having solved these questions he is often able to reconstruct the building. He can then consider the second, wider question as to the builder. He can draw conclusions as to his technical skills, his geometrical knowledge, his artistic taste. Here too he is helped by the fact that the builder was a man with abilities comparable with our own.

In biology both problems are incomparably more difficult. We cannot assume at the outset that "suitability for a purpose" is suitability in the same sense as a machine is suitable for our use; let alone that the "architect" of living organisms possessed capabilities similar to those of man. It is precisely all this that must be the aim of unprejudiced research. The word teleology is to be understood throughout in a fairly general sense, not only in the sense of purpose and aim but in general whenever some sort of over-all plan is involved, e.g., a form to be fashioned. And above all no scale of values is implied. The over-all plan does not have to appear, as judged by us, as "suitable for a purpose".

To begin with, we can limit ourselves to the first step. We will ask questions not only about the suitability of the structure of organs, bones and so on, for their purpose, but will also ask how cell-division is governed by the over-all plan of the organ to be formed, what kind of conformity with a plan there was (and perhaps is) in evolution,[8] and a thousand other questions. There is no reason why research so directed should not be just as "scientific" as the pursuit of causal laws, and be on a footing of complete equality with that pursuit. In both cases we limit ourselves to the determination of the facts, whether they are according to the plan or are causal.

The second step, the question as to the being that made the plan, takes us, it is true, into metaphysics. This is however not in itself an argument against teleology as such. Causal laws do the same. As we have already remarked in the previous chapter the laws of physics are

---

8. A very interesting account of evolution is to be found in the book by the Jesuit palaeontologist Teilhard de Chardin, "Le Phénomène Humain". While we do not have to agree with everything in this book, it is important for us in one respect; the author leaves no doubt that evolution has followed a planned course, with digressions and unsuccessful attempts.

of exquisite mathematical abstractness and beauty. We need only think of quantum mechanics or general relativity, which has recently replaced the laws of gravity and of motion. We have already concluded from this that there must exist outside man a spiritual principle with which the laws of nature as well as our own mathematical knowledge of them are bound up. But if we have already to recognise an extra-human spiritual principle in the context of causal laws, then there is no difficulty in making such a principle responsible for laying down the plan as well, e.g. in evolution. We do not need to seek far in the history of human thought. In a large part of Greek philosophy pure mathematics and particularly geometry was always looked on with profound veneration as a reflection of the divine spirit — as in the Pythagorean doctrine of harmonies or the Platonic doctrine of ideas. It is scarcely necessary to remind ourselves that for the majority of mankind, and often in particular for its intellectual leaders during the most fertile periods of its history, religion was a living fact. So when we use the intentionally rather vague expression "extra-human spiritual principle" we are only describing something that has been accepted as a matter of course throughout practically the whole of human history, in some concrete sense or other.

Thus there is not much difference in the metaphysical situation as between teleology and causal laws, although at first sight there appeared to be. The scientist will in the first place ignore, and be right in ignoring, metaphysical questions, just as he has hitherto done so successfully in the case of causal laws. So we cannot see any objection to a teleologically oriented science.

. . . .

Conclusion

. . . If we apply the same principles as we use in physics to the living body, we will, as we have seen, be unable to understand just the most typical vital phenomena. These include for instance morphology, the form and size of the living body and its organs, its resistance to decay, also evolution of lower to higher organisms, and of course the existence of consciousness in the higher animals and in man. Quite different principles will have to be used if anything of this is to be understood, principles in which the wholeness of the living organism and of its organs in respect of form and function is essential; principles which involve something essentially new, the typical vital element, in which the over-all plan is decisive in the architecture of the living organism as well as in its evolution. We came to the conclusion that in biology teleology must play an important part in supplementing causality, which is not to say that both principles, teleology and causality together, will suffice for a complete understanding of the living body. At any rate the exclusive application of the principle of causality in biology, in particular the exclusive use of physico-chemical laws in living bodies will give us only a very limited excerpt from the science of life, an excerpt more suited to describe the dead body than actual living matter, which bypasses just the most typical vital phenomena. Biology will undoubtedly make further progress along the present lines which stress the causal and quantitative or the physical and chemical aspects, and will certainly achieve even greater success than hitherto. Perhaps some day it will even be possible to synthesise the DNA molecule and proteins. Perhaps indeed these substances will exhibit properties with a remote resemblance to living matter. If a prophecy expressing our own feeling may be permitted, the living things so produced would be caricatures of real living things, homunculus-creatures inspiring only revulsion but devoid of all positive character.

Reviewing what has been said we must admit that contemporary science presents an aspect of the world so restricted that it appears small compared with the problems that have not so much as been touched on, all the magnificent achievements of science notwithstanding. This aspect is concerned only with the material side of the world, which is just the side that concerns man less, save for its technical applications. In particular we see that little justification remains for seeing the world as a causally running mechanism. Belief in a mechanistic universe is a modern superstition. As probably happens in most cases of superstition, the belief is based on a more or less extensive series of correct facts, facts which are subsequently generalised without warrant, and finally so distorted that they become grotesque.[9] A mechanistic living creature presents the grotesque picture of a robot such as is frequently portrayed in comic papers nowadays. The witch superstition has cost innumerable innocent women their lives, in the cruellest fashion. The mechanistic superstition is more dangerous. It leads to a general spiritual and moral drying-up which can easily lead to physical destruction. When once we have got to the stage of seeing in man merely a complex machine, what does it matter if we destroy him?

Perhaps some readers will think that in taking this stand in opposition to the mechanical conception of the world we are hammering at an open door. Philosophical materialism reached its zenith about the end of the nineteenth century and it is probably true that this philosophy is no longer very widely held. But after all it is science more than anything else that calls the tune nowadays.[10] Within science itself however there are as yet only few indications that any trend other than the causal and quantitative is being followed—rather the reverse. Moreover the limitations inherent in this trend have rarely been consciously realised, and even if we do not profess a materialist philosophy this philosophy is being applied increasingly in scientific practice. Nowadays our private philosophy and our science are often two different things. There is no bridge connecting science with our life as human beings, except through material and technical applications, whose character we have already described.

---

9. Even the belief in witches seems to have some factual basis. According to a recent report a chemist is said to have made up the ointment with which mediaeval witches are supposed to have anointed themselves, and tried it out on himself. He passed into a trance state which was alleged to be not unlike the well-known witches' ride.

10. The reader who has read thus far will scarcely attribute this assertion to scientific arrogance on the author's part.

It is generally said that science, which is the search for truth, is neither moral nor immoral, but only that those who put its applications into practice are faced with ethical decisions. In view of our results we can agree with this view only with one proviso. The search for truth can surely not be immoral. But we have seen that modern research is conducted mainly along channels leading further and further away from all that is human. And then this science puts forward a claim to total validity, setting itself up to be the whole and only truth. But a partial truth that claims to be the whole truth may very well be immoral. Is this perhaps the reason for the demonic character of science mentioned in the introduction? At all events this claim to total validity is in danger of destroying all reverence for life.

THE NATURE OF LIFE

A. I. Oparin

The extent of life

Life—the word is so easy to understand yet so enigmatic for any thoughtful person. One would have thought that the meaning of this word would have been clear and the same for all ages and all peoples. Nevertheless, we know that, during the many centuries of human cultural history, there have been irreconcilable conflicts as to how it should properly be understood.

Even the question of what is alive, which of the objects in the world around us are imbued or endowed with life, the extent of the realm of life or its scope, have been defined and are still defined in various totally different ways. We have, as it were, a whole multicoloured spectrum of different opinions. At the one end of this spectrum we find the views of those philosophers and scientists who believe that life is a general property, inalienable from all matter, and who therefore extend the realm of life to cover all objects in the universe.

On the other hand, the philosophers of the opposite end of the spectrum arbitrarily restrict the scope of life to the compass of human existence, or may even maintain that life is the prerogative of one single thinking subject.

The first of these opinions owes its origin to the ancient Greek hylozoists. According to Aristotle, even Thales the founder of the Miletian school of philosophy (who was alive about 600 B.C.) considered

---

"The Nature of Life," Chapter I in *Life: Its Nature, Origin, and Development*, tr. Ann Synge (New York: Academic Press, Inc., 1961), pp. 1–37. Reprinted by permission of Oliver & Boyd, Ltd., Edinburgh.

magnets to be animate on account of their ability to attract iron. More than 2000 years later, in the 17th century, the Dutch philosopher and materialist, Spinoza, maintained that stones think and that all natural bodies are animate, while even 100 years later still (also in Holland), the French philosopher Robinet published a book called *On Nature* in which he acknowledged that all matter was living and even considered the stars in heaven as living organic bodies.

Even in our own times, many engineers and physicists are ready to consider the most complicated modern mechanisms and automata as being alive, just as Descartes compared organisms to water clocks or mills, or La Mettrie referred to man as an extremely well-educated machine. Some present-day chemists and geneticists follow Diderot in an attempt to assign life even to individual molecules of organic substances.

On the other hand, it is understood by anyone that, if some writer or philosopher speaks, in one of his works, about the significance or value of life, or about its aim, then he is referring only to human life, to that "striving towards good" which, according to Tolstoï, constitutes the main aspiration of life and is understood as such by all men.

This last expression of opinion is taken from Tolstoï's treatise *On Life*. In it Tolstoï censures the experimental scientists or, as he calls them, the scribes[1] for using the actual word 'life', in that by cunning sophistry they have invented a conventional scientific Volapük in which words do not correspond with what all ordinary laymen understand by them. Tolstoï justifiably recommends that "a man is bound, by every word, to mean that which all indisputably understand alike".

It seems to me that if we follow this wise advice we shall be able to find a way out of the present confusing labyrinth of contradictory opinions on the question of the delimitation of the realm of life, although the way out which we shall find will be far from the same as that of which Tolstoï approved. Any ordinary person looking at the world around him will infallibly sort it into the kingdom of the lifeless or inorganic, and that of living things. In all places and at all times he will see that life is not simply scattered about all over the place, but only exists in individual organisms which are separate from their environment; so that the sum of these organisms constitutes the realm of life, the world of living things. This world exhibits a colossal variety, including plants, animals and microbes, which are very diverse and which, at first glance, would hardly seem to have anything in common. Nevertheless, anybody, even without any scientific experience, can easily observe what they do have in common and what enables one to include in the one category of 'living being' a man and a tree, a whale and a tiny beetle or blade of grass, a bird and a shapeless mollusc.

When the simple glass polisher from Amsterdam, Leeuwenhoek, first saw microbes of various kinds through his magnifying glass, he unhesitatingly designated them as living things (*viva animalcula*), although some of them, such as the cocci, which Leeuwenhoek drew

---

1. L. Tolstoï is here using the term 'scribe' in the bad sense in which it is used in the gospels "scribes and Pharisees."

with his own hand, could not move and had none of the other external features of living things.

On perceiving that living things have something in common, which relates them to one another, one distinguishes them from the objects of the inorganic world which lack that 'something' i.e. which lack life. Thus, even by his unaided observation of the world around him, any ordinary person can establish the most elementary, but also the most general definition of the extent of life or the area embraced by its natural realm. Life is a property of any organism, from the highest to the lowest, but it does not exist in inorganic natural objects, no matter how complicated their structure may be. It is very possible that, in the unbounded extent of the universe, there exists a multitude of extremely complicated and highly-evolved forms of movement and organisation of matter, of which we, as yet, have no suspicion, but it would be quite unjustifiable to call any of these forms 'life' if they differed in essential principles from that life which is represented on our planet by a whole multitude of organisms of different forms. It would be better to think up a special new word to denote these forms of organisation when it is required.

We have thus marked out the region of nature, the category of objects which are pertinent to our enquiries about life. This means that, in what follows, we can avoid many of the mistakes which are rather common in scientific literature, by keeping strictly to the terms of reference laid down above. Of course, what has been given is not, by any means, a definition of life. To give that one would have to solve the problem of the nature of that 'something' which is characteristic only of the world of living things and which is absent from the objects of inorganic nature.

The conflict between idealism and materialism as to the essential nature of life

From the earliest times, even until the present day, this problem of the essential nature of life has always been a battlefield in the embittered war which has been waged between the two irreconcilable philosophic camps of idealism and materialism.

The representatives of the idealist camp see, as the essence of life, some sort of eternal supramaterial origin which is inaccessible to experiment. This is the 'psyche' of Plato, the 'entelechy' of Aristotle, the 'immortal soul' or 'particle of divinity' of various religious doctrines and faiths, Kant's *'inneres Prinzip der Kausalität'*, the *'Weltgeist'* of the Hegelians, the 'life force' of the vitalists and the 'dominant' of the neovitalists, and other such concepts.

From this point of view, matter, in the sense of that objective reality which we observe directly and study experimentally, is in itself and as such, lifeless and inert. It serves only as the material from which the spirit or soul creates a living being, gives it form, adapts its structure to functional needs, endows it with the power of breathing and moving and, in general, makes it alive. And when the soul leaves the organism and death takes place, there remains but the lifeless material envelope, a rotten, decomposing corpse.

This concept of death as the departure from the body of the soul, which constitutes the essence of life, is, in fact, the basis of a definition of life which is widely held and even appears in a number of encyclopaedias, namely, that life is the contrary of death. This, however, pushes out of sight the fact that the living can only properly be contrasted with the lifeless, not with the dead. It is obvious that the dead body is a product of life for, in the absence of life, that is in an inorganic world, a corpse could never occur on its own.

Even if one starts from idealistic premises one can, of course, make an objective study of particular organisms and their organs, but it is inherently impossible to reach an understanding of the essence of life itself by experimental, materialistic means, as this essence is of a supramaterial or spiritual nature. Only by means of speculative introspection can one approach an understanding of that divine principle which we bear within ourselves. We can only passively contemplate all the rest of the world of living things and marvel at the wisdom of the Creator Who made them. And naturally there can be no question of man making any change or transformation in living nature if one adopts this position.

Materialists approach the problem of the essence of life from a diametrically opposite viewpoint. Basing their arguments on the facts obtained by science they assert that life, like all the rest of the world, is material and does not require for its understanding the acceptance of a spiritual origin which is not amenable to experimental study. On the contrary, objective study of the world around us is, for the materialist, not only a hopeful way of leading us to an understanding of the very essence of life, but it also enables us to alter living nature purposefully in a way favourable to mankind.

Wide circles of biological scientists, either consciously or intuitively, base their investigations on a materialistic concept of living nature and, in following this line, they are always enriching the science of life by their work and bringing us closer to an understanding of the essence of life.

Mechanical and dialectical concepts of life

However, even within the limits of the materialistic concept of life, its essence may be interpreted in various ways.

According to the mechanistic view, which prevailed in the scientific world of last century, and which is partly retained even now, the understanding of life in general comprises simply a complete explanation in terms of physics and chemistry, a complete account of all living phenomena as physical and chemical processes. If one adopts this position there is no place for any specifically biological laws of nature. In reality there is only one law which governs both the inorganic world and all the phenomena occurring in living organisms. This is, in fact, to deny that there is any qualitative difference between organisms and inorganic objects. We thus reach a position where we must say either that inorganic objects are alive or that life does not really exist. Thus, by a logical development of the mechanistic outlook which has been explained, we are forced to a conclusion which is fundamentally opposed to the view which we adopted earlier. However, in contradistinction to this, one must be quite clear that acceptance of the material nature of life does not mean that one must deny that it has specific characteristics and that living things show qualitative differences from inorganic objects. One must not do as the mechanists and regard everything which is not included in physics and chemistry as being vitalistic or supernatural. On the contrary, the forms of organisation and motion of matter may be very varied. To deny this variety is to indulge in oversimplification.

According to the dialectical materialist view, matter is in constant motion and proceeds through a series of stages of development. In the course of this progress there arise ever newer, more complicated and more highly evolved forms of motion of matter having new properties which were not previously present. There can be no doubt that, for a long period after the formation of our planet, there was no life on it. Obviously, all the things which existed on it at that time simply obeyed the laws of physics and chemistry. However, in the process of development of matter on the Earth, the first and most primitive organisms arose, that is to say, life came into being as a qualitatively new form of motion. When this happened, the old laws of physics and chemistry naturally continued to operate, but now they were supplemented by new and more complicated biological laws which had not operated before.

Thus, life is material in nature but its properties are not limited to those of matter in general. Only living beings possess it. This is a special form of the movement of matter, qualitatively different from that of the inorganic world, and the organism has specific biological properties and ways of behaving and does not merely follow the rules governing inorganic nature. Therefore a dialectical materialist will even formulate the problem of understanding life in a different way from a mechanist. For the latter it consists in a more complete explanation of life in terms of physics and chemistry. For the dialectical materialist, on the other hand, the important thing about understanding life is the establishment of its qualitative difference from other forms of matter, i.e. that difference which obliges us to regard life as a special form of the motion of matter.

Attempts to formulate definitions of life

This difference has found, and still finds, a greater or less reflection in the definitions of life formulated and expounded by the scientists and thinkers of last century and those of our own time. It is just in their setting out of this difference between the living and the non-living that one can perceive the objective and essential value of these definitions in spite of their absolute contradictoriness and their astounding variety.

At the beginning of his remarkable book, *Leçons sur les phénomènes de la vie communs aux animaux et aux végétaux* (1878–1879), Claude Bernard produces a large number of definitions of life which had been made before that time, but he does so simply in order to show that, in general, any *a priori* definition of life is always chimerical and scientifically unprofitable. However, he also believes that life can be understood completely if approached *a posteriori*, by establishing the characteristic features which differentiate living creatures from non-living bodies. This is certainly not easy and, in doing it we are beset with considerable difficulties and doubts, but all the time we are getting closer to solving our problem.

In an American encyclopaedia of 1944, it is stated that there is no single satisfactory definition of life, for, while some include too many phenomena, others suffer from too narrow limitations.

We believe that this is because, in most cases, people try to characterise life as a single point while it is, in fact, a long line, comprising the whole of that section of the development of matter lying between the origin of life on the Earth and our own time, and including among its manifestations the most primitive organisms as well as more highly developed plants and animals, especially man. With the appearance of man, however, there arises a new social form of motion of matter which is more complicated and highly evolved than life and which is characterised by its own peculiar features and by the special laws of development of human society.

It is therefore completely wrong to try to characterise the 'line of life' simply on the basis of one point, whether that point lies at the beginning, the middle or the end. In fact, if we try to define life in terms of the characteristics which arose at the very beginning of its emergence on the Earth, we have to exclude from among its features, not merely consciousness, but also respiration, which obviously did not take place among the earliest organisms. On the other hand, if we define life on the basis of phenomena which are typical only of the more highly developed living things, we shall risk relegating the anaerobic bacteria, as well as many primitive organisms, to the category of non-living bodies belonging to inorganic nature.

When Engels made his remarkable definition of life as the "mode of existence of albuminous bodies" he immediately made reservations, indicating the incompleteness of the definition. "Our definition of life", he wrote, "is naturally very inadequate, inasmuch as, far from including *all* the phenomena of life, it has to be limited to those which are the most common and the simplest. From a scientific standpoint all definitions are of little value. In order to gain a really exhaustive knowledge of what life is, we should have to go through all the forms in which it appears, from the lowest up to the highest".

Thus for an exhaustive understanding of life it is necessary to have an understanding of the whole gamut of its characteristic features, starting with those extremely elementary ones, with which the first living beings were endowed, and finishing with the most complicated manifestations of higher nervous activity in animals and man, in which the biological stage of the development of matter culminates. Among this multitude of features characteristic of life, manifested at the very outset of its development and becoming more complicated in the course of its further evolution and increasing complexity, special mention must be made of that clearly defined, specific interaction between the organism and its environment which runs, like a red thread, along the 'line of life' and is a characteristic of all living things, the lowest as well as the highest, but which is absent from the objects of the inorganic world.

The specific interaction between the organism and its environment

An organism can live and maintain itself only so long as it is continually exchanging material and energy with its environment. As food, drink and gaseous material, various substances of a chemical nature foreign to the organism enter into it. In the organism they undergo far-reaching changes and transformations as a result of which they are converted into the material of the organism itself. That is to say, they are turned into chemical compounds which are, in some degree, similar to those of which the living body is already composed. This is the ascending limb of biological metabolism known as assimilation. In the course of the interaction of substances from outside with the material of the organism, however, the opposite process also occurs continually and is known as dissimilation. The substances of the living body do not remain unchanged. They are broken down fairly quickly to liberate the energy latent in them and the products of their breakdown are discharged into the surrounding medium.

Our bodies flow like rivulets, their material is renewed like water in a stream. This was what the ancient Greek dialectician Heraclitus taught. Certainly the flow, or simply the stream of water emerging from a tap, enables us to understand in their simplest form many of the essential features of such flowing, or open systems as are represented by the particular case of the living body. If the tap is not far open and the pressure in the water cistern remains constant, the external form of the water flowing from the tap remains almost unchanged, as though it were congealed. We know, however, that this form is merely the visible expression of a continual flow of particles of water, which are constantly passing through the stream at a steady rate and emerging from it. If we disturb the relationship between the rates of input and output or the steady process of movement of its particles, the stream, as such, disappears, for the very existence of the stream depends on the steady passage of ever-renewed water molecules through it.

On this analogy the constancy of the external form, and even of the most detailed internal structure of the living being, is merely the visible expression of the constancy of the sequence of processes going on within it as a result of the extremely intricate balancing of the two contrary phenomena already noted, i.e. assimilation and dissimilation. The prolonged existence of a living system in which breakdown and decay are going on all the time is entirely due to this balance. In the place of each molecule or structure which breaks down a new and analogous one appears as a freshly synthesised formation. Thus the organism maintains its form, structure and chemical composition unchanged while its material is continually changing.

Organisms are, thus, not static but stationary or flowing systems. Their ability to exist for a longer or shorter time under given environmental conditions does not depend on their being at rest or unchanging. On the contrary, it depends on the constancy of their movement, i.e. their metabolism.

From a purely chemical point of view, metabolism is merely the sum of a large number of comparatively simple reactions of oxidation, reduction, aldol condensation, hydrolysis, transamination, phosphorylation, cyclisation etc. Each of these reactions can be reproduced, even outside the organism, as there is nothing specifically connected with life about them.

The peculiarity which distinguishes life qualitatively from all other forms of motion of matter (and in particular from inorganic flowing systems) is that, in the living body, the many tens and hundreds of thousands of individual chemical reactions, which, in their sum, make up the metabolism, are not only strictly co-ordinated in time and space, not merely co-operating harmoniously in a single sequence of self-renewal, but the whole of this sequence is directed in an orderly way towards the continual self-preservation and self-reproduction of the living body as a whole. They are extremely well adapted to solving the problem of the existence of the organism under a given set of environmental conditions.

The 'purposiveness' of the organisation of living bodies

This flowing character of the interaction of living bodies with the medium around them, and, what is most important, the amazingly efficient adaptation of the organisation of this interaction to the task of self-preservation and self-reproduction of the system under a given set of external conditions, all that which has been referred to by many authors as the 'adaptation of form to function' or 'purposiveness' in the structure of such a system, is so objectively obvious and makes such a forcible impression on the eyes of those who study living nature that, in one form or another, it figures in the majority of even the most varied definitions of life formulated during the course of many centuries and put forward by members of the most dissimilar schools of philosophy and scientific thought.

The presence in all organisms, without exception, of an adaptation of form to function was noted even by Aristotle who, in his writings, was the first to be able to generalise from the extensive accumulation of biological material which was available at the time. Aristotle designated this specific property of living things as the 'entelechy' underlying life or the 'principle having its aim within itself'.

In one form or another Aristotle's teaching about 'entelechy' has left its mark on all idealistic definitions of life. It is reflected in various religious creeds and philosophic teachings and has lasted through many centuries to reach our own 20th century in the works of Reinke, Driesch and other contemporary students of vitalism.

In their investigations of life, however, the representatives of the materialist camp naturally could not overlook this specific feature of it. Many of them, following Descartes, defined the vital phenomena of plants and animals merely as responsive reactions of a specifically constructed bodily mechanism to the external influence of the environment. Others saw the orderly direction of metabolism as the specific property which distinguished organisms from non-living things.

In this connection Claude Bernard wrote:

> L'édifice organique est le siége d'un perpétuel mouvement nutritif qui ne laisse de repos à aucune partie: chacune, sans cesse ni trère, s'alimente dans le milieu qui l'entoure et y rejette ses dechettes et ses produits. Cette renovation moleculaire est insaisissable pour le regard; mais, comme nous en voyons le debut et le fin, l'entrée et la sortie des substances, nous en concevons les phases intermediaires, et nous nous représentons un courant de matière qui traverse incessamment l'organisme et le renouvelle dans sa substance en le maintenant dans sa forme.
>
> L'universalité d'un tel phénomène chez la plante et chez l'animal et dans toutes leurs parties, sa constance, qui ne souffre pas d'arrèt, en font un signe général de la vie, que quelques physiologistes ont employé à sa définition.[2]

"There is one expression which must be applied to all organisms", wrote Engels, "and that is adaptation". Later he puts forward his own definition of life: "Life is the mode of existence of albuminous substances and this mode of existence essentially consists in the constant self-renewal of the chemical constituents of these substances by nutrition and excretion".

In our own times, Perret and later, Bernal, have tried to define life in the following terms which are, perhaps, rather complicated for non-specialists.

> Life is a potentially self-perpetuating open system of linked organic reactions, catalysed stepwise and almost isothermally by complex and specific organic catalysts which are themselves produced by the system.

"The organism represents an entity as a system only in conjunction

---

2. "The organic structure is the seat of perpetual nutritional movement which leaves no part of it at rest: each part nourishes itself, without rest or pause, from the medium surrounding it and discharges its wastes and products into that same medium. This molecular renewal is not perceptible to the eye, but, as we see the beginning and the end of it, the entry and discharge of substances, we can imagine the intermediate stages and we picture to ourselves a flow of matter, incessantly passing through the organism and renewing its substance while maintaining its form.

"The universality of such a phenomenon in plants and animals and in all parts of them, as well as their constancy, which never undergoes arrest, make it a general sign of life which some physiologists have used for its definition."

with the conditions necessary for its life" states a representative of the Michurinist school of biology.

Thus the universal 'purposiveness' of the organisation of living beings is an objective and self-evident fact which cannot be ignored by any thoughtful student of nature. The rightness or wrongness of the definition of life advanced by us, and also of many others, depends on what interpretation one gives to the word 'purposiveness' and what one believes to be its essential nature and origin.

The idealists see this 'purposiveness' as the fulfilment of some predetermined plan of a deity or 'universal intellect'. The materialists, on the other hand, use the expression (for lack of a better one) as the shortest way of characterising the direction of the organisation of the whole living system towards its self-preservation and self-reproduction under given environmental conditions, as well as to describe the suitability of the structure of the separate parts of the living system to the most efficient and harmonious performance of those vitally necessary functions which the particular part subserves.

The extremely highly developed adaptation of the structure of the individual organs to the performance of their functions and the general 'purposiveness' of the whole organisation of life is seen to be extremely precise even on a very superficial acquaintance with higher living things. As we have already pointed out, it was noticed a long time ago and found expression in the Aristotelian 'entelechy'. It had been considered to be essentially mystical and supernatural until Darwin gave a rational, materialistic explanation of the way in which this 'purposiveness' arose in higher organisms by means of natural selection.

'Purposiveness' of structure does not, however, manifest itself solely in the more highly organised creatures, it pervades the whole living world from the top to the bottom, right down to the most elementary forms of life. It is necessary to every living body but in the absence of the living body there would be no 'purposiveness' under natural conditions. It would therefore be fruitless for us to seek its explanation simply in terms of the laws of the inorganic world, i.e. the laws of physics and chemistry. The 'purposiveness' which is characteristic of the organisation of all living things can only be understood if one understands the specific interaction between the organism and its environment in terms of the Darwinian principle of natural selection. This new biological law could only arise on the basis of the establishment of life and therefore lifeless, inorganic bodies lack 'purposiveness'. The striking exception to this rule is the machine.

Attempts to treat the organism as a machine

It is, of course, impossible to doubt that the principle on which any machine is constructed is that of adapting its structure or external organisation to the performance of the particular specific job which is its work. From this point of view the comparison between the machine and the organism forces itself upon one. In the course of many centuries it has been widely used by many philosophers and scientists, in their attempts to solve the problem of the essential nature of life. The only thing that has changed in these attempts, in the course of the various periods of development of science, has been the opinion as to which of the points common to the organism and the machine ought to be taken into consideration, as being the features most characteristic of life. The way in which the problem was posed and the attempt to describe the organism as a machine of some sort or another has, however, remained essentially unchanged. Undoubtedly the ideas of each age tend to be expressed in terms of its technology. In his book,[3] N. Wiener very pertinently refers to the 17th century and the early part of the 18th century as "the age of clocks", the end of the 18th century and the whole of the 19th century as "the age of steam-engines" and our own times as "the age of communication and control".

In the age of clocks the world was represented by man as a huge mechanism which had been wound up once and for all time. People saw, as the basis of all existence, mechanical motion, the displacement of bodies in space, taking place according to Newton's laws of motion. Life was also discussed from this point of view, as being merely a special kind of mechanical motion. The spontaneous movement of animals and their organs through space may serve as the clearest expression of this. According to the ideas of that time, therefore, the organism is nothing but a "very complicated machine, the structure of which is, nevertheless, completely comprehensible. Its movement depends entirely on its structure and on the pressure and on the collision of particles of matter like the wheels of a water clock" (Descartes). Anatomy therefore occupied the most important place in the study of life at that time.

However, in the next period of the development of science, the age of steam-engines, physiology began, to a greater and greater extent, to aspire to this place and the rôle of mechanics in the study of life was taken over by energetics.

The prototype of the living creature was now thought of, not as a watch, but as a heat engine. The analogy put forward by Lavoisier between respiration and the burning of fuel was a great step forward. Food is simply the fuel we throw into the furnace of our organism and its importance can therefore be assessed completely in terms of calories. The guiding principles of that time in connection with the understanding of life were those of the conservation and degradation of energy. The first law of thermodynamics, that of the conservation of energy, was found to be universally applicable, both to organisms and to mechanisms.

The second law was a more complicated matter. This is the law which expresses the statistical tendency of nature towards disorder, the tendency to even out energy and thus to devalue it in isolated systems, which is expressed in general terms as the increase of entropy in these systems. If one were to put such a system in uniform conditions and leave it alone, then all the phenomena occurring within it would very

3. *Cybernetics or control and communication in the animal and in the machine.* New York: Wiley (1949).

soon cease and the system as a whole would come to an end. It would thus attain the unchanging state in which nothing would happen. Physicists call this state 'thermodynamic equilibrium' or 'maximum entropy'.

In organisms, on the other hand, not only does entropy not increase, it may even decrease. Thus, one might say that the fundamental law of physics was a tendency towards disorder or an increase in entropy, while that of biology, on the contrary, was a tendency to increasing organisation or a decrease in entropy. Some idealist philosophers, such as A. Bergson, defined life as the "struggle against entropy" and even saw, in this contradiction between physics and biology, a reason for accepting the supernatural nature of life.

Now, however, we know that the contradiction is only apparent. Living things can never exist as isolated systems. On the contrary, as we have said above, it is characteristic of living organisms that they constantly interact with their environment and, by virtue of this fact, they must be regarded as 'flowing' or 'open' systems. The stationary (but not static) state in which they exist is maintained constant, not because they are in a state of 'maximum entropy', or because their free energy is at a minimum (as is the case in the thermodynamic equilibrium), but because the open system is continually receiving free energy from the medium around it in an amount which compensates for the decrease taking place within the system.

Wiener maintains that the ability to act against the general tendency to the increase of entropy is to be found, not only in organisms, but also in machines which have certain specific ways of interacting with the world outside them. In this way he thinks that machines can create a certain local zone of organisation around themselves.

Cybernetics

This concept ushers in the third and present period of the history of the problem, the age of communications and control which has superseded the age of steam-engines.

"There is, in electrical engineering", he writes, "a split which is known in Germany as a split between the technique of strong currents and the technique of weak currents, and which we (in the U.S.A. and Great Britain) know as the distinction between power and communication engineering. It is this split which separates the age which is just past from that in which we are now living". Communication engineering may make use of currents of any strength and may use enormous motors, but it differs from power engineering in that it is fundamentally interested in the exact reproduction of signals and not in the way in which energy is used.

The energy consumed by an electronic valve may be almost entirely wasted, but nevertheless the valve may be a very effective means of carrying out a necessary operation. Similarly, the efficiency of the work of our nervous systems cannot be calculated simply from the point of view of the rational utilisation of the comparatively small amount of energy which reaches the neurones from the blood stream.

Organisms are effectively coupled to the world around them, not merely by their overall metabolism and energy balance, but also by the flow of communications inwards and outwards, the flow of impressions received and actions performed. The extremely well organised and highly differentiated higher nervous activity of man and animals may serve as a particularly clear example of the relationship. Wiener, however, maintains that it is possible to produce a very far-reaching analogy between this activity and the work of contemporary self-regulating machines and automata. Photo-electric elements and other light receptors, radiolocating systems, apparatus for the registration of the potential of hydrogen ions, thermometers, manometers, all sorts of microphones etc. are the equivalents of the sensory organs and serve as mechanisms for receiving information. The effector organs of the machine may be electric motors, solenoids, heating elements and other similar devices. Between the receptor mechanisms and the effector organs of such machines as, for example, the contemporary quick-acting electronic calculating machine, there are intermediate groups of elements, a central regulating system which might be regarded as being analogous with the brain of animals or man.

The object of this system is to co-ordinate the incoming messages in such a way as to bring about the desired reaction by the executive organs. As well as the information reaching this central regulating machine from the outside world, it also receives information about the working of the executive organs themselves. This is what is known as 'feedback' and it permits recording of the fulfilment or non-fulfilment of its own tasks by the machine itself. "Moreover", writes Wiener, "the information received by the automat need not necessarily be used at once but may be delayed or stored so as to become available at some future time. This is the analogue of memory. Finally, as long as the automaton is running, its very rules of operation are susceptible to some change on the basis of the data which have passed through its receptors, and this is not unlike the process of learning".

Thus, in the transition from the age of the steam engine to the age of communication and control, the prototype of the living thing is becoming the electronic calculating machine, the study of nutrition gives place to the study of the physiology of the central nervous system and energetics is exchanged for cybernetics, which is the scientific study of the reception, transmission, storage, transformation and use of information by regulating apparatus, regardless of whether it is made 'of metal or of flesh', i.e. whether it is a machine or an organism.

Like any new branch of knowledge, cybernetics is developing very quickly. In the very short period of its existence it has therefore succeeded in enriching with new ideas and achievements both science and, especially, contemporary technology, in its efforts at maximal automation in the direction of the productive processes. Furthermore, the latest developments in automats and in calculating machines have already advanced so far that the results of experiments planned or already carried out with them may, in many cases, be used in efforts to achieve a rational explanation of the phenomena which take place during the functioning of the nervous system and in many other processes. The understandable attractiveness of these successes as well as the extensive (though little-justified) use of neurophysiological, psychological and even sociological terminology in cybernetics, has now created a situation in which many contemporary authors are beginning to think that machines which can solve complicated mathematical problems, make translations from one language into another and, in general, carry out many tasks normally considered as brain work, must, in some way, be alive and, therefore, they have come to regard cybernetics as being a fundamentally new and universal road to the understanding of the very essence of life.

Of course, this is wrong. As we have pointed out earlier, attempts have been made, many years ago, to attribute life to machines. The only thing that has changed is the opinion as to what aspect one should concentrate on; movement, energetics, communication or some other property common to organisms and machines which is susceptible to explanation in terms of the laws of physics and chemistry. The basic stimulus which induces investigators to attribute life to machines is always the same. It is as follows. 'Purposiveness' in the organisation of living things is what differentiates them in principle from the objects of the inorganic world. Apart from organisms, machines are the only things which show such 'purposiveness' in their structure. Furthermore, the work of machines can be completely known in terms of physics and chemistry. This identification of living things with machines was therefore viewed as the one and only way of saving science from the mystical entelechy of the vitalists, the bridge which will carry us over from physics and chemistry to biology.

Of course, we may, and should, try to understand the physical and chemical basis of the various vital phenomena by means of the construction and study of models which will reproduce the same phenomena as occur in organisms but in a simplified form. In doing so, however, we must always remember that we are dealing with models and not confuse them with living things. We must always take into account the differences as well as the similarities between the model and the real thing. Only thus can we avoid very dangerous oversimplification and those mistakes which have always cost mankind dear and which have only been corrected by science at the expense of a tremendous effort. However great the complexity or intricacy of its organisation, an electronic calculating machine is still further apart in its nature from a human being than is, for example, the simplest bacterium, although this has not got the differentiated nervous system which the machine imitates so successfully.

Unfortunately this difference is usually slurred over in cybernetic literature. It may be that this is, to some extent, justifiable when we wish to concentrate our attention solely on the general rules of communication and not on any particular systems. However, if the aim of our studies is the understanding of the nature of life, then it is, in principle, impermissible to ignore the difference between organisms and mechanisms.

Appraisal of contemporary mechanistic hypotheses

The first difference between machines and living things to strike the eye is the material of which the different systems are made and their actual nature.

Those who hold the theory that living things are machines usually tend to ignore this difference on the ground that the work of a machine depends, essentially, on its structure and not on the material of which it is made. In this connection Jost has written: "We may construct a machine of steel or of brass and this will certainly affect its durability and accuracy but not the nature of the work it does". One might even construct a machine not of metal but of plastic or some other organic material and thus approximate its composition to the chemical composition of a living thing.

Such considerations are, however, radically unsound. The fact that living things are, in Engels' words, "albuminous bodies", that they include in their composition proteins, nucleic acids, lipids, specific carbohydrates and other multifarious organic compounds is by no means to be regarded as an incidental circumstance of only slight significance. The composition of the living body is the very factor which determines its flowing character. In particular, it is only by understanding the highly specific features of the structure of proteins that we can understand the immediate causes underlying the determinate sequences of individual reactions in metabolism, that is to say, their co-ordination in time.

Any organic substance can react in very many different ways, it has tremendous chemical possibilities, but outside the living body it is extremely 'lazy' or slow about exploiting these possibilities. Inside the living thing, however, organic substances undergo extremely rapid chemical transformation. This is due to the catalytic properties of proteins. If any organic substance is to play a real part in metabolism it must enter into chemical combination with some protein-enzyme, and form with it a particular, very active and unstable intermediate compound. If it does not do so its chemical potentialities will be realised so slowly that they will be insignificant in the quickly flowing process of life.

Owing to its extreme specificity, each enzyme will only form intermediate compounds with a particular substance (its substrate) and will only catalyse strictly determined individual reactions. The rates at which these reactions take place within the living body may therefore vary greatly, depending, in the first place, on the presence of a set of enzymes, and also on their catalytic activity. This latter can be greatly changed by internal physical and chemical circumstances and also by the action of the external medium. This sort of mobile relationship between the rates of individual biochemical reactions is, in fact, a prerequisite for the determinate sequences and concordances of these reactions in the whole complicated network of metabolism.

This sort of organisation of life may, in some ways, be compared with the organisation of a musical work, such as a symphony, the actual existence of which depends on determinate sequences and concordances of individual sounds. One has only to disturb the sequence and the symphony as such will be destroyed, only disharmony and chaos will remain.

In a similar way, the organisation of life is fundamentally dependent on a regular sequence of metabolic reactions and the form and structure of living bodies are flowing in nature. For this reason organisms can only exist for any length of time as a result of the continuous accomplishment of chemical transformations, which constitute the essence of living, and the cessation of which would lead to the disruption of the living system and the death of the organism.

In contrast to this, the basic structure of the machine is static. When the machine is working, only the energy source or fuel undergoes chemical change, while the actual structure remains materially unchanged irrespective of whether it is made of metal or of plastic, and the less it is changed (by corrosion for example) the longer the actual machine will last.

Thus, the actual principle of stability which enables them to exist for a prolonged period is different for organisms and machines. The similarities between them which have been enumerated above are, therefore, only very superficial and, when examined in more detail, they are seen to be purely formal.

We may demonstrate this in the particular case of mechanical movement by an organism. In the muscles of the animal carrying out this movement, the protein fibrils are orientated in a particular way relative to one another. Such a structure, however, cannot be likened in any way to that of a machine. In a machine the structural elements do not play any part whatsoever in the chemical transformation of the energy source. If the component parts of the machine were themselves to undergo chemical transformation during their work, this would, of course, lead quickly to the destruction of the whole mechanism. On the other hand, the elements of construction of the living body, the protein fibrils in this case, themselves take a direct part in the metabolic reactions which serve as the source of that energy which is transformed into mechanical movement. The same may also be said of the comparison of organisms with heat engines in respect of energetics. We now know that the analogy between respiration and combustion is very formal. In combustion the surmounting of the energy of activation, which is necessary for the accomplishment of the oxidative reactions, is done by raising the temperature considerably, whereas in respiration this is not needed. Respiration is based on an enzymic lowering of the energy of activation.

If the transformation of energy took place in the same way in organisms as it does in heat engines, then, at temperatures at which living things can exist, the coefficient of their useful activity would fall to an insignificant fraction of one per cent. It is, in fact, amazingly high, considerably higher than that obtained in present-day heat engines. The explanation of this is that the oxidation of sugar, or any other respiratory fuel, in the organism takes place not as a single chemical act, but by a series of individual reactions co-ordinated in time.

If the oxidation of organic materials in the organism took place suddenly, then the living body would be unable to make rational use of all the energy set free in this way, especially if it was given off in the form of heat. In the oxidation of only 1 mole (180 g.) of sugar about 700 kcal. are liberated. The instantaneous liberation of this amount of energy would be associated with a sharp rise in temperature, the denaturation of proteins and the destruction of the living body. This same energy effect, which is brought about by the organism under ordinary conditions of low temperature, depends on the fact that in the process of biological oxidation, sugar is not converted into carbon dioxide and water suddenly, but slowly, by stages. A process of this sort not only gives the possibility of surmounting the energy of activation at ordinary temperatures, it also enables the living body to make rational use of the energy which is gradually set free. Thus, the more highly organised the metabolism, i.e., the better the co-ordination between the separate reactions comprising it, the higher the coefficient of useful activity.

The principle of evaluating nutrients simply in terms of their content of calories led to many difficulties in its practical application. This principle was only overthrown with great difficulty, as a result of studies of vitamins and essential amino acids, and investigations which showed that, unlike a heat engine, there occurs in the organisms, not only oxidation of energy-providing material, but also transformation of the fundamental protein structures of the living body, which are broken down and resynthesised in the general interaction of the organism with the external medium.

Finally, it must be pointed out that the ways of 'overcoming entropy' used by organisms and contemporary mechanisms or automats also differ from one another in principle. As we have shown above, organisms manage to avoid 'thermodynamic equilibrium' just because they are open or flowing systems. Recent studies of the thermodynamics of such systems have shown them to be essentially different from classical thermodynamics, which is based on the phenomena observed in closed systems. It gives us a perfectly rational explanation of why it is that, in organisms, entropy not only does not increase, but may even decrease.

According to Wiener, a different principle underlies the ability of contemporary cybernetic automats to counteract the tendency to the increase of entropy and to create zones of organisation around themselves. In order to explain this ability, Wiener uses the same idea as Maxwell used in the form of his demons. According to present-day ideas, however, this 'Maxwell's demon' has to be continually obtaining 'information' according to which he opens or closes the doors to molecules of high or low rates of movement. For a number of years the overriding wish to identify the organism with a mechanism forced many scientists to ignore all the increasing factual evidence and look for some rigid, unchanging, static structures in the living body so that these structures themselves might be regarded as the specific bearers of life.

At the end of last century it was widely held among biologists that the organisation of protoplasm was based on the presence in it of a certain machine-like structure formed of solid and unchanging 'beams and braces' interlacing with one another. It was thought that the only thing that prevented us from seeing this structure was the imperfection of our optical methods.

As these methods developed, however, the search for static, 'life-determining' structures was first transferred to the realm of colloid chemical formations and then to the realm of intramolecular structure. In this way there arose the concept that the material carriers of life are to be found in the single molecules of heritable substance which have a static, unchanging structure and form a part of the nuclear chromosomes. This concept is associated with the work of T. Morgan and his followers concerning the gene nature of life. According to H. Muller the "living gene molecule" can only undergo change in detail but is essentially so static that it has maintained its internal life-determining structure unchanged throughout the whole development of life on the Earth. This concept of the Morgan school of geneticists was fully expressed in Schroedinger's well-known book *What is Life?* Schroedinger saw the key to the understanding of life in the fact that the structure which is the only one natural and peculiar to life, namely that of the gene, "is so long-lasting and constant as to border on the miraculous". It is as unchanging as though it were frozen. Thus, according to Schroedinger, the organisation of life is based upon the principle of 'clockwork', the structure of which remains completely constant at room temperature as well as at absolute zero. In his conclusion Schroedinger writes "Now, I think, few words more are needed to disclose the point of resemblance between a clockwork and an organism. It is simply and solely that the latter also hinges upon a solid – the aperiodic crystal forming the hereditary substance, largely withdrawn from the disorder of heat motion."

The only new thing that has been added to the gene theory up to now is that an attempt has been made to give a chemical reality to the previously rather vague idea of the gene molecule in the form of a suggestion that the living molecule may be a particle of nuclear nucleoprotein or, according to the latest evidence, simply the molecule of desoxyribonucleic acid. It would seem that everything else in the cell is to be regarded as merely the medium for the 'living molecule'.

From this point of view the capacity for self-reproduction, which is characteristic of living things, is based only on the strictly determinate, static, intramolecular structure of desoxyribonucleic acid (DNA), on the specific arrangement of purine pyrimidine mononucleotide residues in the polynucleotide chain of DNA. This arrangement represents, in the terminology of cybernetics, the code in which the whole collection of specific characteristics of the living body is stored. The transfer of 'hereditary information' may thus be thought of as something like the work of a stamping machine in which the molecule of DNA represents the matrix which always reproduces a single uniform structure. Such hypotheses are very impressive to the protagonists of the machine theory of life and are therefore very widely supported by contemporary physicists as well as biologists. We shall go into this in more detail in the course of further explanation. All that is needed now is to remark briefly on the present state of the problem. The more concrete the biochemical studies of the self-reproduction of living things, the more obvious it becomes that the process is not just bound up with this or that particular substance or a single molecule of it, but is determined by the whole system of organisation of the living body which, as we have seen, is flowing in nature and is in no way to be compared with a stamping machine with an unchanging matrix. Speaking on this subject at the 4th International Congress of Biochemistry, E. Chargaff said. "It is even possible that we may be dealing with templates in time rather than in space", by which he meant a definite order in which processes occur in the living thing. In any case when we are not making a formal comparison between the phenomena occurring in living beings and those occurring in machines, but are trying to understand what they are really like, we find, not only similarities, but also a profound difference between the two kinds of system. This difference is not merely fortuitous but forms the very essence of their organisation.

In the first place, it is connected with the fact that the 'purpose' which inspires a person to create some machine which is necessary to him has nothing in common with the task of self-preservation and self-reproduction which determines the organisation of living things. The aims in constructing a watch, a steam locomotive or an automatic device for defence against aerial attack are to tell the time correctly, to transport people and goods and effectively to bring down enemy aircraft. Owing to our present ways of thinking and technical habits which have evolved over many centuries we find it far easier to solve these problems rationally by building static structures out of metal or some solid plastic material, and this is what, in fact, we do.

In this way the actual principles of construction of any machine now in existence reflect the character of the person who made it, his intellectual and technological level, his aims and his methods of solving the problems in front of him.

This also applies fully to the various 'cybernetic toys' which are now being made, the point of which is simply to imitate living things, such as Grey Walter's 'tortoise', Shannon's 'mouse', Ducrocq's 'fox' and Ashby's 'homeostat', constructions which have been wittily described by Grey Walter as "machines which can serve no useful purpose". The structure of all these necessarily carries the predetermination put there by those who constructed them and P. Cossa was quite right when, in his book, *La cybernétique* (Paris, 1957), he wrote of them as follows: —

> What is inherent in the living thing (adaptability), is not merely the means but the end itself: the preservation of life, the preservation of the continuity of existence by adaptation to the environment. There is nothing like this in the homeostat, it has no inherent ultimate aim. If a living thing, which has had its equilibrium upset, perseveringly tries out, one after another, all possible means of adapting itself to its new environment, this is explained as an effort to survive. If the homeostat tries out its 390625 combinations one after another it only does so because that is what Ashby wanted of it.[4]

---

4. Retranslation from Russian. A. S.

Of course one may imagine machines of the future which will imitate living things very closely; machines designed as flowing systems in which energy is used by easy stages; they might even be able to reproduce themselves etc. All the same, the organisation of these machines would still reflect the specific task which those who made them had set themselves; they would always bear the marks of their origins.

The insuperable difference in principle between machines and organisms stands out specially clearly when we consider the question of the origin of individual systems. We know that, in its general organisation in which the structure is adapted to the performance of particular tasks, a machine develops first in the mind of its creator and nòt as a real physical system. This idea is then expressed in drawings or plans. These plans usually form the basis for the construction of individual components in accordance with their specifications. These are then assembled and it is only at this stage that the machine appears as a physical object.

The way in which a machine arises is, thus, perfectly clear, but if we try to solve the problem of the origin of living things by analogy with machines, we shall, logically and inevitably, reach an idealistic conclusion.

The book by Schroedinger, which has already been quoted, may serve as a good example of this. In it the author set out to understand life from the point of view of physics, that is, on a purely materialist basis. Nevertheless, in his conclusion, he was forced to characterise life as "the finest masterpiece ever achieved along the lines of the Lord's quantum mechanics", i.e. to put it plainly, he acknowledged the divine origin of life.

There is a difference in form, but not in substance, between this conclusion and those of other attempts to solve the problem of the origin of life which have been made on the basis of purely mechanistic assumptions as to its genetic nature (e.g. those of A. Dauvillier, G. Blum, L. Roka and others). Essentially all these attempts arrive at the same explanation. In the primitive and, as yet, lifeless solution of organic material there somehow arose particles of protein, nucleic acid or nucleoprotein and these, suddenly, on their appearance, had an intramolecular structure which was extremely well adapted to the accomplishment of self-reproduction and other vital functions. Thus, there arose the 'primary living matrix' which could later be elaborated, but the 'purposive' life-determining structure was not necessarily immediately the same as it is to-day. The question then arises as to what were the natural laws underlying the origin of an intramolecular structure which was adapted to the performance of specific functions. Iron can exist in the elementary form in inorganic nature and, under certain circumstances, may take the form of shapeless lumps, but, as Aristotle wrote, even a sword cannot arise in this way without human intervention, for its structure is suited to the accomplishment of a particular end. In just the same way (as we shall see later) those physical and chemical laws, which were the only ones prevailing in the waters of the primaeval ocean, were quite enough to account for the primary formation, in those waters, of high-molecular protein-like polymers and polynucleotides with a more or less irregular arrangement of mononucleotide residues. By themselves, however, these laws are quite insufficient to provide for the possibility of the development of any structures adapted to the performance of particular functions. The supporters of these hypotheses 'explain' so to speak, the functional suitability of the structures of their primary matrices as being due to 'a lucky chance' or 'just pure chance', in which Dauvillier is justified in seeing 'the hand of an eccentric creator'. This 'hand' does not differ essentially from Schroedinger's 'the Lord's quantum mechanics' nor even from St. Augustine's 'divine will'.

In his book, the English edition of which bears the most intriguing title, *The Origins of Life*, A. Ducrocq claims to have given a general explanation of life and its origins based on 'cybernetic theory' and to have demonstrated the laws of the delicate interaction of forces whereby "conglomerates of atoms are transformed into living aggregates", i.e. living things. On closer acquaintance with this book, however, we find that, in the last analysis, the whole thing amounts to a statement that the chain of DNA, which served as the point of origin for the whole series of living things and which was constructed in a specific way, must have appeared in some improbable way in the solution of organic substances, for its appearance "had a probability which was not nil". In what way is this different from those numerous hypotheses, which we have already mentioned, about the chance origin of life?

Physicists assert that, in principle, it is possible that, by chance, the table on which I am writing might rise up of its own accord into the air owing to the simultaneous orientation of the thermal movement of all its molecules in the same direction. It is hardly likely, however, that anyone would conduct his experimental work, or his practical activities in general, with this possibility in view. Furthermore, the experimental scientist attaches value to those theories which open up possibilities for investigation, but how can one study a phenomenon which, at the best, could only occur once in the whole time of the existence of the Earth? The conception of the chance origin of the 'living molecule' is, therefore, completely fruitless from a practical point of view and, as we shall see later, it is also theoretically unsound.

There can be no doubt that the conscious or unconscious attempts to liken the origin of living things to the assembly of a machine also lies at the root of the many contemporary statements to the effect that, in the original solution of organic substances, there were formed various substances which were at once structurally suitable and well adapted to the carrying out of particular vital functions and then, by their combination, they gave rise to the first living body, just as a machine is assembled from separate components the structure of which was already adapted to doing a particular job.

According to these statements the first thing that happened, even before the appearance of the most primitive organism, was the formation of protein-enzymes with their strictly determinate intramolecular structures and their very efficient adaptation to the carrying out of particular catalytic reactions which are very important in metabolism, nucleic acids, which play an essential part in the process of reproduction of organisms and other compounds which are to be found in the very efficient 'rationally constructed' organs of living protoplasm as we know it, though this itself only arose secondarily by the combination of the primary compounds.

Such an idea reminds one of the sayings of the ancient Greek philosopher Empedocles who believed that, when living things originally came into being, individual organs were first formed independently of one another — "Thus there grew up a multitude of heads without necks, naked arms wandered around without their shoulders and eyes moved about with no foreheads." Later these unmatched members joined together and in this way the various sorts of animals and people were formed.

It is only possible to understand life by studying
its origin and development

From the modern Darwinian point of view the falsity, not to say absurdity, of such a theory is perfectly obvious. Any particular organ can only originate and become perfected as part of the evolutionary development of the organism as a whole.

The specialised and complicated structure of the eye and the hand are adapted to their purpose only when considered in relation to the functions which they carry out. It is impossible, even unthinkable, to take seriously the evolution of an individual organ such as the Empedoclean 'eyes with no foreheads' because the very functions which determined their structure would have no meaning under those circumstances. The action of natural selection can, therefore, only affect them as parts of whole living things.

In just the same way enzymes, nucleic acids and so on are only parts of the living body, they are like organs, subserving definite, vitally necessary functions. Thus the catalytic activity of enzymes or the specific functions of nucleic acids are of no importance to the substances themselves but are only important to the whole living body in which the particular metabolic reactions take place. It follows that, when not a part of such a body, before its formation, they would be quite unable to acquire a 'purposive' structure, suited to carrying out their vital functions. It is quite natural and right to suppose that there were successive developments proceeding from simpler to more complicated systems, but, although the individual organs are simpler than the whole organism, we should not be like Empedocles and imagine that animals and people arose by the fusion of individual organs.

Darwin showed the true way in which higher organisms have arisen by the evolution of lower living things which were more simply organised but were still complete systems in themselves.

Similarly it would be wrong to suppose that, in the organically rich waters of the primaeval ocean, there arose proteins and nucleic acids with a 'purposive' structure extremely accurately and well adapted to the carrying out of particular biological functions and that, later, by their combination, the living body itself was created.

All that we can expect from the action of the laws of physics and chemistry, which were the only ones on the still lifeless Earth, is that there were formed more or less randomly constructed polymers with a haphazard distribution of peptides and mononucleotides and thus having no 'purposiveness' or adaptation to the carrying out of particular functions.

These polymers could, however, join together with one another to form complete multimolecular systems though, naturally, these were incomparably simpler than living bodies. It was only as a result of the prolonged evolution of these original systems, their interaction with their environment and their natural selection, that there arose those forms of organisation which are peculiar to the living body, namely metabolism, and with it proteins, enzymes, nucleic acids and those other complicated and 'purposefully' constructed substances which are characteristic of contemporary organisms. Thus there is not even the most remote similarity between the origin of life and the assembly of a machine.

These two sorts of system show a likeness to each other only if we consider them in their finished state, divorced from their origins. Once we start to deal with this question the difference between the machine and the organism immediately becomes apparent and it is obvious that the two kinds of system are essentially of a different quality.

This concept is understandable and even simple, for the origin of life and the origin of the machine took place at very widely separated levels of evolutionary development.

We may note the following important stages in this development from the moment of the formation of the Earth to the present day. For the first milliards of years of its existence our planet had no life on it and all the processes occurring on it were subject only to the laws of physics and chemistry. This stage of development may be referred to as inorganic or abiogenic. Life then arose on the Earth and a new biological stage of evolution began. Now new biological laws were added to the old physical and chemical ones and these new laws have now come to the fore and assumed an ever-growing importance in the progressive development of living things. The crowning achievement of this period was the emergence of man heralding the beginning of the third or social stage of evolution. Now even the biological laws have been driven from the foreground and the laws of development of human society have begun to play the leading part in further progress.

It is very important that, with the beginning of each new stage of development, with the origin of a new form of the movement of matter, the tempo of its evolution increases. The abiogenic period of the existence of the Earth lasted for thousands of millions of years, but the decisive progress of biological evolution only required hundreds or perhaps even tens of millions of years for its accomplishment. The whole development of mankind has only lasted a million years. Social transformations have occurred within thousands of years or even centuries and now we can easily notice substantial changes in human society over periods reckoned in decades.

There can hardly have been any significant biological change in the human race since the time of Aristotle, but it is only during the last few hundred years that man has attained hitherto unimaginable power over his environment. He can cover the ground faster than any deer, swim beneath the water better than any fish and fly through the air incomparably faster and further than any bird. But this is not because he has grown wings or fins and gills during that time. The powers acquired by mankind are not the result of biological but of social development. In particular, machines, which play such an outstanding part in man's conquest of the forces of nature are the fruit of this development, for man could only create them by all-round mastery of the experiences accumulated by his forebears over many centuries, only, in fact, on the basis of the communal life of mankind.

Thus machines are not merely inorganic systems operating in accordance with no laws other than those of physics and chemistry. They are, in origin, not biological but higher, i.e. social forms of the motion of matter. We can therefore only understand their real nature through studying their origin. We shall now discuss some other examples so that this may become clearer to the reader.

On the banks of great rivers, which have worn down thick sedimentary formations, one may find stones made of calcite which are commonly called 'devil's fingers' because of their queer shape, which certainly does remind one of the shape of a finger except that it is sharpened at one end into a cone. In old times people believed that these objects were formed by lightning striking sand and even their scientific name — belemnites — is derived from this supposition as to their origin. If this were the case they should always be associated with mineral formations of the abiogenic, inorganic world. In fact, however, it has been shown that belemnites are the fossilised remains of rostra, which are parts of the insides of molluscs, and that these are characteristic of a particular group of cephalopod molluscs which lived in the Jurassic and Cretaceous periods and were completely extinct by the beginning of the Tertiary period. On the surface of some belemnites one may even find traces of the blood vessels of the mantle, or soft envelope, of the body of the mollusc which once enclosed the belemnite. Thus belemnites, taken on their own without reference to their origin, are clearly completely lacking in life. From the point of view of their chemical composition and also from that of their characteristic physical properties they appear to be objects of the inorganic world. Belemnites, however, could not be formed in that world as a result of the elementary forces of inorganic nature alone. For this reason we cannot understand the essential nature of these objects if we do not know about their biological origin or the history of the development of life on the Earth. In that case they would certainly seem to us to be some miraculous 'devil's fingers'.

I will now ask my readers to let me indulge in fantasy as this will enable me to present my ideas more clearly.

Let us imagine that people have succeeded in making automatic machines or robots which can not only carry out a lot of work for mankind but can even independently create the energetic conditions necessary for their work, obtain metals and use them to construct components, and from these build new robots like themselves. Then some terrible disaster happened on the Earth, and it destroyed not only all the people but all living things on our planet. The metallic robots, however, remained. They continued to build others like themselves and so, although the old mechanisms gradually wore out, new ones arose and the 'race' of robots continued and even, perhaps, increased within limits.

Let us further imagine that all this has already happened on one of the planets of our solar system, on Mars, for example, and that we have landed on that planet. On its waterless and lifeless expanses we suddenly meet with the robots. Do we have to regard them as living inhabitants of the planet? Of course not. The robots will not represent life but something else. Maybe a very complicated and efficient form of the organisation and movement of matter, but still different from life. They are analogous to the belemnites which we have already considered, the only difference being that the belemnites arose in the process of biological development while the robots were based on the higher, social form of the motion of matter.

Life existed in the Jurassic sea and the rostra of cephalopod molluscs played a particular part in it. The life vanished and the belemnites remained, but now they appear to be lifeless objects of the inorganic world. Similarly, automatic machines and, in particular, our imaginary robots, could only develop as offshoots of human (or some similar) society, as the fruit of the social form of organisation and movement of matter, and they have played a considerable part in the development of that form of organisation. But that form was destroyed, it vanished and the robots are on their own, not controlled by it. They are completely subject to the laws of physics and chemistry alone.

Nevertheless, just as one cannot understand what a belemnite is if one has no knowledge of life, so it is impossible to grasp the nature of the 'Martian robot' without a sufficient acquaintance with the social form of the motion of matter which gave rise to it. This would be true even if one were able to take down the robot into its individual components and reassemble it correctly. Even then there would remain hidden from our understanding those features of the organisation of the robot which were purposefully constructed for the solution of problems which those who built them envisaged at some time, but which are completely unknown to us.

When the Lilliputians found a watch in Gulliver's pocket they were not in a state to understand its nature properly, although, according to Swift, the Lilliputians had a very extensive knowledge of mathematics and mechanics. After prolonged deliberation they decided that it was a pocket god which Gulliver consulted each time he started to do something.

If some 'thinking Martian' were to chance on a watch flying about somewhere in space perhaps he too would be able to take it to pieces and put it together again but there would still be a lot about it that would be incomprehensible to him. And not only will the Martians not understand, but many of my readers will probably not be able to explain why there are only twelve numbers on the faces of ordinary clocks although the day is divided into twenty-four hours. This question can only be answered from a good knowledge of the history of human culture and, in particular, of the history of watchmaking.

Similarly, an understanding of the nature of life is impossible without a knowledge of the history of its origin. Usually, however, the nature and origin of life have been regarded, and are even now regarded, as being two completely separate problems. Thus, at the end of last century and the beginning of the present one the problem of the origin of life was denounced as an accursed and insoluble problem, work on which was unworthy of a serious scientist and was a pure waste of time. People tried to achieve an understanding of the nature of life, which is the main problem of biology at present, primarily in a purely metaphysical way, completely isolated from its origin. In principle this amounts to their wanting, crudely speaking, to take the living body apart into its component screws and wheels like a watch and then to try to put it together again.

Even Mephistopheles jeered at such an approach in his advice to the young scholar.

> Wer will was Lebendigs erkennen und beschreiben,
> Sucht erst den Geist herauszutreiben,
> Dann hat er die Teile in seiner Hand,
> Fehlt leider! nur das geistige Band.
> *Encheiresin naturae* nennt's die Chemie,
> Spottet ihrer selbst, und weiss nicht wie.[5]

Of course, a detailed analysis of the substances and phenomena peculiar to contemporary living things is extremely important and absolutely necessary for an understanding of life. That is beyond doubt. The whole question is whether this, by itself, is enough for such an understanding. It is clearly not. Even now, for all our skill in this sort of analysis, we are still very far from being able to point to any way in which life could actually be synthesised although we admit that this synthesis is theoretically perfectly possible.

This is by no means merely because our analysis has, as yet, not been finished, that we still have not found out all the details of the structure of the living body.

"The whole", wrote M. Planck, "is always somewhat different from the sum of the separate parts." It is only possible to understand this whole by knowing it in its maturity and in its development, by studying and reproducing the processes of gradual elaboration and perfection of the more primitive systems which were its precursors.

It is now becoming more and more obvious that a knowledge of the essential nature of life is only possible through a knowledge of its

---

5. Whoso would describe and know aught that's alive
   Seeks first the spirit forth to drive;
   The parts he then hath in his hand,
   But lacks, alas! the spirit-band.
   Encheiresin naturae chemists call it now,
   Mock at themselves and know not how.

Trans. W. H. van der Smissen

origin. Now, too, this origin no longer seems so puzzling as it did not long ago. We are sketching out in more and more detail the actual ways in which life arose on the Earth. It could only have happened as an integral part of the general historic development of our planet. The facts at our disposal indicate that the origin of life was a gradual process in which organic substances became more and more complicated and formed complete systems which were in a state of continual interaction with the medium surrounding them.

Following the path of the emergence of life in this way we encounter neither the 'almighty hand of the Creator' nor machines which made their appearance at a far later stage in the development of matter. We do, however, discover in this way how and why it is that the particular original systems which existed were transformed, in the process of evolution, into those which are characteristic of life instead of into others and how, in that same process of the establishment of life, there arose new biological laws which had not existed before, and also how the 'purposiveness' which we notice in all living things came into being.

In this way our knowledge gives us a real understanding of the essential organisation of the most primitive forms of life and, on that basis, we can easily follow the further evolution of these forms by applying the precepts of evolutionary theory. We can trace the formation of new features characteristic of highly organised living beings, including man, who is the culmination of the biological stage of the development of matter.

Thus we arrive at the main idea underlying this book which had already been formulated by Heraclitus of Ephesus and was included in the works of Aristotle: — "One can only understand the essence of things when one knows their origin and development."

THE RELATION OF QUANTUM THEORY TO OTHER PARTS OF NATURAL SCIENCE

Werner Heisenberg

It has been stated before that the concepts of natural science can sometimes be sharply defined with regard to their connections. This possibility was realized for the first time in Newton's *Principia* and it is just for that reason that Newton's work has exerted its enormous influence on the whole development of natural science in the following centuries. Newton begins his *Principia* with a group of definitions and axioms which are interconnected in such a way that they form what one may call a "closed system." Each concept can be represented by a mathematical symbol, and the connections between the different concepts are then represented by mathematical equations expressed by means of the symbols. The mathematical image of the system ensures that contradictions cannot occur in the system. In this way the possible motions of bodies under the influence of the acting forces are represented by the possible solutions of the equations. The system of definitions and axioms which can be written in a set of mathematical equations is considered as describing an eternal structure of nature, depending neither on a particular space nor on particular time.

The connection between the different concepts in the system is so close that one could generally not change any one of the concepts without destroying the whole system.

For this reason Newton's system was for a long time considered as final and the task set before the scientists of the following period

"The Relation of Quantum Theory to Other Parts of Natural Science," Chapter VI in *Physics and Philosophy: The Revolution in Modern Science* (New York: Harper & Brothers, 1958), pp. 93–109. Reprinted with the permission of Harper & Row, Publishers, Incorporated. Permission covering markets in the British Commonwealth granted by George Allen & Unwin, Ltd., London.

seemed simply to be an expansion of Newton's mechanics into wider fields of experience. Actually physics did develop along these lines for about two centuries.

From the theory of the motion of mass points one could go over to the mechanics of solid bodies, to rotatory motions, and one could treat the continuous motions of a fluid or the vibrating motions of an elastic body. All these parts of mechanics or dynamics were gradually developed in close connection with the evolution of mathematics, especially of the differential calculus, and the results were checked by experiments. Acoustics and hydrodynamics became a part of mechanics. Another science, in which the application of Newton's mechanics was obvious, was astronomy. The improvements of the mathematical methods gradually led to more and more accurate determinations of the motions of the planets and of their mutual interactions. When the phenomena of electricity and magnetism were discovered, the electric or magnetic forces were compared to the gravitational forces and their actions upon the motion of the bodies could again be studied along the lines of Newtonian mechanics. Finally, in the nineteenth century, even the theory of heat could be reduced to mechanics by the assumption that heat really consists of a complicated statistical motion of the smallest parts of matter. By combining the concepts of the mathematical theory of probability with the concepts of Newtonian mechanics Clausius, Gibbs and Boltzmann were able to show that the fundamental laws in the theory of heat could be interpreted as statistical laws following from Newton's mechanics when applied to very complicated mechanical systems.

Up to this point the program set up by Newtonian mechanics had been carried out quite consistently and had led to the understanding of a wide field of experience. The first difficulty arose in the discussions on the electromagnetic field in the work of Faraday and Maxwell. In Newtonian mechanics the gravitational force had been considered as given, not as an object for further theoretical studies. In the work of Faraday and Maxwell, however, the field of force itself became the object of the investigation; the physicists wanted to know how this field of force varied as function of space and time. Therefore, they tried to set up equations of motion for the fields, not primarily for the bodies upon which the fields act. This change led back to a point of view which had been held by many scientists before Newton. An action could, so it seemed, be transferred from one body to another only when the two bodies touched each other; for instance, in a collision or through friction. Newton had introduced a very new and strange hypothesis by assuming a force that acted over a long distance. Now in the theory of the fields of force one could come back to the older idea, that action is transferred from one point to a neighboring point, only by describing the behavior of the fields in terms of differential equations. This proved actually to be possible, and therefore the description of the electromagnetic fields as given by Maxwell's equations seemed a satisfactory solution of the problem of force. Here one had really changed the program given by Newtonian mechanics. The axioms and definitions of Newton had referred to bodies and their motion; but with Maxwell the fields of force seemed to have acquired the same degree of reality as the bodies in Newton's theory. This view of course was not easily accepted; and to avoid such a change in the concept of reality it seemed plausible to compare the electromagnetic fields with the fields of elastic deformation or stress, the light waves of Maxwell's theory with the sound waves in elastic bodies. Therefore, many physicists believed that Maxwell's equations actually referred to the deformations of an elastic medium, which they called the ether; and this name was given merely to explain that the medium was so light and thin that it could penetrate into other matter and could not be seen or felt. This explanation was not too satisfactory, however, since it could not explain the complete absence of any longitudinal light waves.

Finally the theory of relativity . . . showed in a conclusive way that the concept of the ether as a substance, to which Maxwell's equations refer, had to be abandoned. The arguments cannot be discussed at this point; but the result was that the fields had to be considered as an independent reality.

A further and still more startling result of the theory of special relativity was the discovery of new properties of space and time, actually of a relation between space and time that had not been known before and did not exist in Newtonian mechanics.

Under the impression of this completely new situation many physicists came to the following somewhat rash conclusion: Newtonian mechanics had finally been disproved. The primary reality is the field and not the body, and the structure of space and time is correctly described by the formulas of Lorentz and Einstein, and not by the axioms of Newton. The mechanics of Newton was a good approximation in many cases, but now it must be improved to give a more rigorous description of nature.

From the point of view which we have finally reached in quantum theory such a statement would appear as a very poor description of the actual situation. First, it ignores the fact that most experiments by which fields are measured are based upon Newtonian mechanics and, second, that Newtonian mechanics cannot be improved; it can only be replaced by something essentially different!

The development of quantum theory has taught us that one should rather describe the situation in the following terms: Wherever the concepts of Newtonian mechanics can be used to describe events in nature, the laws formulated by Newton are strictly correct and cannot be improved. But the electromagnetic phenomena cannot adequately be described by the concepts of Newtonian mechanics. Therefore, the experiments on the electromagnetic fields and on light waves, together with their theoretical analysis by Maxwell, Lorentz and Einstein, have led to a new closed system of definitions and axioms and of concepts that can be represented by mathematical symbols, which is coherent in the same sense as the system of Newton's mechanics, but is essentially different from it.

Therefore, even the hopes which had accompanied the work of the scientists since Newton had to be changed. Apparently progress in science could not always be achieved by using the known laws of nature for explaining new phenomena. In some cases new phenomena that had been observed could only be understood by new concepts which were adapted to the new phenomena in the same way as Newton's concepts were to the mechanical events. These new concepts again could be connected in a closed system and represented by mathematical symbols. But if physics or, more generally, natural science proceeded in this way, the question arose: What is the relation between the different sets of concepts? If, for instance, the same concepts or words occur in two different sets and are defined differently with regard to their connection and mathematical representation, in what sense do the concepts represent reality?

This problem arose at once when the theory of special relativity had been discovered. The concepts of space and time belonged both to Newtonian mechanics and to the theory of relativity. But space and time in Newtonian mechanics were independent; in the theory of relativity they were connected by the Lorentz transformation. In this special case one could show that the statements of the theory of relativity approached those of Newtonian mechanics within the limit in which all velocities in the system are very small as compared with the velocity of light. From this one could conclude that the concepts of Newtonian mechanics could not be applied to events in which there occurred velocities comparable to the velocity of light. Thereby one had finally found an essential limitation of Newtonian mechanics which could not be seen from the coherent set of concepts nor from simple observations on mechanical systems.

Therefore, the relation between two different coherent sets of concepts always requires very careful investigation. Before we enter into a general discussion about the structure of any such closed and coherent set of concepts and about their possible relations we will give a brief description of those sets of concepts that have so far been defined in physics. One can distinguish four systems that have already attained their final form.

The first set, Newtonian mechanics, has already been discussed. It is suited for the description of all mechanical systems, of the motion of fluids and the elastic vibration of bodies; it comprises acoustics, statics, aerodynamics.

The second closed system of concepts was formed in the course of the nineteenth century in connection with the theory of heat. Though the theory of heat could finally be connected with mechanics through the development of statistical mechanics, it would not be realistic to consider it as a part of mechanics. Actually the phenomenological theory of heat uses a number of concepts that have no counterpart in other branches of physics, like: heat, specific heat, entropy, free energy, etc. If from this phenomenological description one goes over to a statistical interpretation, by considering heat as energy, distributed statistically among the very many degrees of freedom due to the atomic structure of matter, then heat is no more connected with mechanics than with electrodynamics or other parts of physics. The central concept of this interpretation is the concept of probability, closely connected with the concept of entropy in the phenomenological theory. Besides this concept the statistical theory of heat requires the concept of energy. But any coherent set of axioms and concepts in physics will necessarily contain the concepts of energy, momentum and angular momentum and the law that these quantities must under certain conditions be conserved. This follows if the coherent set is intended to describe certain features of nature that are correct at all times and everywhere; in other words, features that do not depend on space and time or, as the mathematicians put it, that are invariant under arbitrary translations in space and time, rotations in space and the Galileo—or Lorentz—transformation. Therefore, the theory of heat can be combined with any of the other closed systems of concepts.

The third closed system of concepts and axioms has its origin in the phenomena of electricity and magnetism and has reached its final form in the first decade of the twentieth century through the work of Lorentz, Einstein and Minkowski. It comprises electrodynamics, special relativity, optics, magnetism, and one may include the de Broglie theory of matter waves of all different sorts of elementary particles, but not the wave theory of Schrödinger.

Finally, the fourth coherent system is essentially the quantum theory. . . . Its central concept is the probability function, or the "statistical matrix," as the mathematicians call it. It comprises quantum and wave mechanics, the theory of atomic spectra, chemistry, and the theory of other properties of matter like electric conductivity, ferromagnetism, etc.

The relations between these four sets of concepts can be indicated in the following way: The first set is contained in the third as the limiting case where the velocity of light can be considered as infinitely big, and is contained in the fourth as the limiting case where Planck's constant of action can be considered as infinitely small. The first and partly the third set belong to the fourth as a priori for the description of the experiments. The second set can be connected with any of the other three sets without difficulty and is especially important in its connection with the fourth. The independent existence of the third and fourth sets suggests the existence of a fifth set, of which one, three, and four are limiting cases. This fifth set will probably be found someday in connection with the theory of the elementary particles.

We have omitted from this enumeration the set of concepts connected with the theory of general relativity, since this set has perhaps not yet reached its final form. But it should be emphasized that it is distinctly different from the other four sets.

After this short survey we may come back to the more general question, what one should consider as the characteristic features of such a closed system of axioms and definitions. Perhaps the most important feature is the possibility of finding a consistent mathematical representation for it. This representation must guarantee that the system does not contain contradictions. Then the system must be suited to describe a wide field of experience. The great variety of phenomena in the field should correspond to the great number of solutions of the equations in the mathematical representation. The limitations of the field can generally not be derived from the concepts. The concepts are not sharply defined in their relation to nature, in spite of the sharp definition of their possible connections. The limitations will therefore be found from experience, from the fact that the concepts do not allow a complete description of the observed phenomena.

After this brief analysis of the structure of present-day physics the relation between physics and other branches of natural science may be discussed. The nearest neighbor to physics is chemistry. Actually through quantum theory these two sciences have come to a complete union. But a hundred years ago they were widely separated, their methods of research were quite different, and the concepts of chemistry had at that time no counterpart in physics. Concepts like valency, activity, solubility and volatility had a more qualitative character, and chemistry scarcely belonged to the exact sciences. When the theory of heat had been developed by the middle of the last century scientists started to apply it to the chemical processes, and ever since then the scientific work in this field has been determined by the hope of reducing the laws of chemistry to the mechanics of the atoms. It should be emphasized, however, that this was not possible within the framework of Newtonian mechanics. In order to give a quantitative description of the laws of chemistry one had to formulate a much wider system of concepts for atomic physics. This was finally done in quantum theory, which has its roots just as much in chemistry as in atomic physics. Then it was easy to see that the laws of chemistry could not be reduced to Newtonian mechanics of atomic particles, since the chemical elements displayed in their behavior a degree of stability completely lacking in mechanical systems. But it was not until Bohr's theory of the atom in 1913 that this point had been clearly understood. In the final result, one may say, the concepts of chemistry are in part complementary to the mechanical concepts. If we know that an atom is in its lowest stationary state that determines its chemical properties we cannot at the same time speak about the motion of the electrons in the atom.

The present relation between biology, on the one side, and physics and chemistry, on the other, may be very similar to that between chemistry and physics a hundred years ago. The methods of biology are different from those of physics and chemistry, and the typical biological concepts are of a more qualitative character than those of the exact sciences. Concepts like life, organ, cell, function of an organ, perception have no counterpart in physics or chemistry. On the other hand, most of the progress made in biology during the past hundred years has been achieved through the application of chemistry and physics to the living organism, and the whole tendency of biology in our time is to explain biological phenomena on the basis of the known physical and chemical laws. Again the question arises, whether this hope is justified or not.

Just as in the case of chemistry, one learns from simple biological experience that the living organisms display a degree of stability which general complicated structures consisting of many different types of molecules could certainly not have on the basis of the physical and chemical laws alone. Therefore, something has to be added to the laws of physics and chemistry before the biological phenomena can be completely understood.

With regard to this question two distinctly different views have frequently been discussed in the biological literature. The one view refers to Darwin's theory of evolution in its connection with modern genetics. According to this theory, the only concept which has to be added to those of physics and chemistry in order to understand life is the concept of history. The enormous time interval of roughly four thousand million years that has elapsed since the formation of the earth has given nature the possibility of trying an almost unlimited variety of structures of groups of molecules. Among these structures there have finally been some that could reduplicate themselves by using smaller groups from the surrounding matter, and such structures therefore could be created in great numbers. Accidental changes in the structures provided a still larger variety of the existing structures. Different structures had to compete for the material drawn from the surrounding matter and in this way, through the "survival of the fittest," the evolution of living organisms finally took place. There can be no doubt that this theory contains a very large amount of truth, and many biologists claim that the addition of the concepts of history and evolution to the coherent set of concepts of physics and chemistry will be amply sufficient to account for all biological phenomena. One of the arguments frequently used in favor of this theory emphasizes that wherever the laws of physics and chemistry have been checked in living organisms they have always been found to be correct; there seems definitely to be no place at which some "vital force" different from the forces in physics could enter.

On the other hand, it is just this argument that has lost much of its weight through quantum theory. Since the concepts of physics and chemistry form a closed and coherent set, namely, that of quantum theory, it is necessary that wherever these concepts can be used to describe phenomena the laws connected with the concepts must be valid too. Therefore, wherever one treats living organisms as physicochemical systems, they must necessarily act as such. The only question from which we can learn something about the adequacy of this first view is whether the physicochemical concepts allow a *complete* description of the organisms. Biologists, who answer this question in the negative, generally hold the second view, that has now to be explained.

This second view can perhaps be stated in the following terms: It is very difficult to see how concepts like perception, function of an organ, affection could be a part of the coherent set of the concepts of quantum theory combined with the concept of history. On the other hand, these concepts are necessary for a complete description of life, even if for the moment we exclude mankind as presenting new problems beyond biology. Therefore, it will probably be necessary for an understanding of life to go beyond quantum theory and to construct a new coherent set of concepts, to which physics and chemistry may belong as "limiting cases." History may be an essential part of it, and concepts like perception, adaptation, affection also will belong to it. If this view is correct, the combination of Darwin's theory with physics and chemistry would not be sufficient to explain organic life; but still it would be true that living organisms can to a large extent be considered as physicochemical systems—as machines, as Descartes and Laplace have put it—and would, if treated as such, also react as such. One could at the same time assume, as Bohr has suggested, that our knowledge of a cell being alive may be complementary to the complete knowledge of its molecular structure. Since a complete knowledge of this structure could possibly be achieved only by operations that destroy the life of the cell, it is logically possible that life precludes the complete determination of its underlying physicochemical structure. Even if one holds this second view one would probably recommend for biological research no other method than has been pursued in the past decades: attempting to explain as much as possible on the basis of the known physicochemical laws, and describing the behavior of organisms carefully and without theoretical prejudices.

The first of these two views is more common among modern biologists than the second; but the experience available at present is certainly not sufficient to decide between the two views. The preference that is given by many biologists to the first view may be due again to the Cartesian partition, which has penetrated so deeply into the human mind during the past centuries. Since the "res cogitans" was confined to men, to the "I," the animals could have no soul, they belonged exclusively to the "res extensa." Therefore, the animals can be understood, so it is argued, on the same terms as matter in general, and the laws of physics and chemistry together with the concept of history must be sufficient to explain their behavior. It is only when the "res cogitans" is brought in that a new situation arises which will require entirely new concepts. But the Cartesian partition is a dangerous oversimplification and it is therefore quite possible that the second view is the correct one.

Quite apart from this question, which cannot be settled yet, we are obviously still very far from such a coherent and closed set of concepts for the description of biological phenomena. The degree of complication in biology is so discouraging that one can at present not imagine any set of concepts in which the connections could be so sharply defined that a mathematical representation could become possible.

If we go beyond biology and include psychology in the discussion, then there can scarcely be any doubt but that the concepts of physics, chemistry, and evolution together will not be sufficient to describe the facts. On this point the existence of quantum theory has changed our attitude from what was believed in the nineteenth century. During that period some scientists were inclined to think that the psychological phenomena could ultimately be explained on the basis of physics and chemistry of the brain. From the quantum-theoretical point of view there is no reason for such an assumption. We would, in spite of the fact that the physical events in the brain belong to the psychic phenomena, not expect that these could be sufficient to explain them. We would never doubt that the brain acts as a physicochemical mechanism if treated as such; but for an understanding of psychic phenomena we would start from the fact that the human mind enters as object and subject into the scientific process of psychology.

Looking back to the different sets of concepts that have been formed in the past or may possibly be formed in the future in the attempt to find our way through the world by means of science, we see that they appear to be ordered by the increasing part played by the subjective element in the set. Classical physics can be considered as that idealization in which we speak about the world as entirely separated from ourselves. The first three sets correspond to this idealization. Only the first set complies entirely with the "a priori" in the philosophy of Kant. In the fourth set, that of quantum theory, man as the subject of science is brought in through the questions which are put to nature in the a priori terms of human science. Quantum theory does not allow a completely objective description of nature. In biology it may be important for a complete understanding that the questions are asked by the species man which itself belongs to the genus of living organisms, in other words, that we already know what life is even before we have defined it scientifically. But one should perhaps not enter into speculations about the possible structure of sets of concepts that have not yet been formed.

When one compares this order with older classifications that belong to earlier stages of natural science one sees that one has now divided the world not into different groups of objects but into different groups of connections. In an earlier period of science one distinguished, for instance, as different groups minerals, plants, animals, men. These objects were taken according to their group as of different natures, made of different materials, and determined in their behavior by different forces. Now we know that it is always the same matter, the same various chemical compounds that may belong to any object, to minerals as well as animals or plants; also the forces that act between the different parts of matter are ultimately the same in every kind of object. What can be distinguished is the kind of connection which is primarily important in a certain phenomenon. For instance, when we speak about the action of chemical forces we mean a kind of connection which is more complicated or in any case different from that expressed in Newtonian mechanics. The world thus appears as a complicated tissue of events, in which connections of different kinds alternate or overlap or combine and thereby determine the texture of the whole.

When we represent a group of connections by a closed and coherent set of concepts, axioms, definitions and laws which in turn is represented by a mathematical scheme we have in fact isolated and idealized this group of connections with the purpose of clarification. But even if complete clarity has been achieved in this way, it is not known how accurately the set of concepts describes reality.

These idealizations may be called a part of the human language that has been formed from the interplay between the world and ourselves, a human response to the challenge of nature. In this respect they may be compared to the different styles of art, say of architecture or music. A style of art can also be defined by a set of formal rules which are applied to the material of this special art. These rules can perhaps not be represented in a strict sense by a set of mathematical concepts and equations, but their fundamental elements are very closely related to the essential elements of mathematics. Equality and inequality, repetition and symmetry, certain group structures play the fundamental role both in art and in mathematics. Usually the work of several generations is needed to develop that formal system which later is called the style of the art, from its simple beginning to the wealth of elaborate forms which characterize its completion. The interest of the artist is concentrated on this process of crystallization, where the material of the art takes, through his action, the various forms that are initiated by the first formal concepts of this style. After the completion the interest must fade again, because the word "interest" means: to be with something, to take part in a process of life, but this process has then come to an end. Here again the question of how far the formal rules of the style represent that reality of life which is meant by the art cannot be decided from the formal rules. Art is always an idealization; the ideal is different from reality — at least from the reality of the shadows, as Plato would have put it — but idealization is necessary for understanding.

This comparison between the different sets of concepts in natural science with different styles of art may seem very far from the truth to those who consider the different styles of art as rather arbitrary products of the human mind. They would argue that in natural science these different sets of concepts represent objective reality, have been taught to us by nature, are therefore by no means arbitrary, and are a necessary consequence of our gradually increasing experimental knowledge of nature. About these points most scientists would agree; but are the different styles of art an arbitrary product of the human mind? Here again we must not be misled by the Cartesian partition. The style arises out of the interplay between the world and ourselves, or more specifically between the spirit of the time and the artist. The spirit of a time is probably a fact as objective as any fact in natural science, and this spirit brings out certain features of the world which are even independent of time, are in this sense eternal. The artist tries by his work to make these features understandable, and in this attempt he is led to the forms of the style in which he works.

Therefore, the two processes, that of science and that of art, are not very different. Both science and art form in the course of the centuries a human language by which we can speak about the more remote parts of reality, and the coherent sets of concepts as well as the different styles of art are different words or groups of words in this language.

APPENDIX

Note on Physics

As stated in the Introduction, some basic knowledge of biology, particularly those aspects that deal with the cell and with genetics, and of the fundamental principles of physics is assumed to be requisite to an understanding of the readings in this book. Since several of the recent papers base key elements of their arguments on notions in contemporary physics, a supplementary discussion of a number of these concepts is supplied for the reader whose background in this area is limited. The following paragraphs contain brief explanations of Planck's constant h, the correspondence principle, the principle of complementarity, statistical laws, entropy, the uncertainty principle (principle of indeterminacy), and quantum theory (quantum mechanics and wave mechanics).

It is considerably easier to specify the limitations inherent in this effort than it is to number its virtues. First, this Note clearly is not a substitute for rigorous development of the meanings of these concepts; it will not provide a shortcut to genuine knowledge. For comprehensive understanding, the reader should refer to the original papers or to responsible accounts of them. On the other hand, the Note is not a "popularizer" of physics, and it makes no attempt to give oversimplified interpretations.

Second, since the discussions are not historical, the background development of these important ideas enters only incidentally. The concepts therefore are not presented as an organized system, according to their logical relationship to one another, and for the most part the statements made about each concept are supported by a minimum of evidence and argument.

Third, the discussions do not include the philosophical interpretations that often attach to the concepts, interpretations that have been used by proponents of many schools of thought in arguments on both sides of many questions. This omission is of course modified by the fact that I have chosen what I think is essential and hence have presented my particular view of these matters.

This leaves the credit side of the ledger quite empty. The presentations are regrettably short and lacking in advanced mathematics, but they are as synoptic and lucid as I can make them.

Planck's *h*

A body emitting radiation at a constant temperature does so over a wide range of frequencies. The energy of the radiation at each frequency varies further over this range, maximizes toward a central value of the range, and approaches zero toward the minimum and maximum frequencies. A graph plotting energy (E) versus frequency (v) produces the curve shown by the solid line in Figure 1.

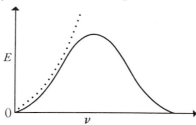

The location of the maximum energy frequency and the total energy (the area under the curve) vary with the temperature of the radiating body, but the general shape of the spectrum is always the same.

Classical electromagnetic theory—that is, Maxwell's electrodynamics—is unable to deduce from its postulates an expression that will reproduce this curve, which symbolizes the observed phenomenon. Classical theory assumes that the radiation derives from vibrating (and hence accelerating) charges; deduced consequences from this theory have the form of the dotted line in Figure 1.

The correspondence of the dotted and the solid curve—that is, of theoretical prediction and experimental observation—is excellent for the low frequencies. However, the overall prediction of classical theory, of a continually increasing quantity of energy with an increasing frequency, clearly is at variance with the observed spectrum. The crucial point is that the theoretical derivation (the dotted curve) is definitive. If classical theory is "correct," results must follow the curve. They do not.

At the turn of this century, Max Planck found a solution to the problem, an equation that produces the solid curve. Two novel assumptions in the equation appear to be unavoidable:

1. The vibrating charges (atomic oscillators) can assume only integral multiples of a basic energy value;
2. This basic energy value is proportional to the frequency of the radiation.

The symbolic expression of the first assumption is $E = \tau h v$, where E is the energy, τ is the constant of proportionality which can take on only the integral values 0, 1, 2, 3, etc., h is the basic energy value ($h = 6.5 \times 10_{-27}$ ergs/second, now known as Planck's constant, the quantum of action), and v is the frequency.

Planck's equation for radiation phenomena is derived from these assumptions. It is an expression that is a function of the frequency and the temperature, that employs the universal constants of the velocity of light (*c*) and Boltzmann's *k* from kinetic theory of gases, and that introduces *h*.

The effect of the first assumption is the quantizing of energy. Unlike classical theory, which permits energy values of any and every amount, Planck's equation considers energy as a packet, or quantum. In other words, energy appears only in discrete amounts; for any and every given frequency, there is a smallest amount—a quantum—of energy (no amount except zero is less than this figure), and all larger quantities of energy are *whole* multiples of this quantum.

Einstein adopted Planck's notion of energy quantization in accounting for the photoelectric effect. Bohr introduced *h* into his theoretical account of the hydrogen atom, and *h* assumes a central role in the uncertainty principle. In fact, it probably is fair to state that *h* is the foundation of quantum theory, for if we accept Planck's conclusions, we must also accept De Broglie's wave equations, Bohr's theory, and many other aspects of contemporary physics.

The correspondence principle

According to the classical laws of electrodynamics, an accelerating electron (for example, one revolving about the nucleus of an atom) must give off radiation; the frequency of the emitted radiation is continuous and proportional to the frequency of revolution of the orbiting electron.

As an outgrowth (not a deduced consequence) of his theoretical account of the hydrogen atom, Neils Bohr introduced into the vernacular a postulate that has come to be known as the correspondence principle. Bohr's account denies the classical explanation of radiation and alleges that an atom emits radiation only when an electron changes from a higher to a lower energy state (states being quantized according to the Planck relationship, $E = \tau h\nu$). There are definite stable configurations for the atom, and the differences among the possible energy levels are multiples of Planck's constant. Hence the spectrum is always discontinuous. If Bohr's model of the atom is interpreted in popular mechanics fashion, in terms of quantum "jumps," the physical occurrence thereby described is very different from that deduced from classical laws.

Using Bohr's theory, it can be demonstrated that the quantitative differences between successive energy states become progressively less as radiation frequencies decrease. In fact, the differences between quantized energy levels—that is, energy levels that are discrete and not continuous, forming a "line" spectrum—become small to the vanishing point. When measured, the energy states, as well as the observed spectrum, *appear* to be continuous, which is the only prediction that classical electrodynamics can deduce. In this limited range of the low energy states, therefore, there is an almost 1-to-1 *correspondence* between the predictions of Bohr's theory and those of classical electrodynamics. It must be emphasized that the correspondence lies only in the circumstance that both theories predict the same observations—the observed spectra—but that the two accounts remain in logical as well as physical contradiction to one another.

The principle of complementarity

Bohr's reflections on the nature of the physicist's enterprise have provided us with what is called the principle of complementarity. Unlike the uncertainty principle and the concept of entropy, this notion does not permit of a precise mathematical expression; it is better likened to a heuristic device.

The principle of complementarity can be illustrated by the following example. Certain phenomena of light, such as the photoelectric effect, seem to require that light be considered as quantized (a quantum of light is called a photon). Other observed phenomena of light, such as the interference pattern produced when light is beamed through small openings onto a screen, seem to require that light be interpreted as possessing wavelike properties. Thus, neither a particulate theory nor a wave theory can account for all the observable facts of light. In the absence of a totally new notion, it is necessary to consider both of these theories in order to render a "complete" description of light. Either view by itself is insufficient, but the two views together *complement* each other and "explain" all known phenomena of light. Similarly, electrons sometimes display a particulate nature but under other circumstances apparently can be accounted for only if wavelike properties are ascribed to them.

The principle of complementarity does not assert that light or electrons have a dual nature. It does seem to imply, however, that an understanding of the essence of a thing may require more than one aspect; moreover, the two conceptions can be mutually exclusive.

Statistical laws

There are at least two distinct kinds of statistical treatment of data that function within physics, and it is necessary to interpret statistical statements that have been manipulated by physicists according to their assumptions about nature.

One typical situation in physics involves the management of data collected during an experiment to test an hypothesis. As a simple case, consider the measurement of a body's time of fall from a fixed distance. Underlying the experiment is the physicist's belief that there exists one true time of fall, the value he searches for. Although he records an array of falling times on repeated trials, experience has taught him to anticipate deviations from the true time, for he recognizes that uncontrollable variations will occur in the starting and stopping of timing instruments, the distance will not remain precisely the same, air currents will vary, and the like. The physicist assumes that these uncontrollable variables fluctuate in a random fashion and that they will negate one another in the long run. He proceeds to treat his data statistically, using what is called the theory of errors.

A second illustration of the same kind of statistical analysis arises when the physicist deals with large numbers. For example, ordinary air confined within a container measuring one cubic centimeter and maintained at standard conditions of temperature and pressure supposedly contains 2.7×10^{19} molecules. Even if all these molecules could be seen at one instant, the number of particles is so great that it is impossible in actuality to treat each one individually.

Kinetic molecular theory handles problems related to this fact—for example, attempts to determine the pressure exerted by molecules against the sides of the container—by the use of statistical laws. The physicist believes his statistical treatment to be a convenience, not a necessity, at least *in principle*. He believes that the impacts between particle and particle and between particle and side of container follow Newtonian laws (e.g., conservation of momentum). In other words, his treatment of such a case gives no predictions regarding the behavior of an individual molecule; rather, it states the probability of a certain event happening to a particular molecule. But the physicist believes that *if* he could determine the position and velocity of each molecule at one instant of time (knowledge he believes possible *in principle* if not in actuality), then, given a computer of sufficient capacity, he could predict with precision the past and future position of each molecule.

A second and different way that statistics operate in physical investigation appears in the study of the metamorphosis or disintegration of radioactive materials. A precise mathematical expression gives the rate at which a large number of atoms will disintegrate in any given time interval. For example, half of any given number of radium atoms will disintegrate (emit an alpha particle and become radon) in 1590 years, half of that remaining half will disintegrate in the next 1590 years, and so on. The law says nothing, however, about individual atoms. It therefore implies that a particular atom's history has no bearing on its future course—namely, disintegration. No matter how many years it has existed as an atom, the probability of its disintegrating within the next increment of time remains precisely the same.

The interpretation given to this phenomenon by many physicists is that the disintegration of radioactive atoms is a completely random event. The question of limitation of measurement—the inability to see or deal with a particular atom—does not enter. Physicists holding this view believe that the phenomenon of radioactive decay is by its very nature a random (i.e., statistical) one and that the phenomenon does not submit to mechanical laws as does the behavior of molecules in a container. These physicists assert that nature is at its very heart random. Quantum mechanics is also to be treated as though its very essence is randomness, in principle as well as in actuality.[1] Statistics —i.e., probabilities—enter into the definition-of-state of a body in this science.

---

1. Note in particular Schrödinger's second example in Chapter I, Section 8, pages 71–74. The diffusion of the permanganate in the water tank can be deduced on the one assumption of complete randomness of motion. Brownian movement, Newtonian forces of collision, and the like need not be assumed at all in order to account for the observed results.

Physicists who believe that the very core of nature is statistical say in effect that our present knowledge is not mechanical *ignoramus* but *ignoramibus*. Those adhering to the opposite view assert that our present ignorance is but a temporary state of affairs and will be removed when the essential laws governing phenomena are discovered. They will not dispute the retention of statistical laws in this domain, but statistical treatment of the first kind described will be all that will be necessary — for the sake of convenience. Learned champions for each camp coexist; the basic issue remains unresolved.

Entropy

The concept of entropy is intimately related to the Second Law of Thermodynamics, the First Law being the statement of the principle of conservation of energy. Entropy has particular relevance to heat phenomena and hence to the motion of molecules.

Imagine an aquarium divided in half by a partition, one side filled with cold water, the other side with hot water. The hot water, by volume, contains more energy than the cold water by virtue of its higher heat content. When the partition is removed, energy can transfer between the two quantities of water.

Applying only the First Law of Thermodynamics, there can be no prediction as to whether the hot water will become hotter and the cold water colder or whether the hot water will become cooler and the cold water warmer. The First Law states only that energy changes will total zero and that energy will be conserved. The Second Law of Thermodynamics expresses the direction in which energy changes can take place.[2] In mathematical terms, the entropy changes in the aquarium, or in any other situation involving bodies initially at different temperatures, T_1 and T_2, can be expressed as follows:

$$\frac{\Delta Q}{T_1} - \frac{\Delta Q}{T_2} = \frac{(T_2 - T_1)\Delta Q}{T_1 T_2}$$

In this formula, the ΔQ represents the change of heat in calories, T the temperature in degrees absolute. Given certain initial conditions, this definitive expression allows the precise calculation of results. When temperatures, masses, and specific heats are measured, it can be shown that the total entropy of a system is greater after an energy exchange

---

2.   More strictly, the Second Law states that the addition of heat to a body cannot be completely converted into work (mechanical energy) and nothing else. For example, if I drop a dime from my hand to the floor, Joule's mechanical equivalent of heat allows me to determine precisely how much heat was produced in the dime as its kinetic energy of fall was converted into heat energy. But were I to supply that amount of heat to a dime on the floor, it could not acquire sufficient mechanical energy to rise to my hand; entropy is a measure of this unavailable energy. This example is in complete accord with experience, of course, for no one has seen a coin rise a fraction of an inch, but on the basis of the conservation of energy alone, this should be a possibility. In fact, why the coin cannot rise is not at all clear — until one renders a statistical interpretation of heat phenomena.

than it was before. The mathematical expression becomes a positive amount, a gain in entropy, only if T_2 is greater than T_1. T_2 would be the temperature of the warm side of the aquarium, and this portion must lose its heat to the cooler side, not vice versa.

Schrödinger (Chapter VI, Section 59) treats this entropy increase as a movement from order to disorder. In our example, the aquarium is more ordered when the hot and cold water are separated than when the entire system is at essentially the same temperature, one intermediate between the two initial conditions. The notion of order and disorder derives from Boltzmann's application of the kinetic molecular theory of heat (which attributes heat to the energy of molecular motion) to the Second Law of Thermodynamics. From the assumption that molecules demonstrate perpetual and chaotic motion — that is, from a hypothesis of molecular disorder — Boltzmann interpreted the law of entropy as a statistical law that assigns high probabilities to the usual states of complete randomness, and vice versa. Thus an unusual state (a majority of high-energy water molecules on one side of the aquarium — the warm water) will *almost* always be followed by the usual state (water at the same temperature throughout the aquarium).[3]

This physical interpretation of entropy differs from the first one given in this section, for it concludes that, although such a phenomenon is highly improbable, the hot side of the aquarium *could* momentarily become hotter and the cool side cooler;[4] the strict expression of the Second Law does not permit of this statistical possibility.

The uncertainty principle (principle of indeterminacy)

Suppose one conceives of a beam of light as consisting of a multitude of photons. If a portion of a rectilinear light beam is directed through a large circular hole in a sheet of cardboard onto a screen placed beyond the cardboard, the light image on the screen corresponds almost exactly with the size of the hole in the cardboard. It is normally assumed that each photon proceeds along the beam in a perfectly straight line, as image formation is treated in geometrical optics. (Whether there *really* is a photon and whether it *really* travels in a straight line is not at issue here.) Thus it is said that the photon's momentum (the product of its mass and velocity) is known with "complete" certainty.

---

3. The falling of the dime adds to the chaotic motion of the silver molecules a uniformly accelerated downward motion, which is the same for all the molecules of the dime. It would be highly unlikely that supplying those molecules with more energy — i.e., heating them — when the dime is on the ground would give all the molecules an upward motion and hence raise the dime.

4. If a spoonful of pepper were carefully placed on top of a spoonful of salt in a small glass and then stirred by a pencil in a clockwise direction for twenty-five revolutions, the contents would appear to be more grey than half black and half white. If the mixture were then stirred twenty-five times in a *counter*-clockwise direction, it is conceivable that the salt and pepper would be separated and replaced in their initial positions, but it is certainly much more likely that the glass would be even more gray throughout than it was after the first stirring.

The exact location of a particular photon in the beam is not known, however. As an hypothetical experiment to determine the position of a single photon, the hole in the cardboard might be made smaller and smaller. Theoretically, the hole could be made small enough to permit only a single photon to pass through it at one instant. But this experimental arrangement produces the well-known interference pattern: concentric rings of light appear on the screen — the image is *not* the size and shape of the hole. While it could then be said with precision where a particular photon is at a particular moment — the instant that it passes through the hole — it cannot be predicted with certainty what path the photon will take from the hole to the screen. It may go straight ahead and produce the spot of light seen at the center of the concentric rings, or it may go off at one of the fixed and known angles. Thus, while the position of an individual photon has been determined with complete certainty, knowledge of its future velocity has been lost, and knowledge of its momentum has become uncertain. Only a probability, albeit a precise probability, can be assigned for the course it will take.

This uncertainty principle was formulated by Heisenberg; its derivation produces the following expression:

$$\Delta p \Delta x \geq h \text{ or } \Delta v \Delta x \geq \frac{h}{m}$$

In this expression, p stands for the momentum (mv), and x stands for a measure of position. The Δ is a symbol that expresses a difference in true values. For example, when a light beam passes through a large hole in the cardboard, the top of the beam could be called x_1 and the bottom of the beam x_2; Δx then stands for $x_1 - x_2$. The h is Planck's constant, and the inequality symbol $\geq$ should be read as "equal to or greater than."

Some meanings of the uncertainty principle should be noted. First, the expression places no restrictions on the type of body under consideration. The simultaneous location of the momentum and position of any body, no matter what its mass or velocity, is subject to an uncertainty that is at least as large as Planck's constant.

Second, as has been stated above, Planck's constant is an extremely small number. Hence, for a mass of ordinary size (say, any visible body), the degree of uncertainty is vanishingly small — zero for all practical purposes. It is never actually zero, but in practice it is incapable of being measured. On the other hand, in the case of a hydrogen atom and its electron, the small mass of the electron divided into Planck's constant yields significant uncertainty. The magnitude of this uncertainty approaches the size of the atom itself, 10^{-8} centimeters. A legitimate interpretation of this fact is that all one can say about the position of an electron in a hydrogen atom is that it is somewhere within the dimensions of the atom.

Finally, if we accept Planck's constant and its related concepts as significant features of physical theory, then we must also accept Heisenberg's derivation of his uncertainty principle. There is nothing uncertain about the uncertainty principle. The physicist's former belief that he could know everything with absolute precision, even in principle, has thus turned out to be a false one. But he does know much more than he ever knew before; with the uncertainty principle, he now knows exactly what he does not and cannot know.

Quantum theory (quantum mechanics and wave mechanics)

The formulations of specific statements for predicting observations of the consequences of atomic and subatomic phenomena, statements frequently expressed in mathematical symbols and language and employing the notions described above, particularly those involving Planck's h, result in what may be called quantum theory. That is, while usage of the phrase "quantum theory" varies with different authors, it is a proper generic title under which "quantum mechanics"[5] and "wave mechanics" can be subsumed. Since uniformity of practice does not exist, however, the reader will have to judge from the context of each paper what meaning the scientist intends.

Wave mechanics originated with De Broglie. His basic expression is

$$\lambda = \frac{h}{mv}$$

in which λ is the wave length or the length of a wave associated with a corpuscle of mass, m, moving with a velocity, v, and h is again Planck's constant. The expression implies that what we have always thought of as particulate has a wave associated with it. In this way, De Broglie's contribution provides the symmetry of the particulate nature of light, heretofore a wave phenomena.

De Broglie's equation has been experimentally verified by the measurement of the wave length of electrons as they form interference patterns. From De Broglie and others, particularly Schrödinger, have come quite complex mathematical statements (Eigenvalues, for example) for dealing with subatomic phenomena. Wave mechanics is the name given to this approach to quantum phenomena. From the early work of Bohr—from Born, Jordan, Dirac, and from Bohr himself—has risen an alternative set of statements for dealing with the same problems. The name given to this set is quantum mechanics.

Quantum theory has not attained its final formulation as yet; modifications, additions, and deletions continue to come from physicists working with the theory. Statistics enters both wave and quantum mechanics, as does Planck's h. Perhaps future scientists will find a completely new theoretical approach, one which appears markedly different from quantum theory and which will ask us to entertain an entirely new view of the world. Even if such a change were to take place, however—and such changes have occurred before in the history of science—Planck's h and the many consequences that follow from it would be no less true than they are today.

---

5. "Mechanics" retains its Newtonian meaning: the science of the motion of bodies (kinematics) and the forces producing the motion (dynamics).

Guide to Inquiry

In order to achieve maximum understanding of any written material, one must ask questions of its author. Unfortunately, learning to ask the *right* questions is by no means as simple an undertaking as it might appear to be. Some questions are appropriate — that is, necessary and fruitful — to any literary product. For example, determining the meanings of important terms in their varying contexts is as essential to the appreciation of a poem as it is to the understanding of a scientific report. Other questions have a particular relevance to a particular kind of material. For example, questions regarding an author's reasons for employing certain stylistic devices (e.g., the insertion of rhyming lines in an otherwise unrhymed play) may be essential in the analysis of imaginative works but may only on rare occasions lead to significant insights into a scientific argument. On the other hand, some questions are right and proper — i.e., have a special relevance — for reports of scientific investigation and reflection.

SECTION A

In Section A of this Guide to Inquiry are seven question types appropriate to the papers collected in this book. The first five sets are generally applicable to the discussion and analysis of any scientific work; the last two have special relevance to the papers in this collection. Number 6 accentuates the fundamental problem of interrelations as treated by individual authors, and number 7 attempts to further enrich the meaning of each interpretation by comparing it with others. As pointed out in the Introduction, each set of questions should be asked of each reading. The order in which the questions are asked is only suggestive and certainly will vary within and among the selections as critical examination and comparison progress. Furthermore, prescription of questions is contrary to the experience of dialogue; the answers generated by a fruitful query will suggest subsequent questions.

1. What is the author's problem, the question he sets out to attack?

2. What is his answer to the question? his conclusion? Is it dogmatic? or does it permit of alternatives?

3. What are the author's key terms (e.g., "biology," "physics," "explanation," "vitalism," "mechanism")? Has he defined them explicitly, or must their meanings be inferred from context? Does each term retain a constant meaning throughout the paper?

4. What evidence does the author consider crucial to his case? How is the particular data included related to his conclusion? What evidence that might well be relevant to his argument has not been considered? Does he argue from firmly established theories? Does he focus on one theoretical consequent and ignore others?

5. What *kind* of an argument does he utilize in advancing his conclusion? Does he generalize inductively from the data? Does he reason deductively from a set of premises? (If so, what are his premises, his basic axioms, either explicit or implicit?) Is the argument one from analogy? Is it a *reductio ad absurdum*? (If so, are *all* alternatives considered and eliminated, save his one?) Is his approach essentially one of persuasive rhetoric rather than rigorous logic? Is the form of his argument valid? Does he argue on the basis of history? extrapolate into the future? The case for his conclusion should be extracted, outlined, and critically examined; his unstated premises will then appear.

6. What does the author consider to be the proper subject matter of biology? of physics? Does he believe that there is a particular methodology appropriate to research in biology or in physics? (Are the methods the same or different for each science?) What, to the author, constitutes fundamental explanation in biology? in physics? What does he consider to be the goal of biology? of physics? Do recent data and/or theoretical constructs in either science modify or invalidate his position?

7. Why do the authors reach different conclusions about the nature of the relationship between biology and physics? A careful inspection of the answers to the questions raised above (particularly 4 and 6) should provide helpful clues. Another approach is to ask how one author would criticize another, and vice versa. The reader should also keep in mind that several men may agree on the present state of the relationship but may prognosticate quite differently.

SECTION B

The sample questions in Section B illustrate the preceding general sets through specific application to one or more of the readings. There are, in most cases, two examples of each of the sets in Section A, and they appear in the same order; that is, the questions on the Bohr and

Commoner readings correspond to questions 1 and 2 in Section A, those on Russell and Heitler to question 3, and so on. I have supplied discursive answers to the questions in order to demonstrate the process of analyzing an author's statements to determine his implicit or explicit meanings. The answers and comments are succinct and hence incomplete, but they include page references to the portions of the readings that I would cite to support them. These discussions do not necessarily represent my actual position on the general issue of the relationship between the sciences; they simply indicate what I believe to be defensible responses according to what each author has written.

Bohr

QUESTION: What is the basic question to which Bohr addresses himself? What is his answer to it?

ANSWER: Although Bohr raises and answers several questions, the one that dominates this paper is: Can the phenomena which typically characterize biology (e.g., "self-preservation and propagation of individuals") be accounted for by contemporary physics (pp. 108, 114)? His answer is no.

DISCUSSION: Bohr's argument is an analogical one based on the comparability of (1) the known limitations of analysis of the fundamental processes of individual atoms and (2) the essence of what makes an organism an organism.

Commoner

QUESTION: What is the question to which Commoner addresses himself, and what is his answer to it?

ANSWER: Can the biological sciences and the natural processes of metabolism, photosynthesis, biosynthesis, division, growth, cessation of growth, etc. (p. 130) be reduced to — that is, explained by — the science of physics? Commoner's answer is no.

DISCUSSION: In addition to rhetorical devices appealing to the healthy growth of all branches of science and references to the methodology of the sciences (pp. 131–132, 137), Commoner cites the evidence of three distinguished physical scientists who conclude as he does.

Russell

QUESTION: A key assertion in Russell's development of his position — one that characterizes the so-called organismal, or organistic, view of biology, in fact — is that "the whole is something more than the summation of its parts" (p. 57). What does this phrase actually mean?

ANSWER: In some way a machine is a sum of its parts, but a living organism is not (pp. 57–58). A machine differs from an organism in the relationship of parts to whole (pp. 58–59), and the two differ in their purposes (pp. 59–61).

DISCUSSION: This is not a very satisfactory answer to a crucial question, and textual analysis of Russell's paper provides few additional clues. Clearly, the meaning of the phrase depends on the analogues of the terms "whole," "sum," and "parts." We see that Russell uses "sum" as a synonym for "relationship," and hence we can infer that "sum" is not restricted to "arithmetic addition" (as in 2 + 2 = 4).

Recently, Ernest Nagel has subjected this statement to careful logical analysis.* The reader is urged to refer to his paper. Nagel finds that "whole," "sum," and "parts" have quite different meanings in diverse contexts. For example, the rules for adding two or more vectors are different from those for adding numbers in the usual arithmetical way. The given vectors are the equivalent of "parts"; the resultant vector — the "whole" — is the "sum."

Nagel's conclusion, one in which I concur, is that the truth of the statement remains open to question; that is, while it may indeed be true that the whole is greater than the sum of its parts, there has not as yet been a satisfactory and rigorous demonstration that this is so.

Heitler

QUESTION: What does Heitler mean by "teleology"?

ANSWER: Teleology is to be understood as an extrascientific — metaphysical or mystical or theological — principle (p. 174) that serves as a guide for a *scientist* in his research. Such a guiding idea affects the form of scientific "laws" in that it affects the structure of statements advanced to account for natural phenomena (p. 174). Hence it gives a distinguishing characteristic to the *science* that develops: the principle of teleology states that any relationship in nature is part of an overall plan, a larger order, and it becomes a premise in arguments adduced in support of scientific laws (pp. 174, 177).

As a particular principle it may vary from scientist to scientist (p. 175), but it is never a "causal" principle (p. 176). A particular teleological belief may lead either to scientific laws identical to those discovered on the basis of another extrascientific principle (e.g., that all laws of science are of a simple mathematical form, p. 174) or to laws that are not logically equivalent to usual ones (pp. 175–176).

The metaphysical concomitants of a particular teleological position do not determine the value of that position to science (". . . no scale of values is to be implied," p. 181). Rather, the value of the position should be assessed in terms of its fruitfulness as a guiding idea for the scientist.

The Structure of Science (New York: Harcourt, Brace & World, Inc., 1961), pp. 380–397.

Novikoff

QUESTION: What evidence does Novikoff consider critical to his contention that there are distinct sciences, each higher level requiring new and separate laws which are not derivable from lower levels of organization?

ANSWER: Novikoff cites many research papers (see his bibliography) and quotes the conclusions of other scientists as well as advancing relevant data of his own. One example of his method follows:

The quotation from Dobzhansky claims that "the rules governing the genetic structure of a population are, nevertheless, distinct from those governing the genetics of individuals. . ." (p. 165). Presumably, "rules" are "laws." Certain mathematical expressions permit statistical deductions regarding the progeny that result from the mating of two individuals of a species, and there are mathematical laws regarding the persistence of a trait in a population. Neither of these laws can, at this time, be mathematically derived from the other or from any third set of concepts (*cf.* the Heisenberg selection).

Oparin

QUESTION: Oparin argues that the processes of life are *not* the same as those of a machine. He states that life, the fundamental property of an organism, is a specific, developed form of matter in motion (p. 189), a "given," a fact of nature, and that it is in accord with fundamental principles of dialectical materialism. How does Oparin argue for his position?

ANSWER: He subjects the machine analogy to careful scrutiny and finds that its proponents, both past and present, have ignored fundamental features of it. For example, Oparin contends that, *unlike the machine*, (a) the materials that make up the parts of an organism are crucial to its existence, (b) the existence of an organism is contingent upon its continual operation, (c) the parts of an organism can and in fact must undergo change, (d) the nature of energy changes in an organism (particularly in regard to entropy) are *qualitatively* different from those in a machine, (e) the origin of an organism is completely different from that of a machine, (f) the nature of an organism's purpose is unrelated to that of a machine, and so on (pp. 198–207). On the basis of the differences he elucidates, Oparin concludes that life is not analogous to a machine and hence that life cannot be reduced to physics and chemistry.

Müller

QUESTION: What is the *form* of Müller's argument for the existence of a vital principle or force and the nonreducibility of biology to physics?

ANSWER: The form of Müller's argument can be outlined as follows:

a. "2. . . . The laws of action of the nervous principle are totally different from those of electricity" (p. 17).

b. Electricity is a branch of physics.

∴ c. The laws of physics differ from the laws of action of the nervous principle.

d. If the laws of action of physics cannot account for biological phenomena, of which nervous phenomena are examples, then some other principle must account for biological phenomena.

∴ e. Some nonphysical principle accounts for biological phenomena.

f. The possible other principles are the mind, animal magnetism, or a vital (creative organic) force.

g. The mind does not account for biological phenomena (p. 10).

h. Animal magnetism does not account for biological phenomena (p. 13).

∴ i. A vital force is *the* principle.

DISCUSSION: To attack this argument, one might focus on the truth of statements (a) and (f), for (i) follows logically from the prior statements. It would be difficult to establish criteria for the truth or falsity of (a), partly because of the ambiguous phrase "totally different." On the other hand, the truth of statement (f) depends upon its including *all* possible alternative explanations, a condition that scientists practically never can satisfy, save in those instances where a simple dichotomy exists (e.g., either the shortest line from a point to a line is the perpendicular from that point or it is not; the *reductio ad absurdum* proof in the geometrical case is complete). Hence, statement (i), the conclusion, is vulnerable.

Bernard

QUESTION: In the final section of the Bernard selection (his exchange with Gerdy on the different outcome of patients treated in a like manner, p. 41), what is the form of Bernard's argument and how conclusive is it?

ANSWER: Assuming that identical treatment is applied to given sets of conditions, Bernard asserts:

a. If the initial conditions of several experiments are identical, the results of the experiments will be identical.

b. The results were not identical.

∴ c. The initial conditions were not identical.

DISCUSSION: This is a valid form, the contrapositive. Since both gentlemen accept statement (b), the conclusiveness of the argument rests on the truth of statement (a). Statement (a), of course, is one of the main points Bernard attempts to establish in his book. Apparently, however, Gerdy will not accept statement (a) when the phenomena of life are involved. Thus there remains little that Bernard and Gerdy can discuss with one another at this juncture, reiterations of personal faiths being their only recourse.

Heisenberg

QUESTION: How does Heisenberg support his contention that a "new closed system" of concepts in natural science will be needed to account for the phenomena of biology?

ANSWER: On the basis of his assumption that a set of concepts consists of a group of definitions and axioms capable of being mathematically formulated (see Heitler for a criticism of this view), which leads to the deduction of consequences testable against experience, Heisenberg finds four (possibly five) extant sets inadequate (pp. 215–216). The premises of his argument are advanced from and supported by his interpretation of the history of science from Newton through quantum physics. The form of his argument may be outlined as follows:

a. Throughout the history of science, men have "created" ("evolved," "developed") systems to account for various classes of phenomena.
b. Different systems have been subsumed — i.e., shown to be special cases — by more recently created systems, which in turn involve new concepts and hence a new set of definitions and axioms capable of mathematical symbolization and logical analysis.
c. Biology cannot be accounted for by any current system.
d. History repeats itself — that is, events that have occurred in history will, in a similar situation, reoccur in a like (but not identical) manner.
∴ e. A new system will be formulated to account for biology, presumably a system with quantum physics as a special case.

More abstractly and succinctly, the argument may be outlined thus:

a–b. H (the history of science) reveals P (a pattern of man's activities, "inventing" or "discovering" systems).
c–d. H will persist.
∴   e. P will result.

Or, stated symbolically:
$$\frac{\begin{array}{l} H \to P \\ H \end{array}}{\therefore \quad P}$$

Clearly Heisenberg supports H→P, but even he questions whether history will "repeat itself."

Haldane

QUESTION: What constitutes fundamental explanation in physics and biology for Haldane?

ANSWER: Physical, or physicochemical, explanation is equivalent to a mechanistic explanation (p. 45). It is a causal explanation (pp. 49, 56). It is the analysis of a phenomenon into "separable events or processes occurring in separable material units" (p. 43), an analysis which is then subjected to pre-quantum (p. 54) physical and chemical theory for the purpose of obtaining a coherent conception of the phenomenon (p. 47).

Biological explanation, on the other hand, is neither causal nor mechanistic (p. 56), nor is it vitalistic (pp. 44–48). Rather, it consists of a particular (p. 52) demonstration of the connections (p. 49) of those processes characteristic of life (particularly coordinates maintenance and reproduction), i.e., of function (p. 53). Said another way, biological explanation requires that a phenomenon be seen as having a certain function of its own, as being an individual whole, and as having an indefinitely large number of relationships with other phenomena in its existence as part of a larger or largest whole.

Simpson

QUESTION: What constitutes "science" for Simpson?

ANSWER: Science is a collection of statements that explain — not describe — natural phenomena. They answer questions like "what for?" as well as "how?" (pp. 156, 159). The statements are neither teleological nor metaphysical nor vitalistic nor mystical; they lead to objective knowledge, and they have a time (historical) dimension (p. 159).

DISCUSSION: Simpson also maintains that physics is only a branch of science, not the roots or trunk — that is, not the essence of science — and hence cannot explain biology.

Mayr and Heitler

QUESTION: Is Mayr's analysis of the concept and role of "teleology" in science the same as Heitler's?

ANSWER: No.

DISCUSSION: Mayr carefully distinguishes between two different meanings — indeed, between two different terms, "teleology" and "teleonomy." Teleonomy designates a factor in the life of an individual organism, the "genetic improvement [by] evolutionary adaptation controlled by natural selection" (p. 145); it is a part of causality and hence is within the domain of science. Teleology refers to evolution or to a larger, overall plan of the universe; it is outside of causality and science.

Heitler, however, focuses on the scientist *qua* scientist and on how teleology is a part of human nature. He argues that, in his investigation of nature, a scientist presupposes a plan existing in nature. Teleology, then, is a part of a scientist, because a scientist is human. Thus teleology, for Heitler, plays an essential role in the structure of resulting scientific laws and in the arguments adduced in support of these laws. (*Cf.* the question on Heitler.)

Schrödinger and Delbrück

QUESTION: Schrödinger and Delbrück agree that quantum physics has a significant relevance to the problem of the relationship of biology to physics. However, each predicts a different future relationship. Why?

ANSWER: Schrödinger emphasizes the Heitler-London derivation from quantum theory which accounts for "the structure of molecules, their binding-energies, their stabilities at different temperatures" (Sections 33–35, pp. 82–84), notions that Schrödinger finds readily amenable to both the permanence and the mutability of genes. Thus he is optimistic in his view of a future unity of the sciences via quantum theory.

Delbrück, on the other hand, focuses on those aspects of quantum theory that are the products of Bohr and Heisenberg, viz., complementarity and the uncertainty principle. The need for an extremely large sample of identical organisms, the importance of individual atoms in key structures, and the interference of the observer with what is observed are consequences of quantum theory that he believes will always preclude a researcher's being able to obtain the information necessary for a description of replication by physics (pp. 125–128). Thus Delbrück foresees that no unity of the sciences will result from the discoveries in quantum theory.

DATE DUE

JA 29 '68			
AP 9 '68			
MY 6 '68			
May 21			
MY 21 '68			
JUN 0 1 1993			
GAYLORD			PRINTED IN U.S.A.